WM11 LEC

Lectures on the History of Psychiatry

The Squibb Series

Edited by
R.M. Murray
T.H. Turner

Lectures on the History of Psychiatry

The Squibb Series

GASKELL

Typeset at the Alden Press,
Oxford, London and Northampton
Printed in Great Britain

Contents

List of contributors

Patricia Allderidge, Archivist at the Bethlem Royal Hospital, Monks Orchard Road, Beckenham, Kent

Virginia Berridge, Senior Research Officer at The Institute of Historical Research, University of London

German Berrios, Consultant Psychiatrist and University Lecturer in Psychiatry at the University of Cambridge, Addenbrooke's Hospital, Cambridge

James Birley, President of the Royal College of Psychiatrists, and Consultant Psychiatrist at The Bethlem Royal and Maudsley Hospitals, London

William F. Bynum, Reader in the History of Medicine, and Director of the Academic Unit at the Wellcome Institute for the History of Medicine, London

Thomas Gruffydd Davies, the author of several papers on the History of Psychiatry in Wales, and Consultant Psychiatrist at Cefn Coed Hospital, Swansea

Edward Hare, Emeritus Psychiatrist, The Bethlem Royal and Maudsley Hospitals, London, and Editor of the *British Journal of Psychiatry* 1973–77

Michael MacDonald, Professor of History, University of Michigan, Ann Arbor, USA

Roy Porter, Senior Lecturer in the Social History of Medicine at the Wellcome Institute for the History of Medicine, London

Andrew Scull, Professor of Sociology, University of California (San Diego), La Jolla, California, USA

Trevor Turner, Consultant Psychiatrist at St Bartholomew's Hospital and Hackney Hospital, London

Alexander Walk, was Honorary Librarian of the Royal College of Psychiatrists for many years before his death, and Editor of the *Journal of Mental Science*

Acknowledgements

The editors wish to thank Squibb for subsidising the publication of this book and for funding the series of lectures at the Institute of Psychiatry over the years.

The lecture by E.H. Hare (Chapter 6) is reprinted from *Psychiatric Developments* volume 3 (1985) with the permission of Oxford University Press. Figure 2 in that chapter (depicting two statues by Cibber) is reproduced with the permission of the Bethlem Royal Hospital and The Maudsley Hospital Health Authority, and the photographs are by courtesy of the Board of Trustees of the Victoria and Albert Museum, London. The lecture by W.F. Bynum (Chapter 8) is reprinted from *The Anatomy of Madness. Essays in the History of Psychiatry*, volume 1, *People and Ideas* (edited by W.F. Bynum, R. Porter and M. Shepherd), with the permission of Tavistock Publications. The lectures by M. MacDonald (Chapter 5), R. Porter (Chapter 9), A. Scull (Chapter 10) and T. Turner (Chapter 11) are reprinted from *Psychological Medicine*, with the permission of Cambridge University Press.

Introduction

TREVOR TURNER

The series of Squibb lectures on the history of psychiatry, initiated in 1973, has for some years been a lonely outpost of historical exposition in the world of psychological medicine. The subject has been largely dropped from the Royal College of Psychiatrists' examination curriculum, has no academic base within the psychiatric establishment, and little following among the younger generation of more 'scientific' psychiatrists. Quoted in James Birley's 1974 lecture are the words of Alfred Whitehead, that "a science which hesitates to forget its founders is lost". Amidst the complex developments of modern psychopharmacology, molecular genetics, nuclear magnetic resonance imaging and psychoneuroendocrinology, questions as to the relevance of history seem pertinently apt.

But it is also reasonable to state that the great majority of psychiatrists are not laboratory workers at the forefront of high-tech medicine. They are clinical practitioners, looking after a range of variably ill patients in certain social and architectural settings. Many are based in asylums built in the Victorian age, asylums due for closure as the moves towards community care gather momentum. The problems of understanding the organisation of services, the popular, public attitudes to madness, the effects of enthusiastic therapy, and the meaning of diagnosis are recurring and difficult. Why are things as they are? What has been tried, in human terms, to alleviate the distress of mental illness? What is genuinely new and what is merely fashionable? Where can we discover the successful enterprises and how did they succeed?

These questions cannot of course be answered directly by history. But an historical understanding can refine them and lead to proposals of useful areas of research. For example, if it can be shown that schizophrenia has persisted across time and space, that similar symptoms were noted in Victorian Sussex as are seen in 1980s New York, it is reasonable to exclude certain modern toxins, such as 'junk food' or nuclear waste, from aetiological speculation. The 1987 lecture attempted to show just this sort of chronological consistency. Likewise, if we review the ways in which a false science can lead to inappropriate therapy, as Andrew Scull's 1986 paper outlines so wonderfully, we are likely to review our own practices in a more rigorous fashion. The relationship between certain modern psychological therapies and the activities of Hans Mesmer, who often treated patients in groups, cannot be ignored, nor can the oddly variable prevalence of hysterectomy across differently funded (private or public) health systems.

Apart from their intrinsic worth, these essays also reveal the changing emphases in historical research. Far from indulging in deference to great men, their concentration on primary sources and the contemporary social context has led to a renewed interest, by historians rather than clinicians, in the history of ideas defining the concept of madness. As Roy Porter makes clear in his 1985 discussion of a "madman 17th-century style", importance lies in "the task of exploring where the boundaries between sanity and insanity were perceived in any particular age, how they shifted over time, so that one age's cognitive coherence might prove another's cognitive disturbance". While such an approach may well lead to tensions between psychiatrists and historians, as to how one should understand mental illness, there is little doubt that psychiatry as a discipline is likely to be enhanced. For by incorporating attitudes about madness into the mainstream of popular history there will be an increased popular awareness of the role of psychological health in ordinary people's lives. Furthermore, if this new interest can stimulate psychiatrists to explore more critically their own professional history, it could give them a much more authoritative voice in, for example, the present community care debates. Patricia Allderidge's 1978 lecture neatly displays the parochial circularity of much of this whole controversy.

Perhaps most interesting to many modern doctors, accustomed to viewing medical history as a succession of scientific (and moral) advances, may be the discovery of unwanted skeletons behind the facade of altruistic progress. Apart from Andrew Scull, Dr T. G. Davies in his elegant 1979 exposition of Ernest Jones, and Virginia Berridge in her 1982 searching analysis of the disease theory of addiction, make one think twice about the motives and intellectual quality of our predecessors. Also our continued ignorance as to the changing patterns of disease is evocatively demonstrated by Edward Hare's 1981 "Old familiar faces", while German Berrios (1988) has outlined the need for a revision of the "cognitive paradigm", using an erudite range of European sources too often neglected by modern clinicians. With such examples in mind how will our successors view our diagnostic habits? The prevalence of parasuicide, and the extraordinary concern over anorexia nervosa (the research interest of four current London professors) are peculiarly contemporary phenomena. Yet such diagnoses, viewed in the continuum of history, may make much more sense as social fashions, the understanding of which is minimally improved by assertions of psychiatric aetiology.

Of course, history also has a plain tale to tell. The account given (in 1983) by W. F. Bynum, of the separation between neurology and psychiatry in the 19th century, is impressive in its details, and provides a rich contrast in style to Alexander Walk's 1975 lecture on the Medico-Psychological Association and the Maudsley Hospital. Both have a narrative to expound, and do this well. But Walk's almost automatic deference to Henry Maudsley as a 'great man' limits his piece to being more a description of achievement, viewed with hindsight, rather than a critical assessment of how things were.

Perhaps an implicit theme to these pieces is the stigmatising effect of mental illness on those foolhardy enough to set themselves up as doctors of the mind. 'Quack', 'mad doctor', 'alienist' and 'shrink' are hardly terms of admiration. That such stigma exists, in such phrases as 'You are the only sane psychiatrist I know!', seems undoubted, although many of us would prefer not to acknowledge the doubts harboured about us by our non-psychiatric colleagues. Which inhibition may also be the reason for our relative neglect of our history, much of which is not very pretty, littered with foolish practices and only occasionally enlightened by a few extremely brave individuals.

In this context Michael MacDonald's 1980 lecture, on insanity in early modern England, is arguably the most fundamental of them all. Not only is he persuasive in his description of how political and religious forces defined the meanings of madness, but his notion of "a society divided not merely by differences in wealth and status, but also by differences in mentalite" is truly shocking. He points out that traditional beliefs about mental disorder "survived among the lower orders of society well into the 19th century", but who can say with certainty that this cultural gap does not still persist? Yet it is this limited ability to communicate to the public a non-stigmatising and rational view of mental illness that still bedevils, literally, psychiatric progress. The association between violence, sexual abnormality and 'psychiatrists' remains very strong in the tabloid and more serious press.

There are many adages about knowing the past so as to understand the present, but perhaps the most obvious lies in the routine of clinical practice. For what sort of doctor would dream of making a diagnosis without eliciting a good history?

So this collection has been published in the belief that there is an intrinsic importance in the history of psychiatry, which must not be neglected. It also demonstrates, quite openly, the trend towards historical scholarship, in that while the first five lectures were delivered by medical practitioners, three of the last five are by professional historians. Likewise the detailed references of the modern work are missing from the earlier lectures, indicating a more demanding use of sources and a more scientific approach to historiography. Yet such historical analysis equates closely with the biopsychosocial approach of psychiatric assessment, sharing methods and concerns. That such interest also needs to be fostered and assisted by psychiatrists seems undeniable, and it is hoped that many colleagues will turn with questioning curiosity to their own past.

Note The lectures by Denis Leigh (1973), Jonathan Miller (1976) and Richard Hunter (1977) are sadly unavailable for publication. That by Michael Shepherd (1984) has attained publication as a book in its own right and thus could not be included here.

1 The history of psychiatry as the history of an art

JAMES BIRLEY

T. S. Eliot, standing on his doorstep, with his *Boston Evening Transcript* in his hand, "turned wearily as he would turn to nod goodbye to Rochefoucauld if the street were time and he at the end of the street". The same weary gaze characterises the attitude of most psychiatrists towards important figures in the history of their subject. A crude indication of this state of affairs is the total absence of any historical questions in most psychiatric examinations. For its jobbing practitioners, psychiatry might as well exist in a historical vacuum. And why not? History has its own snares and delusions. Henry Ford called it "bunk". Alfred North Whitehead remarked that "a science which hesitates to forget its founders is lost". And Karl Popper (1972), who has done a thorough demolition job on the concept of 'historicism', has warned us that "if our civilization is to survive, we must break with the habit of deference to great men". In contrast to psychiatrists, students of art study its history for at least a year. If we regarded psychiatry as an art, how does our history look then?

Time is of little or no relevance to the artist. The shapes of nude human figures, of landscapes, of clouds and of the sea have not changed over the centuries, and neither has the spectrum of colours available and the means of applying them to a surface. An art student learns the use of distortion, of perspective, of colour, of chiaroscuro and other techniques which have been discovered, abandoned, and rediscovered over the centuries. There are many examples of the profound impact of one art form on another, although they have been separated by a considerable gap of time; the rediscovery, or reappraisal, of Greek and Roman art, for instance, in the 13th and 14th centuries in Europe; or more recently, the impact of Japanese and Chinese art on painting and drawing. These unfamiliar forms are not merely appreciated and understood, they can be actually used and incorporated. It is this which gives them their impact. A past style can be once again put to use; the past becomes a useful tool for the present. Solutions to a particular artistic problem can be seen, admired, and assimilated.

If we look at the history of psychiatry for what are the equivalents of the

1

use of distortion, perspective, colour and so forth, and how they have been used over the centuries, then I would suggest that the equivalent is the use of theory. There are ony a limited number of theories which we use in psychiatry, just as there are a limited number of basic variables in painting or music or sculpture. There are, for instance, theories of possession, of physical disturbance, of social causes, and of psychological functioning, such as learning theory or theories of the unconscious. Even these, you may say, are too many and overlap with one another. If we look at the history of psychiatry, not so much as the history of people, but the history of theories, then time starts to contract and the distant figures at the other end of the street seem suddenly a great deal nearer; and sometimes they turn out to be remarkably like ourselves.

As an example, let us first take what one may call 'organic theory': that psychiatric disturbance is caused by, or at least accompanied by, physical changes in the body affecting the brain. This is an ancient theory and was certainly held by Hippocrates and his school. He insisted, for instance, that epilepsy, which was, and still is, frequently explained in demonological terms, was due to a physical condition of the brain (see Chadwick & Mann, 1950). But he also regarded psychological phenomena in physical terms. This, for instance, is what he says about dreams:

> "There are special interpreters, with their own science of these matters, for the god-given dreams which give to cities or to individuals foreknowledge of the future. Such people also interpret the signs derived from the psyche which indicate bodily states; excess or lack of what is natural, or of some unusual change. In such matters they are sometimes right and sometimes wrong, but in neither case do they know why it happens, whether they are right or wrong, but nevertheless they give advice so you shall 'beware of taking harm'. Yet they never show you how you ought to beware, but merely tell you to pray to the gods. Prayer is a good thing, but one should take on part of the burden oneself and call on the gods only to help."

> "The *facts* about dreams are as follows: those that merely consist of a transference to the night of a person's daytime actions and thought, which continue to happen in normal fashion just as they were done and thought during the day, are good, for they indicate a healthy state. This is because the psyche remains true to its daytime cogitations, and is overcome neither by excess nor by emptiness, nor by any other extraneous circumstance. But when dreams take on a character contrary to daytime activity and involve conflict or victory over them, then they constitute a sign of bodily disturbance. The seriousness of the conflict is an indication of the seriousness of the mischief. Now concerning this I make no judgement whether or not you ought to avert the consequence by appropriate rites. But I do advise treatments of the body, for an excretion resulting from some bodily superfluity has disturbed the psyche. If the opposing force be strong it is a good thing to give an emetic and to administer a gradually increasing light diet for five days, or order frequent early morning walks, gradually becoming more brisk, and gymnastics for those accustomed to this form of

exercise, proportionate in severity to the increase of diet. If the opposing force be weaker, dispense with the emetic, reduce the diet by a third and restore the cut by a gradual measure over five days. Strenuous walks and the use of vocal exercises will put an end to the disturbance."

Hippocrates believed in, but certainly did not originate, the humoral theory that health depended on a balance of the four humours: blood, phlegm, yellow bile and black bile, corresponding to the qualities of heat, cold, dryness and moisture. In the last 200 years this theory has been elaborated and its propositions made more specific, as our knowledge of brain function and structure and biochemistry has increased.

Whatever the details of such theories, the therapeutic and social consequences remain the same. Treatment is by physical means, and the patients are regarded as having an illness, like any other sort of physical illness, and should be treated in an ordinary hospital. There should be no stigma and no magic surrounding mental illness, either for the patients or for the staff looking after them. The following will serve as illustration.

> "Two causes contribute powerfully to retard our knowledge of and control over insanity. The first is the prevailing notion of its mysterious origin and nature, as if it involved some deep moral stigma or was inseparably bound up with something of horror and altogether beyond the influence of the ordinary laws of animate nature. The second is the popular notion of the cruel treatment of lunatics, and the great aversion thence arising either to have the patients removed to an asylum or even to admit that insanity really exists. Every effort is consequently made by both patient and friends to suppress and conceal the truth, and treatment is deferred from the early stage in which it can generally cure to that later stage in which all the resources of art are too often unavailing. Before full justice can be done to the unhappy lunatic, these prejudices must be destroyed, and the wholesome and comforting truth made widely known, that insanity is neither an anomalous visitation of a mysterious Providence, nor an affliction involving any stigma, or incapable of cure. The public must be taught to regard it simply as a disease of the body arising from natural causes, governed by the ordinary laws of the animal economy and, like other diseases, amenable to proper treatment when early attended to; and they must be led to regard asylums as infirmaries for the cure and kind treatment of that disease, and resort to them with the same confidence as they now do to other infirmaries for a fracture or a fever. Insanity, rightly considered, involves no moral stigma any more than consumption or inflammation, and the sooner the atmosphere of mystery and horror is cleared away from it, the happier for the unfortunate sufferers". (Quoted by Goshen, 1967)

This was written in 1850 by Andrew Combe, the Scottish phrenologist, at a time when phrenology was very much in vogue. His opinion is almost word for word the same as that of my old mentor, Dr William Sargant, whose own particular organic theory might be called 'Pavlovology', and it is not very different from what the DHSS, advised by the psychiatric profession, is saying now. It can be called 'optimistic' or 'manic' organic theory, and we should remind ouselves that it is liable to be followed by a pessimistic or depressive side – a feeling that when the gamut of physical therapy has been run, there is nothing further to be done. The patients are regarded as suffering from an incurable disease, and on the whole doctors are never at their best when asked to cope with the incurable. Certainly this depressive view began to prevail during the hundred years which followed Andrew Combe's pronouncements, when organic theory was affected by ideas of 'degeneration' and genetic predestination, and it reached its psychotic nadir with the final organic solution of the mental hospital population of Germany in the 1930s and '40s.

Another example is that of social theory: that it is the environment in which people live which makes them ill and that the environment in which they are treated affects the outcome of their illness. This concept has to be kept distinct from the idea that the State has a responsibility for looking after its sick members. This is a very old idea, but the relationship of the environment to the causation and treatment of insanity is comparatively recent and, I suspect, has its origin at a time when people became more aware of their ability and their responsibility to control their environment. The year 1792–93 is often regarded as a pivotal date in European history, and we can, without too much sophistry, regard it as a year of importance, if not for social theory, then for social practice. It was then that, in York, a group of Quakers planned the opening of a house for the mentally ill, as a reaction to the poor care which one of their number had received at the York Asylum, which was soon to be the scene of one of the many scandals which have affected, and improved, the life of the psychiatric patient. In France, Dr Philippe Pinel , as a member of the National Guard, witnessed the execution of the King on 21 January 1793. Later, as we all know, he returned to civilian life and proceeded to release the chained inmates of Bicêtre. The Tukes at York were humane laymen; Pinel, besides being a doctor, was a sophisticated mathematician, with strong views on the need for statistical inquiries in psychiatry. Together, we can see them as products of the Age of Enlightenment which began to impose a more humanitarian view about the 'right environment' for the mentally ill, and ushered in the era of 'moral treatment'. The initial success of these methods led to the strong advocacy for a society and way of life which could reduce the amount of mental ill-health or prevent its occurrence – the concept of preventive psychiatry and mental hygiene. Once more we are on familiar ground.

> "I doubt if ever the history of the world, or the experience of past ages could show a larger amount of insanity than that of the present day. It seems, indeed, as if the world was moving at an advanced rate of speed proportionate to its approaching end; as though, in this rapid race of time, increasing with each revolving century, a higher pressure is engendered on the minds of men; and with this there appears a tendency among all classes constantly to demand higher standards of intellectual attainment, a faster

speed of intellectual travelling, greater fancies, greater forces, larger means than are commensurate with health."

This was the position in 1857, according to Dr John Hawkes, an assistant medical officer to the Wilts County Asylum – not perhaps, to our eyes, the most frenetic of places. He had positive proposals to deal with this situation:

> "Just as we appoint officers of public health, whose business it is to hunt out fever and contagious maladies, the offspring of ignorance and neglect, and to trace them to their lair, and to strangle them at birth, let us think how the same principles of prevention may be applied to diseases of the mind."

He felt the whole community should be involved in this programme:

> "Let us endeavour to promote mental sanitary reform by combining to introduce those changes in the social conditions, more especially of the working classes, by which that high pressure system, so prejudicial to the health of the mind, shall be slackened, and the strain, which it occasions, relaxed. Let the hours of labour be abridged and let childhood no longer share the curse of the Fall. Let the multitudes, who have not the means or opportunities of learning from books, be instructed by public teachers the first principles of mental as well as physical hygiene."

These statements are taken from Professor Rosen's (1959) delightful article illustrating the earlier days of social psychiatry in the 18th and 19th centuries. Halcyon days they seem in some ways, with the blossoming of moral treatment giving grounds for the general humanitarian optimism of so many of the psychiatrists of that time, and leaving us, too, with a curious feeling of *déjà vu*.

The history of theories of the unconscious has been so fully documented by Dr Ellenberger and others that it would be impertinent to attempt a mere précis. Since at least the time of Plato there have been many fascinating and promising theories and observations about the unconscious, especially during the 19th century. The dogmatic acceptance of Freudian theory, for which Freud can only be partly blamed, has led to a rather static period in this particular field. I would, however, like to use the Freudian episode as an example of the effect of different types of theory, and in particular to contrast 'limited' with 'comprehensive' theories, and for this purpose to contrast the teaching of Hippocrates with that of Galen. Hippocrates' theory is, in addition to being non-magical, practically non-theoretical. He is humble, in so far as he says that medicine is very difficult, and he reports patients who die in spite of treatment. He believes that prognosis is the best guide and the most reliable indicator of the nature of the illness. He is an avid and accurate observer of physical and psychological signs and symptoms, and he can be taken as a model for the 'natural history' approach to disease. The physician is the observant naturalist, putting his data together to fit his experience, treating as best he can, avoiding making the patient worse, and relying on nature to play her part. It is not a particularly curious or inquiring approach, but it is modest, not too biased, and self-perpetuating on the basis of 'experience'.

It was just this last characteristic that aroused the objection of more analytically minded doctors such as Galen, who commented that "there is no standard by which a thing can be judged as having been seen very many times. The conclusive number is decided arbitrarily by the observer himself". This problem of validation has bothered philosophers and scientists both before and since Galen's time. Galen, who lived from 130 to 200 AD, was a prolific writer with an analytical mind. In addition to writing some 500 treatises on various subjects, including logic, ethics, and grammar, he found time to make a number of experimental observations which were far ahead of his time. He made accurate observations of the effects of total and partial transections of the spinal cord, and noted the two different sets of nerve roots. (Their separate function was not elucidated for another 1700 years.) He found that in those cases in which the facial muscles were paralysed with the rest of the body the lesion was in the brain, while if it was in the spinal cord the face was spared. He made observations on the regional causes of convulsions which anticipated those of Hughlings Jackson. So far so good; but Galen also wrote equally convincingly of the three Platonic spirits and the three fundamental members, and he extrapolated his findings of the anatomy of the bodies of numerous animals he had dissected to the body of man, which he had not. These opinions persisted for some 1500 years (Riese, 1963).

Galen provides us with a good example of a brilliant analytical mind which perpetuated a number of totally fallacious but very persuasive theories – theories which lasted for many centuries. It is instructive to consider why his influence was so powerful. Partly, perhaps, because he was such an outstanding person, partly because his ideas were irrefutable, and partly because they followed the same line of thought as those of Plato and Aristotle, two philosophers who profoundly influenced, and were adopted by, Christianity. Galen's theories thus became institutionalised in very powerful company. Today, we can still make contrasts between cautious, limited, 'open' theories, and bolder, all-embracing, 'closed' theories. The latter persist today for the same reasons; they are irrefutable and systematic, and derive much support from influential opinion.

So far I have developed and illustrated my initial theme that in the teaching of its history it is useful to regard psychiatry as an art and its theories as art forms which have a certain immediacy to us, though separated by centuries. For the second half, the themes, like the teams in a football match, must be reversed, and I must develop the theme that art is a science, or at least as much of a science as psychiatry. As I am neither an artist nor an art historian, I need an artist to assist me. So I have selected John Constable, for three reasons: firstly, because he is an English artist whose work is familiar; secondly, we know a good deal, from his letters and memoirs (Leslie, 1951), about his personal and artistic development and his view on art; thirdly, and perhaps most important, he has already been examined by the creative mind of Professor Ernst Gombrich (1972) in his marvellous book, *Art and Illusion*.

John Constable lived from 1776 to 1837, 60 years which covered the end of one era and the beginning of another, both for art and for science. Two years before his birth, Priestley announced the discovery of oxygen; in the year before his death, Magendie could claim that pathological phenomena were a consequence of altered physiological processes, and therefore the aim of medicine should be to study normal and abnormal 'pathological physiology'. During his life, psychiatry had moved into the flourishing era of moral treatment. In the field of poetry, Crabbe had described the new realities of rural life in the old style of Augustan couplets; Wordsworth had taken things a good deal further by recording his own and his sister's rural experiences in the form of "experiments to ascertain how far the language of conversation in the middle and lower classes of society is adapted to the purposes of poetic pleasure".

Seen retrospectively, Constable was of this movement. In particular, he had artistic affinities with Wordsworth, and one of the first people to recognise his talent, although he never liked his style, was Sir George Beaumont, Wordsworth's patron. "Painting", he said, "is a science and should be pursued as an inquiry into the laws of nature. Why, then, may not landscape painting be considered a branch of natural philosophy, of which pictures are but the experiments?" Like Wordsworth, he hated 'style' for its own sake. "The great vice of the present day", he said, "is 'bravura', an attempt to do something beyond the truth. Fashion always had, and will have, its day; but truth in all things only will last, and can only have just claims on posterity. The deteriorations of art has everywhere proceeded from similar causes, the imitation of preceding styles with little reference to nature". "Observe that thy best director, thy perfect guide, is Nature. She is above all teachers, and ever confide in her with a bold heart, especially *when thou beginnest to feel that there is a sentiment in drawing*." This advice, with the last clause underlined, he copied from a book by Cennino Cennini, a pupil of Agnolo Gaddi, whose father painted under Giotto for 24 years.

What did this mean in practice? In the first place, Constable was an extremely accurate observer of the English countryside, in particular of that small part of Suffolk and Essex which he loved so dearly. The son of a miller, he had worked a windmill himself, and he understood the sky. Many of his paintings and sketches of the sky have the date, the time of day, the direction of the wind, and other details written on the back. They remind one of the notebooks of a naturalist, such as Gilbert White, a man he greatly admired. "The mind that produced the 'Selborne' is such a one as I have always envied," he wrote. "The single page of the life of Mr White leaves a more lasting impression on my mind than all that has been written of

Charles V or any other renowned hero. It shows what a real love of nature will do."

If he was an accurate observer, he was also an accurate painter of the countryside: for instance, of the order in which reapers work, or the order in which cows drink at a pool. But he chiefly insisted on accurate light and colour, and particularly on allowing the colour green to return to the landscape. Conventional taste had banished it. "I believe that the beauty of pictures", wrote a contemporary critic, "is in inverse ratio to their fidelity, and that nature must be stripped of her green livery and dressed in the browns of the painters, or confined to her own autumnal tints in order to be transferred to the canvas". His friend, Sir George Beaumont, sub-scribed to this view, and recommended the colour of an old Cremona fiddle for the prevailing tone of everything. Constable replied by laying on old fiddle on the green lawn in front of the house. "What a sad thing it is," he wrote to his friend, Leslie, "that this lovely art is so wrested in its own destruction. Used only to blind our eyes to prevent us from seeing the sun shine, the fields bloom, the trees blossom and from hearing the foliage rustle; while old, black, rubbed-out and dirty canvases take the place of God's own works."

And, finally, Constable emphasised again and again the importance of long and arduous application in studying nature, to understand it and to attempt to transfer this understanding to canvas. He regarded painting of 'pure imagina-tion' as a resource of the technically and imaginatively destitute.

But if we see Constable as a faithful copier of nature, we do him an injustice. A picture is not a reflection, it is the product of a creative act brought about, to use one of Constable's favourite expressions, by "uniting imagination with nature". When painting Wivenhoe Park, for instance, he writes to his fiancée: "The great difficulty has been to get so much in it as they wanted. On my left is a grotto, with some elms, at the head of a piece of water; in the centre is the house over a beautiful wood; and very far to the right is a deer house which it was necessary to add, so that my view comprehended too large a space. But today I have got over the difficulty and begin to like it myself." When his two friends went to visit Flatford soon after his death, they were astonished to find so much of the material for most of his major works to be concentrated in a small space. But they often found that he had combined and varied the materials. For "The Haywain", for instance, he had "increased the width of the river to great advantage", while "the appearance of Dedham Mill is greatly improved, in every picture which Constable painted of it, by his showing the water-wheel which is in reality hidden". The cows in front of Salisbury Cathedral have no horns; they are not Wiltshire but Suffolk cows, and to Constable's eyes, probably thus "greatly improved".

"Rien n'est beau que le vrai" – Constable copied out this saying of Boileau into one of his notebooks – "only what is true is beautiful", a phrase echoed later by Keats, but, in order to reach an artistic truth, nature, which

Constable so loved and revered, has to be reinterpreted: a river widened, a lake shortened, a hidden water-wheel revealed, or a cow deprived of its horns.

A work of art is a human statement of a particular theory about the way experience can be represented in a symbolic form. In arriving at an artistic truth, a process of selection and distortion goes on to produce a symbolic representation of the original. This process of transformation depends on the symbols which are available to the artist. Constable, with his scorn of mere copying, stated that: "When I sit down to make a sketch from nature, the first thing I try to do is to forget that I have ever seen a picture." But his pictures are recognisably his very own and bear the powerful imprint of his symbols as well as of the Suffolk landscape. When trying to represent what we experience, we are all limited by our own schemata, our own range of available symbols.

As psychiatrists, we too are faced with the problem of transforming the data about the patient, by a process of symbolic representation, into what we feel to be a truth. Like Constable faced with Wivenhoe Park, we may feel "the difficulty of getting so much in" to our picture, and we have to get over that difficulty by selection. What we select depends on the schemata which we have acquired from our own personal experience and from our professional training. As it is human beings who are concerned, there is a considerable interaction between ourselves and our patients, who may suggest different schemata if we have eyes and ears to perceive them, or who may be persuaded to adopt our own. As an example, take the picture of one of the famous demonstrations given by Charcot of hysteria. The patient is beginning to adopt the characteristic position of the 'hysteric'. On the wall is a picture of the position which everybody expects her to adopt. This process of suggestion has been regarded by some writers as being the essential activity of psychiatry. It is, in my opinion, a caricature, but it is no good dismissing Dr Szasz's or anybody else's theories on the basis of a personal opinion. The schemata which we adopt in assessing and treating our patients are all based on theories. The only difference between artistic and scientific theories is the nature of the truth with which they are concerned, and in particular the way in which they can be tested.

It is here that Karl Popper's writings are so helpful. He has clarified the false dichotomy between 'science' and 'meaning'. We must accept that much of what is most meaningful in our lives does not fall into the purview of science and may never do so. He has also propounded a solution to the problem of 'validation' which so troubled Galen and many others. This is that the essential aspect of a 'scientific' theory is that it should suggest refutation rather than proof; and thus a theory can only be called scientific if it predicts means by which it can be refuted. There is no absolute truth, no 'laws' of nature. Scientific 'truth' is a man-made theory which explains, in symbolic form, the largest number of phenomena, but remains refutable. A 'better' scientific theory is one which not only explains the phenomena accounted for by a previous theory but also those for which the previous theory could not account. Artistic truth is also a man-made theory, using symbols and "uniting imagination with nature", but its only 'proof' is by human experience, based on validation. A 'better' scientific theory includes and replaces its predecessor. A better artistic theory may replace its predecessor and become, in Kuhn's (1962) terms, the fashionable paradigm, but after a time, the previous theory may be revived to replace it once more.

The field of psychiatry is at present littered with a mixture of irrefutable theories which explain a great deal, and refutable theories which explain only a very little. There are, I believe, two main reasons for this. The first derives from the considerable difficulties of method and measurement in testing the theories which we may hold. The second is our laudable therapeutic concern. 'Explanation' in itself reduces anxiety both in ourselves and in our patients. Leibnitz showed that any phenomenon was open to an infinite number of explanations, and Popper has demonstrated that a self-contradictory theory can embrace all statements. We have a tendency to regard the outcome following treatment as a test of the validity of its underlying theory. This is quite unwarranted, whether for ECT or for psychoanalysis.

So what is left may be legitimately called an artistic exercise. Indeed, psychiatric education provides a curious mixture of life class and a debating society. We need to be explicitly aware of this, for three reasons. Firstly, in any art form there is good and bad art, and never a great child artist. Art is a branch of natural philosophy which requires arduous application. Secondly, it can become just as hidebound and resistant to new ideas as can science, especially by 'totalitarian' or 'comprehensive' theories. Thirdly, for those with a sense of our history, it is clearly a prey to fashion. The wanderings of psychiatric theory have been to some extent circular. This is because the theories are still 'myths', or art forms, rather than scientific theories. We are thus still in a maze, and in order to find our way out we must look for a scientific thread. Indeed, we will have to spin one, and, like the most creative of all threads, it will be a spiral one, spun between conjecture on one side and refutation on the other, and every important turn will involve somebody apparently going round the bend. Just at present, we are, artistically speaking, in an optimistic phase, but we have been there before, some 150 years ago when 'moral treatment' and 'non-restraint' were flourishing, and Constable was studying the wind and the clouds and the corn fields waving beneath them.

"The readers of the *Boston Evening Transcript*", said T. S. Eliot, "sway in the wind like a field of ripe corn." Does that apply, too, to the readers of the *British Journal of Psychiatry*? If, instead of turning wearily, we gaze intently at the figures at the other end of the street, we may notice that they are trying to give us an answer.

References

CHADWICK, J. & MANN, W. N. (1950) Hippocrates, *The Medical Works*, pp. 194–195. Oxford: Blackwell.

GOMBRICH, E. H. (1972) *Art and Illusion*. London: Phaidon Press.

GOSHEN, C. E. (1967) *Documentary History of Psychiatry*, pp. 561–562. London: Vision Press.

KUHN, T. S. (1962) *The Structure of Scientific Revolutions*. Chicago.

LESLIE, C. R. (1951) *Memoirs of the Life of John Constable*. London: Phaidon Press.

POPPER, K. R. (1972) *The Logic of Scientific Discovery*. London: Hutchinson.

RIESE, W. R. (1963) In *Galen on the Passions and Errors of the Soul* (trans. P. W. Harkins). Ohio: Ohio State University Press.

ROSEN, G. (1959) Social stress and mental disease from the eighteenth century to the present: some origins of social psychiatry. *Millbank Memorial Fund Quarterly*, **37**, 5–32.

2 Medico-psychologists, Maudsley and The Maudsley

ALEXANDER WALK

Four circumstances (in addition to my own limitations as a historian) have determined my choice of subject for this evening. Last November, this Institute celebrated its jubilee, that is, the 50th anniversary of the recognition of the Maudsley Hospital as a School of the University of London. In the following month, the one-time Medico-Psychological Association, which owed its very name to a suggestion by Henry Maudsley, and has now developed into the Royal College of Psychiatrists, moved into its new headquarters in Belgrave Square. Since then we have had to mourn the death of Sir Aubrey Lewis, one of whose outstanding contributions to the Association, and to psychiatric history, was his Maudsley Lecture of 1951, devoted to the work and influence of Henry Maudsley.* Moreover, the early '70s are the centenary years of Maudsley's period of office as the senior editor of the *Journal of Mental Science*, now the *British Journal of Psychiatry*, with which I myself have long been associated. So it seemed that it might be appropriate for me to tell you something about the history of the Association, about Maudsley's relations with it, and about the various ideas, proposals and actions which eventually led to the foundation of this Hospital and Institute. In doing this I hope to furnish a few footnotes, as it were, to Sir Aubrey's Maudsley and Mapother lectures, and these will be my personal tribute to one whom so many of us have held in affectionate admiration.

When Henry Maudsley was born in 1835, two major influences on his future career were already prominent. His first introduction to psychiatry was to be at Wakefield Asylum, now Stanley Royd Hospital; this was a county asylum founded by avowed admirers of the York Retreat and where it was intended to apply the humanitarian principles of the Retreat on a large scale. Here the Medical Director, Dr (afterwards Sir William) Ellis, had been able to pioneer many innovations such as the employment of

---

* Sir Hubert Bond's Maudsley Lecture of 1931 was entitled "Maudsley – Testimonied in his own Bringings-forth". Unfortunately this was never published, and its contents are unknown.

patients in industrial work and in individual occupations; he gave the more stable increased freedom and enlisted the sympathy and help of local residents. He was the first to advocate and to take practical steps towards the after-care of discharged patients, and he expressed the highest hopes and ideals for the future of mental nursing. Among other things, Ellis asserted the claim to independence of the Medical Director, as being the specialist on mental disorders, against the rival pretensions of the visiting general physician, and here the controversy foreshadowed a much later one which was to be an integral part of the pre-history of the Maudsley Hospital.

The other major influence was that of John Conolly, Maudsley's future father-in-law, who a few years earlier had published his *Indications of Insanity*. There is in the library of this Institute a copy annotated by the author in his own hand, and in these notes he says among other things that in any future edition the last chapter (Chapter XI) might be omitted. But to us it is this chapter that is of the greatest interest, for it sets out in a few words what is really a scheme for a National Mental Health Service. Every asylum, he says, should be the property of the State and all the officers should be appointed by the Secretary of State. Medical officers and keepers should be ready at all times to attend to insane patients at their own houses and as soon as signs of insanity appeared there should be an immediate visit by a medical officer. Every asylum should be a school of instruction for students and for keepers, and medical practitioners of the district would be medical associates of the asylum and become accustomed to attend to insane patients. Patients out of the asylum would be the majority, and so better arrangements might be made for the smaller number in the public asylums or 'central houses of reception'.

When a few years later Conolly became Resident Physician to Hanwell Asylum, no such reforms had been initiated, and instead of being able to treat patients at the very outset of their illness, he was on the contrary overwhelmed with chronic cases who had been retained in workhouses by Poor-Law officials who considered troublesomeness rather than curability to be the proper criterion for transfer to the asylum. Meanwhile he established his reputation as the leader of the 'non-restraint' movement. In the small world of English psychiatry of the time, the years 1840 and 1841 looked as though they were to be remembered chiefly as years of dissension and controversy between those practising the new 'system', as they called it, and their opponents. Reading the correspondence in the *Lancet* during those years I have been led to wonder whether the term 'non-restraint' was being applied to a style of journalism rather than to a mode of treatment.

Yet, in that same year of 1841, a few courageous men made their successful attempt to join into one Association doctors who seemed to be showing so much disunity. Prominent among these were two who bore the prophetic name of Samuel – Samuel Hitch and Samuel Gaskell – and a few words about each of these may serve to show how progressive were those founder-fathers in their ideas and practices.

Samuel Hitch was Resident Physician at the Gloucester Asylum, which as Horton Road Hospital has recently celebrated its 150th anniversary and at that time was a 'mixed' asylum for both private and county patients. Besides having the highest recovery rate in the country, he was the first to grant trial leave to convalescent patients, and he countenanced voluntary admission to the extent that, as the Commissioners put it, "ten or twelve pauper lunatics appear to have ingress and egress from the asylum at all times at their own discretion" – both practices heavily frowned on by the Commissioners and the latter suppressed for many years. He employed a female nurse in a male refractory ward, and he created a small self-governing unit for the patients who worked in the gardens, who enjoyed almost unlimited freedom. And lastly he encouraged young doctors and students and "young ladies of education" to come into the asylum and join in social gatherings with the private patients and his own family.

The name of Gaskell is familiar to those of you who may have competed for the Gaskell Medal and Prize of the College (as many of the staff of the Maudsley Hospital have done from its inception), or who may be thinking of competing. Samuel Gaskell had his first psychiatric experience at the Manchester Lunatic Asylum, at that time still in its cramped and unwholesome quarters in the centre of the city before its removal to Cheadle, where Maudsley was to be its superintendent. In 1840 Gaskell became Resident Superintendent of Lancaster Asylum and here he virtually revolutionised the living conditions of both patients and nursing staff. He not only did away with restraints, but gave active encouragement to mutual assistance among the patients. He became specially interested in the idiot children who at that time were admitted to the asylum, and placed some of them in the individual care of adult women patients; and his description of what was being done for the mentally defective in Paris was the starting point of the movement which led to the foundation of Earlswood and other institutions for the mentally defective in this country. Later, in 1860, when he had been a Commissioner for some years, he wrote the short article entitled "On the Want of Better Provision for the Labouring and Middle Classes When Attacked or Threatened with Insanity", in which he advocated voluntary admission of "mild, transient, incipient and convalescent cases" to a new class of houses specially provided for the purpose. Besides what I have said about Samuel Hitch's practice, the case for voluntary admission had in fact been forcibly argued 30 years earlier by Matthew Allen, better remembered, if at all, for his connection with John Clare and with Tennyson. But Gaskell had some success here, for voluntary admission to licensed houses and to registered hospitals, although not to public asylums, was legalised within a very few years.

So the body known for its first 15 years as the Association of Medical Officers of Asylums and Hospitals for the Insane – the oldest society of its kind in the world – came into being and made a good start with its first annual meeting in Nottingham. Besides the official minutes, we possess an account of this meeting by a foreign observer, who has much praise for the way it was conducted – the careful scrutiny of the institution and the detailed discussion of its features, the absence of "misplaced vanity or professional jealousy" and the members' resolve to try out every suggested means of treatment before the next meeting. The original impetus seems to have been lost after the first two or three years; the revival came in the early 1850s with the increase in membership consequent on the building of many new county asylums under legislation which made this mandatory. Regular meetings were now held, a permanent presidency was instituted, and above all the Association undertook the publication of a journal. Although this made the most modest start under the unpretentious title of *The Asylum Journal*, yet in the 'Prospectus' prefaced to the very first number its editor, Dr (afterwards Sir John) Bucknill, was asserting the claim of psychiatry to be a specialty, and the need for the psychiatric physician to undergo "a second education" because, as he put it, "in the psychical mode of cure the vehicle, as it were, in which the medicine is administered is the person of the physician himself". Within a very few years he had added the words '*of Mental Science*' to the original title, then dropped the '*Asylum*' prefix, and changed the format to something more suitable for a scientific periodical. He planned to deal with "mental science in its practical, that is in its sociological point of view" and to cover "mental physiology and pathology with their vast range of inquiry into all things which tend to cause mental disease or preserve mental health". This he achieved, to the extent that so discerning a critic as Sir Aubrey Lewis could say that, reading these early volumes, he had become convinced that in the Association there was as much capacity and erudition as might be found now – that is in 1950 – in a much larger circle of our members, and perhaps more vitality; and, also in 1950, our then President-Elect, going through these volumes in search of ideas for his address, was struck by the ferocity and outspokenness of the early editors, whom he described as wielding flails and scorpions. It was this journal to which Maudsley sent his first essays and which he himself later edited.

Maudsley joined the Association in 1858, when he had completed his first experience of asylum work at Wakefield. Officially the 'house surgeon', he was in fact locum superintendent. Thus in psychiatry he was entirely self-taught, but he must have assimilated some of the Ellis tradition; and he was so highly esteemed that it was the permanent superintendent who took office after his departure, J. D. Cleaton, afterwards a Commissioner, who recommended him to the Committee of the Manchester Lunatic Hospital, by then happily removed to Cheadle, of which he was given the charge at the age of 24.

During these first years of his membership of the Association, Maudsley must have read the memorable addresses given by successive presidents of outstanding personality – Conolly, Sir Charles Hastings and Bucknill, the discussions and comments on the Report of the Select Committee of 1859, perhaps the Report itself and the evidence presented to it, and the review of Arlidge's book *On the State of Lunacy*, and he must have become aware of the anxieties and frustrations expressed by his colleagues; in fact the high hopes of curative treatment with which the asylums had been founded were being dissipated, first by seemingly immovable obstacles to early treatment, and then by the inordinate growth of the asylums and the utter inadequacy of means for the study and care of individual patients. Removal of the stigma of pauperisation and authority to admit voluntary patients were two of the reforms demanded by the Association and reiterated by its presidents.

Then Maudsley, writing from Cheadle, began to contribute to the *Journal* that series of philosophical and psychological articles most of which have been fully summarised and evaluated by Sir Aubrey, beginning in 1860 with his "Correlation of Mental and Physical Force". In his autobiographical note, however, Maudsley recalled that it was his article on the life and infirmities of Edgar Allen Poe that excited most attention and made him favourably known. In this article, only mentioned in passing by Sir Aubrey, are seen some of Maudsley's most characteristic approaches: his compassion towards "the feeble being struggling in the midst of the irresistible, grasping painfully after development in untoward circumstances"; his scorn for "the censorious and complacent in their stuccoed villas" whom he stigmatised as "the stuccoed man"; and, on the other hand, his doomwatching preoccupation with degradation and degeneracy, where he asserts that the poor children that might have been born to the drunken Poe and his cousin wife would assuredly have been blind or deaf, strumous, epileptic or mad.

Having thus made himself known both for his literary works and for his achievements at Cheadle, Maudsley, in his own words "became restless and threw himself on to London". He arrived almost as a young man seeking his fortune, for in 1862 he was living in what must have been modest quarters in Camden Town. But in 1864 he was appointed as one of the two physicians to the West London Hospital, another example of how much brilliance and reputation, rather than experience, were valued in those mid-Victorian times.

Now it so happened that in 1862 John Bucknill was appointed Lord Chancellor's Visitor in Lunacy and thereupon resigned his office as Editor of the *Journal*. As his successor he recommended Lockhart Robertson, the Association's General Secretary; Robertson was the superintendent of what was then the Sussex County Asylum at Haywards Heath, and a prolific contributor to the *Journal*. He was duly elected, and immediately announced that Maudsley had promised his cooperation; and in the following year the matter was regularised by Maudsley's election as joint Editor with Robertson. To succeed Robertson as Secretary, the 1862 meeting elected Harrington Tuke, who owned and superintended a licensed house, the Manor House at Chiswick (incidentally, he was in no way related to the

Tukes of the York Retreat) and who was married to the elder of John Conolly's daughters. These details have to be given because of the part Tuke played in Maudsley's later history.

At this 1862 meeting both Conolly and Maudsley were present, and Conolly took the opportunity to express the hope that the *Journal* would advance a cause dear to him, namely the need for schools for clinical instruction in the nature and treatment of mental maladies, and the need for this study to be "placed in that rank which it ought to have among the departments of medical science". He also wished the *Journal* to give attention to "a larger intercourse with our foreign brethren, a more intimate knowledge of what is doing". Undoubtedly Maudsley took these pleas to heart; we shall see presently what he did about the first, but the second he responded to at once, for from 1863 onwards the *Journal* included a bulky section at first called "Report on the Progress of Psychological Medicine" and later "Psychological Retrospect", which consisted of abstracts of psychiatric literature from the leading countries. Maudsley was already a favourite of Conolly's, and not long afterwards he married Conolly's younger daughter, Ann. Then, shortly before Conolly's death in 1866, he took over the running of Lawn House at Hanwell, which had been Conolly's residence since he had left the great asylum nearby, and which was also a tiny licensed house accommodating no more than six ladies. This became his home for many years, and in 1911 he showed his abiding filial piety by presenting to the local council part of the grounds, to be known as Conolly Dell, together with a fountain commemorating the work of his predecessor there.

As one of the Editors, Maudsley now took an increasing part in the affairs of the Association. Almost his first intervention in one of its debates concerned the future of Bethlem Hospital, many years later to be closely linked to his own creation. The problem was this. On the one hand there was a demand for the establishment, to serve the London area, of a 'middle-class' hospital, similar to those in the provinces such as Coton Hill or the Retreat, catering for those above the pauper level but unable to afford the fees of licensed houses, and it was suggested that Bethlem should become that hospital. On the other hand it was generally felt that the building in St George's Road was now outdated and unsuitable for its new role, and that the hospital ought to be removed to a country site perhaps eight or ten miles away. An offer for the old site had in fact been made by the Governors of St Thomas's Hospital, which was about to be displaced from its home in the Borough; but the two institutions had been unable to agree on terms, and the Bethlem Governors were inclined to let their hospital stay where it was. At the meeting the merits of town and country were being argued, as well as the hope that under new conditions Bethlem might become a place of instruction in mental disorders. Maudsley's contribution to the discussion was in total and startling contrast to his views and actions of 40 years later. The irony of it demands that I should quote his actual words: "Can a hospital for mental diseases in a large town be a hospital for that purpose? Does it not rather become a prison? Are not intercourse with nature and employment absolutely necessary? We should not be discussing whether patients should be confined in a large town. A 'hospital' for mental diseases so situated is surely miscalled."

We may, however, think that the Governors' decision against removal was all to the good, since when the union with the Maudsley Hospital eventually took place, Bethlem was able to bring to the marriage a set of modern and well planned buildings, instead of what might have been erected in the 1860s. But, apart from this, Bethlem did go some way towards meeting the general demand – it became a hospital for the 'educated classes', established a country branch and agreed to take a small number of post-graduate pupils. Then, in 1865, Maudsley made a fresh approach to the problem of clinical instruction in mental disorders, through the Medical Committee of the University of London Convocation, and it was resolved that a certificate of a course of instruction should be required for the final MB and that the examination should embrace the subject of insanity. Yet the General Medical Council (GMC) did not make this very modest requirement compulsory until 1885.

In the same year, 1865, Maudsley gave the Association the name by which it was to be known for over a century. It was at his suggestion that the name 'Medico-Psychological Association' (MPA) was adopted. True, this must have been in imitation of the French 'Société Médico-Psychologique'; it was good, nevertheless, to have a title indicating the spread of psychiatry beyond the bounds of institutional care. In fact, membership was now opened to all doctors sufficiently interested to want to join; and some members wished to go further, admitting lawyers and other laymen and forming a society embracing all persons concerned with the welfare of the mentally ill. Maudsley opposed this vigorously and upheld the medical character of the Association; and so the matter was decided.

In 1870 a new threat arose to the very existence of the MPA; this was the proposal by the Royal Medical and Chirurgical Society that all the existing London medical societies should amalgamate with it and lose their identity. Maudsley spoke powerfully against this, and once more helped to preserve the Association as an independent body able to undertake activities which would have been impossible for a mere section of a medical academy. I should add that a similar crisis arose, many years later, still within Maudsley's lifetime, when the Royal Society of Medicine was formed; by this time the MPA's scope was nationwide and the decision was easier.

Maudsley was by now the senior Editor of the *Journal*; as a sample of the contents, I will anticipate a little and take the issue for July 1875. Professor Thomas Laycock of Edinburgh writes on "Organic Laws of Personal and Ancestral Memory"; a set of Morisonian Lectures, begun by David Skae and continued by Clouston follows; then we have Hughlings Jackson on "Syphilitic Affections of the Nervous System"; and an instalment of a study of the "Morbid Psychology of Criminals" by David Nicholson, soon to be Superintendent of Broadmoor; numerous clinical notes and case reports, and the Psychological Retrospect already mentioned; and lastly those verbatim reports of Association meetings that are so precious for the understanding of our predecessors' thoughts and attitudes.

So back to 1871 and Maudsley's Presidency of the MPA. His inaugural address has been touched on by Sir Aubrey in the context of the pithy criticism it received from Clouston – that Maudsley had pronounced it useless to give eugenic advice, useless to send a patient to an asylum, and useless to administer sedative drugs; and to this Maudsley had replied by admitting to scepticism, but in the good sense of examining and looking into things. He had in fact looked most carefully, as far as the knowledge of his time would allow, into the perplexities of genetic counselling; and he had spoken discriminatingly about the indications for admitting patients or for refraining from doing so; thus, referring to young patients whose insanity he wrongly believed to be caused by masturbation, he rightly asserted that in asylums they sank into a hopeless state and that the one thing wanted for them was "some intelligent and judicious person of higher education and position than an attendant who will take a genuine interest in them and gain their confidence". And as to attendants, although he did not go so far as to propose a training scheme, he was perhaps the first to suggest that the MPA might do something towards raising their status by organising an office for the keeping of a register of those who had proved their merit.

Maudsley ceased to be Editor of the *Journal* in circumstances which certainly reflect the dissensions and strife in matters of belief which were so acute in the Victorian age, but from which the small world of psychiatry was generally free. It will be remembered that Maudsley and Harrington Tuke were related by their marriages to John Conolly's daughters. Tuke was now no longer the General Secretary of the Association and had passed the Presidential Chair. At the annual meeting in 1877, when the re-election of the Editors was proposed, he rose to announce that Maudsley would shortly be resigning and moved that Dr Bucknill should be recalled as Editor; he went on to say that certain doctrines were being taught in the *Journal* which were repugnant to him and others, and against which he felt bound to protest. The ensuing discussion did not touch on these tenets and doctrines, and eventually Maudsley was re-elected, although he stated that he did in fact intend to resign before long, and he did so the following year. It seems possible that Harrington Tuke had put pressure on him privately and would have attacked him more openly had he resisted.

I have been at pains to discover what there was in Maudsley's writings in the *Journal*, as distinct from his books, that could cause such hostility. Clearly, Harrington Tuke was a man with strong religious convictions; in his presidential address he had welcomed the opening to patients, by the appointment of chaplains, of "that refuge in which the most miserable may hope for solace"; in no branch of medicine was religious consolation more necessary than in the treatment of mental depression. There is in fact very little to be found in Maudsley's articles that would contradict this; but two passages might be cited. First, from the article on Swedenborg, written in 1869: "It is true that the wrath, the folly, the madness of men are made to praise Him whom sun and moon, winter and summer . . . and the holy and humble bless and magnify, but whom systems of theology and the prophets thereof have so often dishonoured". Second, from the Presidential Address: "Morality has hitherto been the exclusive possession of religion. But so-called moral laws are laws of nature and must come within the scope of scientific study. Has there not been more practical morality in certain scientific discoveries and their application than in half humanity's creeds?" But both these passages were written several years before 1877, so the puzzle remains as to what finally caused Harrington Tuke to lose patience.

After Maudsley's resignation, the *Journal* was continued under the editorship of Clouston, Daniel Hack Tuke (who *was* of the Retreat family, being the son of Samuel Tuke and great-grandson of William Tuke – but we shall meet with yet another unrelated Tuke before long) and George Savage of Bethlem. A few landmarks in the history of the MPA up to the foundation of the Maudsley Hospital might be conveniently mentioned here. After 1885, when, as I have said, a reluctant GMC was persuaded to make some knowledge of mental disorder compulsory, the Association initiated a 'Certificate in Psychological Medicine' (the MPC), an elementary forerunner of the DPM and the MRCPsych. Next the training of mental nurses was taken in hand, and lectures and examinations for the MPA's nursing certificate were introduced – the first nursing qualification to be organised on a national scale – and this was followed by prolonged and eventually successful efforts to have mental nurses included in any scheme for state registration. I will come presently to some other aspects of its activities, and will only add here that in 1892, after having been advised that a petition for a charter would not be well received, the Association applied to the Home Office for permission to use the prefix 'Royal', but this too was refused. As is well known, both ambitions were achieved in 1926.

Maudsley himself continued to attend and speak at meetings of the MPA, and one noteworthy speech of his was in 1887, in a discussion on a proposed Lunacy Acts Amendment Bill, which in modified form eventually became the Lunacy Act of 1890. He denounced the Bill in the strongest terms; it proceeded, he said, entirely upon the incarceration point of view and made the treatment of acute and recent cases impossible. He urged that there should be "some simpler forms to suit fresh cases" and that only after six months or so should all the proposed restrictions be brought in. The reluctance to certify and admit to asylums brought about by the recent agitation had, he said, led to increased cruelty and neglect towards patients kept at home. Such fears were voiced by others, even after the modified Bill had become law; still, one must remember that the changes applied only to private patients, the provisions for the vast majority still officially called paupers being virtually the same as before.

Mysteriously, however, Maudsley's name disappears from the list of members of the MPA after 1890, and he never rejoined. Yet he continued to contribute articles to the *Journal of Mental Science*; two, on "Optimism and Pessimism" and on "Materialism and Spiritualism", were published in 1917, the year before his death, and one was published posthumously in 1919. Thus his writings for our *Journal* cover a span of 60 years. This last group of articles, coming so close together, and followed by his bequest to the MPA, seem to me to have been a gesture of reconciliation, if ever one was needed.

I come now to the great constructive act by which Henry Maudsley is today best remembered – the "living organism", as Sir Aubrey Lewis called it, which he created to be his heir. Sir Aubrey thought that the genesis of the project lay in Maudsley's concern, in the 1860s, with early treatment and in his discussions with Baron Mundy and Crichton-Browne, but here I am compelled to differ. As I have already shown, nothing was further from Maudsley's mind than the creation or the retention of a hospital for mental disorders in London, and what he actually advocated for many years was the treatment of early or mild cases in private houses, or in villas in the grounds or neighbourhood of asylums – a policy which was in fact successfully carried out by George Mould, who succeeded him at Cheadle. The credit for first proposing what we would now call a Maudsley-type hospital should instead go to Dr J. G. Davey, who had been one of the two so-called superintendents at Colney Hatch; in 1867 he was the proprietor of a licensed house near Bristol, but he had not lost his interest in the mental health problems of London, and at a meeting of the MPA he read a paper entitled "On the Insane Poor of Middlesex". With much eloquence he contended that poverty was at the root of mental disorder in these classes, and that reformed and progressive legislation would before long so greatly diminish poverty that insanity too would decline. The great asylums should be regarded as places for mere protection and care, and what was needed for London was "a hospital for the insane poor, one of the most approved construction and embracing all the means essential to the relief and cure of the disordered mind". It must not contain more than 250 beds, otherwise it would be no hospital. He added that he had proposed this to the Committee of Colney Hatch as far back as 1851, and had been met with laughter and impatience.

In the discussion that followed a complementary proposal was put forward, I believe for the first time, by Dr Belgrave, formerly of the Lincolnshire Asylum and then a consultant in London. "In this large metropolis," he said, "there is no institution where the poor may in their incipient condition apply to receive advice or relief. I suggest that some of us should establish a dispensary or hospital for diseases of the brain or nervous system." Dr Bucknill approved of both Davey's and Belgrave's proposals; but Dr Henry Monro was taken aback by this entirely new idea and asked in a puzzled way whether the out-patients were insane or persons you suspect of going insane, and how could you get such patients to attend for treatment?

Maudsley was not present at this meeting but as one of the Editors he must have read Davey's paper and the discussion, and may have retained some memory of these suggestions in later years. In the meanwhile nothing was done to give effect to them, and the 'hospital' idea remained dormant for a decade or more. But in the 1880s it came to life again, now in a more diffuse form and in more than one context. This can best be illustrated by examples. Thus, in 1885 and 1886 Dr Strahan of the Northampton County Asylum (now St Crispin) published two articles on the necessity for hospital treatment of the curable insane; what he was advocating was the establishment of small hospitals of 30 or more beds in connection with each asylum; each hospital would have a physician solely in charge and would admit only curable cases; it would be in the asylum system but not of it. A different approach was that exemplified by Sir W. W. Gordon JP's letter to the *Lancet* in 1882; here the recommendation was for Receiving or Reception Houses in each county, "to which all lunatics should be sent until each case had developed itself". Much attention was given to a successful experiment in Australia, the Reception House run by Dr Manning in Sydney; he described its working to the MPA in 1887, and it was generally agreed that as a combined observation ward and short-term treatment centre it was decidedly superior to the English Poor-Law infirmary wards. Again, reports of the work of the psychiatric unit at the Charité Hospital in Berlin raised hopes of some similar venture in this country; but in general the teaching and other voluntary hospitals were uncooperative.

Thus 20 or more years of dissatisfaction with the asylum system were now crystallising into a demand, a general clamour as Strahan called it, for 'hospital treatment' in one form or another. Undoubtedly this trend was much influenced by the growing prestige of the teaching hospitals and by the prevailing, somewhat euphoric view of the progress of medical science. It was from one of the teaching hospitals that the next move came, and a very controversial move it proved to be; but it seems to have been heralded by the provocative action of a psychiatrist of repute.

You will remember that I promised to introduce yet a third family of Tukes, unconnected with the others, and I now bring forward the name of Dr, afterwards Sir John, Batty Tuke. In the early 1870s, as Medical Superintendent of the Fife and Kinross Asylum (now Strathdene Hospital), he had worked out an open-door system which had spread in modified form to a number of other Scottish asylums. He was now the proprietor of a private asylum near Edinburgh, and had been elected to Parliament. Early in 1889 he published an article in the *Nineteenth Century* entitled "Lunatics as Patients, not Prisoners", in which all the defects of the existing asylums were exposed, and the need for a specifically medical approach was strongly urged. Now it so happened that almost at the same time the newly formed London County Council was holding its first meetings; one of its members was Mr Brudenell Carter, who at the time was ophthalmic surgeon to St George's Hospital, but who had previously shown interest in nervous disorders, particularly hysteria. On 11 April, taking his cue from Batty Tuke, he moved "That a Committee be appointed to inquire and report on the advantages which might be expected from the establishment, as a complement to the asylum system, of a hospital with a visiting medical staff for the study and curative treatment of insanity". Thus existing asylums were to be complemented or supplemented, but not in any way improved or reformed. Not unnaturally another member proposed as an amendment that there should be a report on the asylums as a whole, with recommendations "with the view to securing more thorough medical attention to each individual case as well as the most modern and advanced methods of treatment". Had the two proposals been combined, much good might have resulted, but Brudenell Carter had his way and the committee, over which of course he presided, duly reported in accordance with his wishes.

It may be worthwhile to examine this committee's proceedings and report a little more closely. Their witnesses included numerous neurologists and the Presidents of the two Royal Colleges, but only two psychiatrists of standing, Batty Tuke and Crichton-Browne. We can only regret that Maudsley was not called and that his views at that particular time can never be known. The Council's own medical superintendents were not called, but a questionnaire was sent to superintendents all over the country, so worded that they could either approve, which the majority did, or offer somewhat feeble objections. The report dwelt at length on the well known defects of asylums: their unwieldy size, superintendents burdened with non-medical duties and assisted by inexperienced juniors, lack of contact with general medicine, and so on; but for these crying needs the committee proposed no remedies. Instead, they reasoned as follows: in recent years there had been great advances in medical science and in surgery, and particularly in the understanding of brain function; these advances had emanated from the great general hospitals; therefore if physicians (mainly neurologists) and surgeons on the staffs of these hospitals were appointed to treat the insane in a special hospital, they would be able not only to find the cause of each patient's disorder but also to treat the case by means of remedies already known to them. The logical fallacies were obvious to at least one distinguished physician, Clifford Allbutt, who also pointed out that the visiting doctors would only be able to give a very small part of their time to the proposed hospital and moreover that no cure had yet been found for many of the grosser brain diseases which these physicians already treated. But the discussion was vitiated by irrelevant arguments about the merits of moral versus medicinal treatment. Its low level can be judged from a passage in the report depicting an imaginary case of melancholia caused by liver disease; moral treatment might eventually result in improvement, but the general physician would cure the depression instantly by means of a dose of calomel.

After causing much controversy and resentment the project came to nothing. The Council decided that such a scheme would be of national rather than of local interest, and that it could take no action on it. Probably the decision was influenced by the question of cost; the population of London was still rising and the Council was advised that new asylums would be needed before long; they were indeed built and were of the same inordinate size which the report had so severely condemned.

Meanwhile, in 1889, the Presidential Chair of the MPA was occupied by one of its wisest and most devoted councillors, Hayes Newington of Ticehurst House. In his address, after a spirited defence of the best asylums, some of which, he said, attracted large classes of medical students, he gave a clear-sighted analysis of the hospital question. He distinguished two kinds of hospital, both desirable. The first was the county hospital for curable patients, to be built in connection with each asylum, although not adjacent and preferably out of sight; it was to be fully equipped and staffed and curability was to be the criterion for admission. A few years later, as Chairman of the East Sussex Asylums Committee, he was able to incorporate such a hospital in the plans for Hellingly Asylum. In fact 'hospital villas' so-called became a regular feature of asylums from about this time, although for the most part they failed to serve the intended purpose because it became a matter of routine to pass all admissions through them without any selection being made.

The second kind of hospital envisaged by Hayes Newington he called the 'educational hospital' – an institution intended primarily for teaching and research, to be established close to a medical school, with up to 250 patients carefully selected for the purpose of instruction. He wished the medical staff to be mainly psychiatric, but with some visiting general physicians. In fact, Newington gave a detailed description of a Maudsley-type hospital and, even more prophetically, a profile of its ideal chief psychiatrist which might have been modelled on the man who in due time actually filled this role, Edward Mapother.

Newington's scheme, although much nearer to what was eventually achieved, stood no more chance than Brudenell Carter's of being put into effect at the time. But the London County Council (LCC), while building its 2000-bed asylums such as Bexley and Horton, did not lose sight of other possibilities in the mental health field. The appointment in 1895 of Frederick Mott as pathologist and Mott's achievements at Claybury have been fully documented by Professor Alfred Meyer's article in the *British Journal of Psychiatry*. In 1899, possibly stimulated by Mott, the LCC revived the 'receiving houses' idea of the '80s; the Lunacy Commissioners and the London Poor Law Guardians were favourable, and the Council promoted a Bill empowering it to provide such houses. The Council may have been influenced in its action by the success of the psychiatric wards operated by

Dr John Carswell in one of the Glasgow hospitals. There patients were visited in their homes and classified as suitable for either the local asylum or the special wards, and if the latter they were admitted without formality for short-term treatment. However, in the proposed London receiving houses compulsory detention was envisaged and this gave rise to some criticism.

But this scheme too was frustrated, this time by the dilatoriness of parliamentary procedure. The Council's Bill was introduced in successive sessions, but made no progress. In 1902 it was turned into a public Bill and given Government support, but still remained crowded out. The Liberal victory in the 1906 election made no difference; the Bill passed the House of Lords but the Commons could not find the time for it. Meanwhile the Radnor Commission on the Care of the Feeble Minded had had its terms of reference extended to the whole field of mental health, and so at last, after seven years of effort, the Council decided not to proceed with the Bill, but to await the report of this Royal Commission instead.

It was at this point that Mott's writings became decisive. Hitherto he had pinned his hopes on the realisation of the LCC's scheme. His plea, in the preface to the 1903 volume of his *Archives of Neurology*, for means of intercepting uncertifiable cases of incipient and acute insanity was, of course, in accordance with views then widely prevalent and which had, as we have seen, been put into effect by Carswell and others. In the 1907 volume he put the emphasis rather on the psychoneuroses, on "neurasthenia, psychasthenia, obsession, mild impulsive mania, hysteria and hypochondria"; this too reflected prevailing trends and interests. A shining example of what could be done on a small scale by voluntary effort had been provided two years earlier by Dr Helen Boyle at Brighton, in what afterwards became the Lady Chichester Hospital; her models had been Carswell and the German clinics, Berlin, Munich and Göttingen. Mott's hopes, after similar visits to Germany, were more ambitious; continuing his 1907 article he wrote: "The L.C.C. scheme for Receiving Houses would probably include the establishment of an acute hospital, to which a clinic might with advantage be attached. If suitable post-graduate training in medical psychology and neuropathology were established the universities etc. might be induced to establish diplomas on the lines of the D.P.H." As we have seen, however, the LCC abandoned its scheme even as Mott was writing.

It was now that Maudsley intervened with the offer of a munificent gift which would enable the desired hospital to be built. Sir Aubrey Lewis in his Mapother Lecture attributes Maudsley's initiative to his having read and welcomed Mott's pronouncement; I believe that in addition it must have been borne in upon Maudsley that without outside help no progress would be made.

Maudsley's offer was reported to the LCC, at first anonymously, early in 1908, and the subsequent planning negotiations, delays and eventual completion of the project have been well described elsewhere.

A hospital was being created – a *mental* hospital, for it was under this hitherto unknown title, "A Mental Hospital – its aims and uses", that Maudsley wrote an article at Mott's request in the 1909 volume of *Archives of Neurology and Psychiatry*. To extract precise aims and uses from this article is not easy, as they are wrapped up, as it were, in an essay on the nature of insanity, just as, many years earlier, Maudsley's obituary notice of Conolly was wrapped up in an essay on obituary notices. The emphasis is throughout on insanity – neuroses are not mentioned – and as far as medical studies are concerned, what they chiefly needed was to be taught how to write "a good and sufficient certificate of insanity". But, rising above such old-fashioned trivialities, Maudsley indicates possible lines of pathological, social and genetic research; he lays great stress on close touch with the medical work and thought of general hospitals, on "the attendance of many persons, physicians and students, stimulating one another by constant intercourse", and on the "surrounding atmosphere of sanity" from which the insane patient could hardly fail to benefit. And he had not overlooked the needs of the asylums in which the great majority of patients would continue to be treated – he hoped that his mental hospital would supply a succession of trained medical men imbued with the scientific spirit available to take office in county asylums; and also that it might be a training ground for nurses who would afterwards go into service in large asylums, fitted with "a sense of responsibility to patients as mental beings".

In an editorial in the *Journal of Mental Science* for 1908, the MPA gave the project its warmest approval. The atmosphere was now quite different from what it had been 20 years earlier, and the new hospital was welcomed as fulfilling one of the Association's own aims, since for years it had campaigned for facilities for early treatment, for the creation of psychiatric clinics, and for financial support for research. The only criticism made in the *Journal* was that the proposed "metropolitan Mental Hospital" ought not to be completely independent, but should work closely with one of the great teaching hospitals. In any case there was no doubt that it should take its name from its founder and should be called 'The Maudsley Mental Hospital'.

Unknown to the writer, and to Maudsley himself, the Radnor Commission in that same year had recommended that all asylums should be renamed 'mental hospitals', and at Cardiff City the title was at once adopted by Dr Edwin Goodall. The LCC followed in 1918, and so the Maudsley Hospital escaped the stigma which soon attached itself to the adjective 'mental' as it had to the well meant title of 'asylum' a hundred years earlier.

In fact much had been done for the asylums since they had been so pointedly ignored in the Brudenell Carter report. Those newly built by the LCC were better planned, better equipped, and better staffed. Mott's hope that examining bodies might institute a DPM was being realised, largely through the efforts of the MPA, and the Association was engaged in framing proposals designed to improve the conditions of service and raise the status of asylum medical officers. Even before this an outstanding medical superintendent like Hubert Bond was able, as Sir Aubrey has reminded us, to attract to his hospital, Long Grove, a brilliant team, including Bernard Hart, Henry Devine, Ernest Jones, and the most junior, Edward Mapother, who was to be the Maudsley Hospital's first chief. Thus it came about that when the hospital at last opened, it was staffed primarily by asylum-trained psychiatrists, Mapother himself, Petrie, Dawson and others, together with a number of clinical assistants, many of whom achieved great distinction elsewhere.

As is well known, Henry Maudsley lived to see the erection of his hospital, but not its opening. He died in 1918, before the end of the war, which in a prophetic posthumous article scorning "fatuous humanitarian optimism", he had seen as the forerunner of future conflicts. By his will he made a further bequest for the benefit of his hospital, and another to the Medico-Psychological Association to be used for any purpose they might think fit. And the Association decided that the name of Maudsley should henceforth be bound to it by means of an annual lecture. There was at first some hesitation about the form this should take: whether each lecturer should deliver both a popular and a scientific lecture, or whether it should be popular and scientific in alternate years. Now the custom is for the lecturer in alternate years to be a psychiatrist or a person of distinction from another specialty or profession. And assuredly, one of the finest of these lectures has been the one dealing with the work of Henry Maudsley, to which I have been endeavouring to supply some footnotes.

As I have said, in doing so I wish to pay my tribute to the lecturer, Sir Aubrey Lewis, and so I will ask you to allow me to end with some words of his instead of with a peroration of my own. These words referred to Maudsley and to Mapother, but I believe they could justly be applied to Lewis himself. He said: "I recognize that in each generation there are men of rare gifts, severe in self-discipline, with strong and consistent purpose, who, in psychiatry as in other fields, accomplish much good and leave behind a lasting memorial".

3 Hospitals, madhouses and asylums: cycles in the care of the insane

PATRICIA ALLDERIDGE

The received version of the history of the care of the insane consists largely of myth and folklore, tempered by a strong dash of wilful ignorance, and is capable of absorbing any number of incongruous features. It runs roughly as follows, give or take a century or two here or there (which is about the accepted level of precision): from the dawn of history, or just before, or just after, until about the middle of the 19th century, nothing happened at all: or (depending on *where* you received your version) the mentally disordered were indiscriminately exorcised, or burnt, or left to wander at will, or chained up and beaten, or all four. From the middle of the 19th century they were all rounded up and driven into enormous asylums (where, according to a subtle sociological variation, mental illness was invented) and were left to vegetate until the 1950s. Around 1960 dawned the enlightenment, and it was suddenly revealed that everything that had ever happened before – whatever it was – was completely wrong and probably intentionally malicious too: and over the years following there were gradually also revealed a number of brand-new ways of putting it right, all different and mutually incompatible (not to mention expensive), and revealed respectively to different Departments of State, working parties, committees and unions – or sometimes successively to the same one.

I don't see it quite like that. And I propose now to outline to you another version of the subject: the one which has forced me to conclude that we have all been going round in circles for at least the last 750 years; that there are very few, if any, ideas on the public and institutional care of the mentally disordered which have not been round at least once before; and that on the evidence of past experience the likelihood that we are yet at the millenium, if only we had the money, seems remote.

Faced with the problem of where to begin, I have decided, rather reluctantly, not to begin with the Anglo-Saxons. This is partly because I know nothing about them, but chiefly because I don't think that anyone else does either, at least in relation to their treatment of the insane. In an apparently reputable book on medicine in Anglo-Saxon England I learned, for example, that throughout the Dark and Middle Ages, and indeed until the end of the 17th century, the theory of demoniacal possession as the cause of insanity held sway. This does not inspire confidence. If true, it would invalidate most of the rest of my paper and would therefore hardly provide an auspicious beginning; if not true, why should one believe either such statements as: "Mental disease was usually regarded by the Anglo-Saxons, as it was in the New Testament, as the result of possession by a devil"? Why believe this anyway, when all that the evidence *could* indicate is that cases which were regarded in the New Testament, and possibly also by the Anglo-Saxons, as possession by a devil would probably now be regarded as cases of mental disorder (which is a rather different proposition)?

In looking at the social history of the care of the insane, and perhaps this does not apply quite so strictly to the medical history, it is necessary to look at those cases which were regarded at the time as cases of lunacy and not as possession by devils – or even sainthood, come to that: it is usually forgotten by the demoniac theorists that if you opted for crying in the wilderness rather than during a church service you would have a better chance of ending up as a saint. Anyway, I really do not believe that there has yet been accumulated sufficient information to enable us to draw any useful conclusions for the Anglo-Saxon period.

The evidence for the early medieval period is also scattered and fragmentary, but there is sufficient to suggest that in many instances the insane were regarded as, and treated alongside, the sick of other categories, although it is worth bearing in mind that one reason we hear so little about it during this period may be that insanity did not present a very large problem. Whether we consider hospitals (once they existed) or healing shrines and other centres of therapeutic activity is immaterial to the point at issue, which is that everyone was treated together.

One record of this is found in the series of early-13th-century windows in the Trinity Chapel of Canterbury Cathedral, depicting miracles wrought at the tomb of St Thomas à Becket. Here the saint is seen dealing at large with swollen feet, epilepsy, fever, wounds, leprosy, congenital lameness, dropsy, blindness, death by drowning, and insanity. Two windows show the curing of the insane. In one, a pair of roundels depicts Henry of Fordwich being brought to the tomb. The first scene is inscribed *"Amens accedit"* – "Mad [mindless, or deprived of his mind] he comes"; the second *"Orat. Sanus recedit"* – He prays. Sane he goes away". "Mad", we should note, not "possessed by devils". Whether or not one is convinced of the efficacy of St Thomas's healing properties, the point is that others were, and they regarded him as being as good for insanity as for swollen toes.

The manuscript in the British Museum known as *The Book of the Foundation of St Bartholomew's Church* (see Moore, 1923) relates to the healing powers of St Bartholomew, in the previous century. It recounts miraculous cures taking place at the church, which include the healing of the deaf, dumb, blind, palsied, and cripples of all kinds, as well as several cases of insanity.

One such concerns a knight called Ralph, who was riding to London when "by the dome [the doom, decree or judgement] of God he was ravashid of a feende, and made woid [mad] . . .". How much of this is the language of symbolism, and how much of belief, is uncertain; but it does illustrate the difficulty in deciding where to draw the line between those who were thought to be possessed and those who were acknowledged insane but whose insanity was reckoned to be caused by the Devil or devils. (This is not, of course, the same thing, as the Devil could cause many sorts of sickness and trouble.) In any case, after tearing his clothes, flinging his money about, throwing stones at everyone, and terrorising those who came to take him, which everyone could recognise as pretty bizarre conduct for a knight, Ralph was finally captured and brought to the church: "and whan he hadde taryed ther. ii. nyghtys, he come to his mynde again" (Moore, 1923, f. 67). Another case, without any supernatural cause attributed, is that of a little child who had been mad for about three weeks. He was brought by his mother, who had carried him round to various shrines before this without obtaining relief: but St Bartholomew did the trick, and after watching and praying and petitioning the Saint she "optenyd to her-self gladnes And to the childe helth" (*ibid*, f. 75v). (This is possibly one of the earliest examples of family therapy.)

These St Bartholomew cases are slightly confusing, because we are dealing with miracles performed in the church and not medical cures performed in the adjacent hospital; but there is other evidence that medieval hospitals did care for the insane. The foundation deed of Holy Trinity Hospital, Salisbury, for example, probably dating from around the middle of the 14th century, provides for 30 beds where "The hungry are fed, the thirsty have drink, the naked are clothed, the sick are comforted, the dead are buried, the mad are kept safe until they are restored to reason . . ." (Clay, 1909, p. 90). In a petition of 1414 for the reformation of hospitals it is stated positively that they exist, among other things, to maintain those who have lost their wits. Some alms houses, on the other hand, expressly prohibited the admission of the insane, such as those at Croydon, Ewelme and Coventry, strongly suggesting that in the absence of a specific embargo they would be expected to take such cases.

At this period, therefore, the provisions for the insane might be held to fall into that category currently being put about by the DHSS as a new development, the district general hospital with a psychiatry department – not to mention that other recognisable modern phenomenon, the district general hospital *without* a psychiatry department – with the shrines acting perhaps in the role of out-patient clinics. Or perhaps the various places of pilgrimage should be seen as equivalent to the larger teaching hospitals; and when one remembers the unfortunate mother who had trundled her child round from one shrine to another before getting satisfaction, perhaps the analogy with the National Health Service is not so far-fetched.

One medieval hospital was unique, and was to remain so for several centuries: this was Bethlem Hospital. It is possible that other monastic hospitals existed at various times in which the inmates were all, or mostly, insane, but if they existed in any numbers they did not survive long enough to leave much mark. Indeed, it seems very unlikely that there would be congregated anywhere except in London enough insane persons to occupy a hospital solely for this purpose, over any substantial period during the Middle Ages.

The Priory of St Mary of Bethlehem was founded by Simon Fitzmary in 1247, on the site of his own property in Bishopsgate. By 1403 there were in the house, among other sick people, six insane men, and it is clear that from soon afterwards the hospital was concerned exclusively with this category of patient. Around the middle of the century, a one-time Lord Mayor of London called William Gregory wrote of it thus: "A chyrche of Owre Lady that ys namyde Bedlam. And yn that place ben founde many men that ben fallyn owte of hyr wytte. And fulle honestely they ben kepte in that place; and sum ben restoryde unto hyr witte and helthe a-gayne. And sum ben abydyng there yn for evyr, for they ben falle soo moche owte of hem selfe that hyt ys uncurerabylle unto man" (see Gairdner, 1876, p. ix). This indicates that people came, or more accurately, were brought, to the hospital with the intention that they should be cured and discharged, but that if they were not, they could be provided with continuing shelter. Gregory also clearly contemplated the possibility of deliberate cure, procured by human intervention (whether or not this was actually going on in Bethlem is another matter). There is no detailed information, however, about the sort of patient there, and how they came to be admitted, until 1598.

By then the administration had undergone a radical change through the dissolution of the religious houses, a disruption which had particularly important repercussions for those who had previously been cared for in hospitals and charitable institutions of all kinds. In 1547 the City of London acquired the custodianship of Bethlem, retaining it until 1948: but its purely local commitment was already being eroded by the end of the 16th century. Of the 21 patients in the hospital in 1598, at least three came from outside London. Six appear to have been supported out of the hospital's own funds, one from parish funds, and for the rest maintenance was paid by their friends, relatives or patrons; or in the case of a member of the Chapel Royal, out of his own wages (so presumably he was on sick leave). The method of admission is not very precisely defined: the patients are all described as having been "sent in by" various people (not always the person who is paying their maintenance) and their length of stay in the hospital up to that time varies from one month to 25 years. There is evidence that at this time admission might depend on the patient's friends or relatives negotiating a satisfactory rate of maintenance with the keeper: what is fairly certain is that the patient himself had little say in the matter. Admissions might therefore be described as informal, but far from voluntary.

Bethlem remained on its original site in Bishopsgate until 1676, and in its original monastic buildings. It held only about 15 to 20 patients for most of this time, being enlarged to take 50 or 60 around the 1630s; and although it took an increasing number of people from outside London as time went on, its place in the overall pattern of treatment of the insane throughout the country is seen to be very small and specialised. (See Allderidge (1979) for a brief history of Bethlem Hospital up to 1633.)

For those who were not in hospital, of course, there was only one place to be – outside it: and thus we come to the first great era of community care, in the 17th century. We actually come to it in the 17th century because that is when the records start telling us about it; but I have little doubt that something which could be described thus had been going on, one way or another, for a good deal longer. The information comes through records of the activities of the Justices of the Peace in their Courts of Quarter Sessions; but it should be remembered that the cases recorded are only those which did, for various reasons, come before the magistrates: they may be considered typical of what could often also be done without magisterial interference.

One of the legal provisions under which the magistrates came to be involved is well known. This is the Poor Law legislation of the reign of Elizabeth I, and especially the great consolidating Act of 1601, which brought together and finalised many of the measures which had already been passed in increasingly desperate attempts to hold back the flood-tide of poverty – or rather, of the poor. The principal provisions which we need to keep in mind are: that the Churchwardens of every parish, together with two to four substantial householders were to be nominated annually by the County Justices to be Overseers of the Poor for that parish: and that these Overseers should, under the supervision of the Justices, set to work such people as had no means to maintain themselves, and raise sufficient money by taxation "for and towards the necessary Relief of the Lame, Impotent, Old, Blind, and such other among them, being poor, and not able to work . . .".

Increasingly savage legislation against vagrancy and begging meant that more and more of the insane would have to be dealt with under this last provision. How this part of the Act was interpreted by the Justices themselves in relation to the insane is shown in the contemporary manuals written expressly for their guidance. Thus we find in the 1618 edition of Michael Dalton's *The Countrey Iustice* (sub 'Poore'): "Next here is consideration to be had of three sorts or degrees of poor. 1. Poor by impotency". This includes "The aged, and decrepit", "The infant, fatherless and motherless", and "The persons naturally disabled, either in wit, or member, as the Idiot, Lunatick, Blind, Lame &c . . . All these (being impotent, or not able to work) are to be found, and provided for by the Overseers, of necessary relief".

It does not appear that the Justices recognised any specific responsibility for the care of lunatics before the enactment of the Poor Laws; but there was another, far earlier legal provision under which cases of lunacy might come to their attention. This will require rather more explanation, because you are unlikely to find anything about it anywhere else.

It is generally accepted now that the first statute law providing for the confinement of the dangerously insane is contained in the vagrancy legislation of 1714, but little has been said about the Common Law position in this matter. Although it is acknowledged that the Common Law did have a position, everyone seems content to quote 18th-century writers, for example that under the ancient Common Law "persons deprived of their reason might be confined until they recovered their senses . . .".

However, in Dalton's 1618 edition we find the following (sub 'Surety for the Peace'): "though Assaults and Batteries be for the most part contrary to the peace of the realm . . . yet some are allowed to have a natural, and some a civil power (or authority) over others: so that they may, (in reasonable and moderate manner only) correct and chastise them for their offences . . ."; and among the list of chastisers and chastised are "any man" and "his kinsman that is mad". And later, in further elucidation: "It is lawful for the parents, kinsmen or other friends of a man that is mad, or frantic (who being at liberty attempteth to burn a house, or to do some other mischief, or to hurt himself or others) to take him and put him into an house, to bind or chain him, and to beat him with rods, and to do any other forcible act to reclaim him, or to keep him so as he shall do no hurt". In an earlier manual of 1581 is a more succinct version: "Every man also may take this kinsman that is mad, and may put him in a house, and bind him and beat him with rods, without breach of the Peace" (Lambard, 1581, p. 138).

With regard to the beating with rods part, I would only comment that, since this was considered to be one of the appropriate remedies for insanity at the time when the law was formulated, it must be interpreted in this light rather than as a punishment *per se*. This provision is literally neither more nor less than the authorisation of compulsory treatment. Other more modern analogies may come to your minds here, but I don't intend to be drawn into that controversy.

These are merely statements of the law as it existed by the end of the 16th century, but thanks to the dependence of the Common Law on precedent we can trace it further. In the margins against these passages we find the cryptic message "22. E.4. 45", and "22. lib. Ass. plac.56". "Lib. Ass." refers to that favourite legal bedtime story-book the *Liber assisarum & placitorum corone* (Rastell, 1513), or *Book of Assizes and Pleas of the Crown*, citing the 22nd year of Edward III, Plea 56, which we will leave for the moment. "22. E. 4." refers to a Year Book, for the 22nd year of the reign of Edward IV, or 1482; and here I must prevaricate a little.

Year Books are the law reports of the Middle Ages, which have been in print since shortly after the introduction of printing itself to this country. In them are cases which embody the precedents on which the whole Common

Law system is based, and they also provide first-hand evidence of the state and development of the law as it went along. One problem, however, is that they are all printed in an exceptionally dense and opaque black-letter type, evidently set by a myopic printer who had yet to learn the art of proof-reading (and my copy also happened to have the page numbers omitted, which, since the "45" eventually turned out by trial and error to be a page reference, was definitely bonus points to the printer). They also happen to be written in what was then the language of the courts, medieval legal French. This is a quaint, but debased, form of Anglo-Norman, which is itself a spirited pidgin variant of the language brought over by the Conqueror 400 years earlier, for which the rules could be made up as you went along and usually were. And the words are only half there. I don't mean only half the words: I mean only one half of any single word – the rest being represented by a helpful abbreviation mark, to let you know it is not there.

This is just to explain why I am not yet in a position to tell exactly what happened in the Court of King's Bench on that memorable day in the Hilary Term of 1482, though I am still working on it. However, I can give you the gist of the story; and I would remind you that this case is the precedent according to which it was lawful for the next 200 years to lock up a potentially dangerous lunatic. It was an action for false imprisonment. The defendant had imprisoned somebody's wife – I am almost sure it was the wife of the plaintiff in the previous case, who had also been imprisoned, but they said that was all right because he was a Scot. I thought at first that he had imprisoned her in a tall chimney, but now suspect that he met her in the highway (the exact role of the '*hault chimin*' is temporarily obscured by the memorable phrase in the preceding passage, '*fuit supp obvia m̄ cey*'). The defendant claimed that he had imprisoned her because she "*fist au tiel countenance qil semble qi el fuit fere come un qi fuit lunatyk & l[e] def[endant] en eschewyng le pluis graund myschief qi poet ensuer p[ar] luy, luy prist & mitta en son meason . . .*" – "She had such an expression that it seemed that she was wild like one who was lunatic, and the defendant, in eschewing the great mischief which might arise on account of her, took her and put her in his house . . .", or her house (or someone's house). This defence was said not to be good, because he only thought she looked wild like a lunatic; a good defence would have been to say that she *was* wild and he thought that she was going to kill him or do some other mischief like setting a house on fire. (Year Book *De Termino Hillarii Anno xxij. E.iiij* (no date), f.45, collated with another edition (?1520), untitled and unpaginated.) This is really what the case boils down to. But of course the judgement here was merely a statement of the law as it already stood: this just happens to be the case in which it was expounded and which came to be cited as the precedent. What was being said was that it was lawful to imprison someone if he were mad and you believed that he was going to do some mischief like burning down a house.

Returning briefly to the case in the *Liber assisarum*, this dates from 1348 and is undoubtedly the precedent from which was derived the authority to beat one's mad relatives with rods. I have established that someone was indeed mad, or was said to be, and that his kinsmen imprisoned him and beat him with a rod; but what happened subsequently to either them or him I am not yet prepared to say.

We now know, then, that from at least 1348 it was lawful to beat one's mad kinsfolk with a rod if with nothing else, and that from some time before 1482 it was lawful to imprison a lunatic provided you could be fairly sure he was going to burn down a house, and that from around the end of the 16th century these two circumstances began to appear in the Justices' manuals. We can now go back to seeing how this law, together with the Poor Laws, were actually operated in the 17th century. Quarter Sessions records all over the country show the same kind of activity. Friends, relatives, or neighbours of the insane person, having been either reduced to penury or driven to distraction in their efforts to cope with the situation, would present a petition setting out the details and asking for action. In the case of actual or predicted violence or mischief-making, the Justices would order the person's detention, usually but not always in the local house of correction, and would also make an order for maintenance to be paid out of the parish funds or, if the person had sufficient means of his own, would order this source to be managed so as to provide for his keep. In other cases they would simply order certain sums to be provided by the parish for relief of the lunatic or his family, or again they might order his affairs to be managed to pay for his maintenance; so not all these cases can be said to come directly under the Poor Law provisions. The overseers and church-wardens were the people who had to see that these matters were dealt with, and together with the petitioners and the Justices might, I suppose, be called the primary care team. The therapeutic team, I am sorry to say, must often have consisted of the keeper of the house of correction and his assistants, but paid voluntary helpers seem to have played their part too.

In the Somerset Quarter Sessions records of 1612/13, for example, we find an order for six people, some of whom are clearly relatives, to take upon them the keeping of a lunatic "in his own house if they can rule him there, or otherwise that they shall cause him to be sent unto the Bridewell", and they are to sell his goods as necessary towards his financial relief (see Bates, 1907, vol. 1, p. 88). Another case comes from the Taunton Sessions of 1613: Emma Carter of Frome, being now a lunatic, "whereby her neighbours stand greatly in doubt lest she should put in practice some mischievous attempt to set on fire where she dwelleth: Ordered that she be sent to the House of Correction at Ivelchester [Ilchester] where she ought to be kept in such manner as the law requireth for all such dangerous and disordered persons" (Bates, 1907, vol. 1, p. 99). The petitioners of Somerset were obviously well versed in the Common Law, as this is not the only case where they mention the fear of houses being burnt down, and the provisions of the law for such persons are often emphasised too.

Another Taunton case, for 1628, shows how the community could take action for itself. One Henry Collard of Hill Farrance had lately become lunatic "in so much that he is bothe unruly and dangerous and for the prevention of further mischiefe the Inhabitants of the said parish have placed the said Collard with one John Appledore . . ."; and since Collard had sufficient means to maintain himself, the Justices ordered that he remain with Appledore and be relieved out of his own means (Bates, 1907).

A typical Poor Law case comes from the Warwickshire records for Easter 1651. "Whereas the Co[urt] was this day informed That one Goldingale an Inhabitant of Aston parish is growne Lunatick and that a great Charge is fallen upon ye parish by Reason thereof which cannot bee borne by any p[ar]ticular Hamlet And therefore it was prayed that according to ye Lawe the whole parish might contribute by way of Leavy to the mainten[a]nce of the said Lunatick And that the Overseers of the poore may see him provided for as poore of the parish wch this Co[u]rt thought fitt & doth Order the same accordingly" (Warwick County Record Office, Quarter Sessions Records, QS40/3, f.44v.). And from Warwickshire again, in 1646, we have a particularly interesting example of true communal care: "It is ordered that Daniell Hancox a poore Ideott who was borne in Weston under weth[er]ly in this County and is now in the care and custody of William Mulliner gent[leman] on[e] of the Inhabitants there shalbe forth-with Clothed by and out of the stock of money given to the Inhabitants there to that purpose And it is further ordered that the said Daniell shalbe forthwith removed from the said Mr Mulliner and be kept and provided for by the Inh[ab]itants of the said parish from house to house as heretofore hee hath beene there mainteyned and kept" (QS40/2, vol. 1, f.138v.).

In Lancashire, the actual petitions have been preserved; and from these comes a direct and poignant picture of the hardships and problems caused by insanity in the 17th-century community, which, not surprisingly, turn out to be similar to those faced today. The petition of John Sandholme of Inskip cum Sowerby, labourer, was delivered in 1681: "Humbly sheweth unto your good wor[shi]pps that his wyffe is exterordnary troubled with Melancollie distemper in soe much that shee is in danger to distroy her selfe if shee should be Left in the house Allone but for the space of halfe an houre and he hath A Child that is but About A munthe Above halfe A yeare old which he nurseth and hee is A very pore Mann and hath nothinge to Maintayne him selfe nor his wyffe and Child but his owne hand Laboure & he can not Leave his wyffe to worke unlesse he hier An able p[er]son to stay & Looke to his wyffe for feare shee distroy her selfe . . ." (Lancashire Record Office, Quarter Sessions Records, QSP 537/6).

The experience of people such as John Sandholme has been summed up thus: "Living with people who have had or who are recovering from mental illness can place heavy strains on a family. . . . If the mother is ill, the father may find himself having to take time off work and the family income may fall. Special arrangements may need to be made for the care of the children . . . . The family may become afraid to leave a withdrawn and uncommunicative member alone; and they too may become virtually housebound, often giving up sources of income. . . ." This comes from the Department of Health and Social Security's 1975 White Paper, "Better Services for the Mentally Ill", which assures us elsewhere that "there has for years been general recognition of the significance of the social and environmental aspects of mental illness". They can say that again! Three hundred years, to my certain knowledge.

Community psychiatry did not actually work terribly well the first time round, as is shown by the gradual move during the following century towards the next cycle of development – more hospitals. But first, we have at the end of the 17th century the setting up of an institution which does not fit very well into any major category. I think we might call this, with something less than wholehearted conviction, the therapeutic community experiment.

Some rather bold claims are sometimes made for the role of St Peter's Hospital, Bristol, in the care of the mentally disordered: for example, that it was the first public mental hospital; the first hospital where pauper lunatics received treatment; and that the unique policy of Bristol laid the foundations for the later development of county asylums. The facts are slightly different. In 1696 Bristol obtained an Act of Parliament called The Bristol Poor Act. This enabled all the parishes to join together in a union known as the Corporation of the Poor and to provide together for all the poor of the city instead of parish by parish. What Bristol was in fact pioneering was thus the parish union system, which was eventually adopted throughout the country and, through the workhouses which were its outward manifestation, led to one of the most degrading chapters in English social history. But I think we should allow that the Bristol citizens did not intend, in 1696, that things should go quite the way they did.

Part of the original plan was to establish workhouses in which the able poor, and separately the poor children, could be profitably (if compulsorily) employed, educated and disciplined. In fact, the Corporation bought the premises of the redundant Bristol Mint in 1698, and here the children, together with the able-bodied, infirm, sick and aged poor alike, were brought into residence. Later the Mint Workhouse was renamed St Peter's Hospital: but even in the 1820s one of its governors complained that this was misleading, and that it was a workhouse and should be recognised as such.

The admission of the first lunatic to the Mint Workhouse is recorded in 1707 (three years earlier, incidentally, the Corporation of the Poor had made arrangements for a patient to be sent to Bethlem Hospital in London); and from then on there were always a number of such patients, accommodated in a separate ward by 1767. By the early 19th century, St Peter's was recognised as the general lunatic asylum for Bristol; but even so the proportion of lunatic to other workhouse inmates was always small. The house could take 300 people comfortably, but in 1820, for example, it had 436, of whom 97 were classified as sick or insane. Only about 30 of these would actually be insane, even after the numbers had increased in the 1820s. In 1844 St Peter's was declared by the Lunacy Commissioners to be totally unfit, but it was not until 1861 that the patients were removed to the new City Asylum, now the Glenside Hospital. (See Johnson (1826) and Butcher (1932) for detailed accounts of the Bristol Corporation.)

I do not think, therefore, that we should take too seriously any claim for St Peter's as a prototype mental hospital, but its interest for us lies in the fact that it establishes a recognisable pattern, to be repeated for well over 100 years. Wherever workhouses, poor-houses, or houses of industry were set up, these were the most usual places to be used for the accommodation of pauper lunatics.

We must return now for a moment to what was, *pace* the Bristol claimants, really the first and still the only public hospital for the insane poor in England. By 1674 the pressure for admission to Bethlem, together with the appalling state of the building, led to its being rebuilt on a grand and palatial scale to the design of Robert Hooke, friend and collaborator of Christopher Wren. This building was intended, incidentally, to accommodate 120 insane patients, but principally to be an ornament to the City; and what it became, as is well known, was one of London's great tourist attractions in the 18th century, rivalling the lions at the Tower and the tombs in Westminster Abbey.

Whatever the actual facts, however, Bethlem Hospital was always intended for a curative establishment, and from at least this period on, one of the conditions for entry was supposed curability. Patients were discharged after 12 months if not cured (earlier, of course, if recovered) and were released on a month's trial leave of absence before final discharge. Another condition of entry was poverty. As soon as the endowment was large enough, patients sent in by their friends and relatives were taken free, although the parishes had to pay for their own patients. After the rebuilding, an increasing number of parish patients were sent from different parts of the country (I have already mentioned one such from Bristol); and this should be remembered as providing a limited (but very limited) alternative to any other local provisions we may be considering.

Local enterprise is the hallmark of hospital development in the 18th century. First off the mark is the Bethel Hospital, Norwich, somewhere between 1713 and 1724, to which we must give credit for being the first hospital to be specifically founded for the care of the insane. The amazing work of one woman, the daughter of one of Norwich's richest citizens and widow of a local clergyman, it owes its origins to a unique set of circumstances, the combination of wealth, piety and very special motivation. "Whereas it hath pleased almighty God", writes Mrs Mary Chapman in her will, "to visitt & afflict some of my nearest relaċons and kindered with Lunacy but hath hitherto blessed me with ye free use of my reason & understanding as a monument of my thankfulness to God for this invalueable mercy . . . & in Compassion to ye deplorable State of Such p[er]sons as are deprived of ye Exercise of their reason & understanding & are Destitute of relacons or friends to take care of y^m ", she bequeaths her newly built house for the convenient reception and habitation of poor lunatics "wch I will shall be called according to the desire of my well beloved Husband by ye name of Bethel". It is to be first and foremost for poor inhabitants of Norwich afflicted with lunacy (but not fools or idiots from birth), their clothes, food and medicines to be paid for out of the charity. If there is room, then people from the county and elsewhere can be admitted, their friends and relations to pay for them according to their ability: and persons of means from the city can also be accepted if they are paid for over and above the cost of their maintenance. There is no suggestion that the paying patients are to receive different treatment from those on the charity. (Norfolk Record Office, Consistory Court Wills, 1724, 219, copy of Mary Chapman's will.)

Mary Chapman had built the house by 1713, and died in 1724, hence the uncertainty about dates. Other benevolent citizens increased the charity, and the hospital was enlarged from time to time. In 1730 it accommodated 27; in 1761, 45; by the early 19th century it took just over 50. Like Bethlem, it tried to be a hospital for cure, but there does not seem to have been any general time limit on the residence there, although some were discharged as being unlikely to receive further benefit.

The Bethel Hospital, although apparently acceptable to God, to Whom it was dedicated, for 250 years, has not met the more stringent requirements of the DHSS; and Mary Chapman's memorial to the preservation of her wits is unlikely to survive in any form that she would recognise. From its foundation it has remained unique among hospitals for the insane as the gift of a single individual, most of the 18th-century hospitals being financed and set up through the initiative of local subscribers. One small exception is perhaps the lunatic department of Guy's Hospital. Thomas Guy founded his hospital for people excluded from other hospitals as incurable, and he specifically mentioned in his will that there was to be accommodation for 20 incurable lunatics. It opened in 1728 with a separate 'lunatic house', rebuilt at the end of the century. (In fact, although Guy had actually named incurables from Bethlem as being particularly fit objects for his charity, Bethlem was taking this matter in hand too, and by 1733 two wings had been added to the building for 100 incurable patients.)

In 1751 there opened in London the second specialised public hospital for the insane, St Luke's, established by public subscription. As stated in the fund-raising prospectus, the reasons for founding another hospital for lunatics were that "[they are] incapable of providing for themselves and Families, are not admitted into other Hospitals or capable of being relieved (as in other diseases) by private charity", and that "the Expences necessarily attending the Confinement and other means of Cure, are such as People even in midling Circumstances cannot bear, it generally requiring several Months, and often a whole Year before a Cure is completed".

Again, these are not unfamiliar problems. There is also the interesting rider that as more medical men make a study of this branch of physic, it stands to reason that "the Cure of this dreadful Disease will hereafter be rendered more certain and expeditious, as well as less expensive".

St Luke's stood on the far side of Moorfields from Bethlem; an appropriate situation, since its founders intended to correct in their own establishment some of the worst abuses committed across the way. Its terms of admission, however, were very similar to those of Bethlem, though it was much smaller, starting with 57 patients.

The second half of the 18th century saw the establishment of public subscription hospitals in a number of provincial towns, and this movement often extended to include the insane. Manchester, Liverpool, Newcastle, Exeter, Hereford, Leicester and York had all provided hospital accommodation for lunatics by the end of the century. Those who believe that only modern, sophisticated, think-tank methods of research could arrive at the concept of associating the district general hospital and psychiatric services in one establishment, and who might not be convinced by my medieval analogies, might like to know that this was the system adopted from the outset in some of these towns. As there was no central directive to ensure a tidy uniformity, however, the benevolent subscribers were able to follow the retrograde policy of doing what seemed to them to be best suited to the local requirements.

Thus Manchester, which was the first, opened its lunatic hospital (in 1766) as an annexe to the Infirmary, as did Liverpool. The County Infirmary at Leicester is another example of this type, although when it opened in 1771 "persons disordered in their senses" were originally excluded. Ten years later, on the assurance of a legacy, it was decided to build an addition for lunatics, but as the legacy failed to materialise, the building stood empty for ten years more. Finally it was altered, and opened for 20 patients in 1794. Alas! The Asylum seems always to have been the most neglected part of the Infirmary – again, I will refrain from drawing any modern parallels – and was eventually closed in 1837, when the remaining patients were transferred to the new County Asylum. (See Frizelle & Martin (1971) for a history of the Infirmary.)

At York and Newcastle, on the other hand, completely separate lunatic hospitals were built; and there was already a school of thought by the end of the century which held that lunatic hospitals (or asylums, as they were coming to be called) should be distinct institutions set in the country, although near to a town, where the advantages were pure air, plenty of space for amusement and exercise, and opportunity for occupation in gardening and other healthy employments.

So far, we have only considered public institutions, but in fact the most numerous establishments for the care of the insane at any one time, from the early 18th to the late 19th century, were the private madhouses. Although private in the sense of being run as business ventures, they were by no means occupied only by self-financing patients. Until the compulsory building of county asylums in 1845, the practice of contracting out pauper lunatics in private madhouses, where they were paid for from parish funds, was increasingly common; and the natural response to the growing demand was a growing number of madhouses, many of them catering largely for paupers.

The private madhouse system seems to have its origin in the practice which we have already seen in the 17th century, that of placing insane patients individually under the care of other individuals. Mr Appledore, whom we met at the Taunton Assizes in 1628, can be regarded as one prototype of a private madhouse proprietor, while at the more up-market end of the trade members of the wealthier classes might find themselves boarded out in the custody of a medical man or a clergyman. By the beginning of the 18th century there were already established a number of such places taking more than one patient, and from then on the industry grew, until by 1848 a network of 145 madhouses was spread across the country (see Parry-Jones, 1972).

The variety of these institutions makes it impossible to generalise, but in the early days at least they were more likely to be owned by lay than by medical proprietors, and even when owned by a medical man might well be in the day-to-day charge of a lay-man or lay-woman. Brooke House, Clapton, for example, set up by Dr John Monro (of the famous family of Bethlem physicians) in 1759 , was still owned by the family, still physicians, a century later, but in 1841 it was in the charge of the Misses Pettingal; and from the founder onwards none of the Monros themselves had ever lived nearer to Clapton than Cavendish Sqare.

Holly House, Hoxton, was one of the least notorious of the madhouses which had made the name of Hoxton a byeword in satirical literature since at least the 17th century. Andrew Marvell wrote in 1672 of someone as being "fit for nothing but Bedlam or Hogsdon"; and in 1895 John Hollingshead, who had been brought up in a house overlooking the yard of the largest and *most* notorious, Hoxton House, where Charles Lamb once spent a voluntary six weeks, wrote that "Hoxton had been celebrated for its madhouses (and conventicles) for the best part of two centuries" (Hollingshead, 1895). Holly House was generally known as Burrows's House, being owned in the late 18th century by John Burrows and then by his widow and son. Comprising three separate houses, it accommodated 120 and more patients, of whom 100 might be paupers, and was described by the Lunacy Commissioners as "extremely inconvenient for the purpose".

A very different sort of establishment is seen through the eyes of Charles Lamb, whose sister Mary was confined in a private madhouse at Islington in 1796, after stabbing her mother to death in one of her recurring paroxysms of madness. The story of Mary Lamb's life, with its repeated periods of confinement interspersed with years of normal life at home with her devoted brother, is astonishing when one remembers that she had actually murdered her own mother; and it still remains to be explained how such leniency came about. Writing to Coleridge shortly after the murder, Lamb says that it will cost £50 to £60 a year for her to stay at Islington, but "she shall not go into an hospital. The good Lady of the mad house, and her daughter, an elegant sweet behaved young Lady, love her and are taken with her amazingly, and I know from her own mouth she loves them, and longs to be with them as much. . . . She will, I fancy, if she stays, make one of the family, rather than of the patients, and the old and young ladies I like exceedingly, and she loves dearly. . . ." The lady's medical acumen may be judged from her advice that in the interests of economy he might "dismiss immediately both Doctor and apothecary, retaining occasionally an opening draught or so for a while . . ." (Lucas, 1905, pp. 45–46).

William Cowper also struck lucky with Dr Nathaniel Cotton's private madhouse at St Albans, known as the Collegium Insanorum, to which he was removed during a spell of suicidal depression in 1763. Cowper was so well satisfied that he stayed on for nearly a year after his recovery, and when he left he took with him as a servant the attendant who had looked after him throughout his illness – not without some opposition from the doctor (Cowper, 1816, pp. 71–80; Wright, 1904, pp. 23–24).

The other side of the private madhouse coin is exemplified, however, by Mr Spencer's establishment at Fonthill, Wiltshire, whose conditions were revealed in evidence to a Parliamentary Select Committee (1815, pp. 43 ff.) on the state of madhouses. Part of the accommodation consisted of six cells about 9′ by 5′, opening on to a passage which in turn looked out on to a pigsty and dung-heap. The walls were unplastered, damp greenstone; there was no light or ventilation except when the cell doors were opened; three cells were floored only with bare earth. The patients were chained to beds consisting of long boxes raised from the ground and filled with straw. Of the 14 male patients, only one was not confined in irons.

Moor Cottage at Nunkeeling, in the East Riding of Yorkshire, is an example of the kind of small establishment which might be set up during the period of maximum speculation, though not, perhaps, entirely typical, in that its proprietor appears to have eked out the fees by acting as a depot for local smugglers. It was opened in 1821 by John Beal, a former attendant at the Friends' Retreat (the famous Quaker establishment at York), who had previously run a house for the insane at Gate Helmsley and brought the occupants with him. It closed in 1851 (Bickford & Bickford, 1976).

The abuses known to exist in private madhouses led to the first legislation designed to protect the insane from society – the first legislation to protect society from the insane was the clause, already mentioned, in the Vagrancy Act of 1714. This empowered Justices of the Peace to order the confinement of "Persons of little or no Estates, who, by Lunacy, or otherwise, are furiously Mad, and dangerous to be permitted to go abroad", and to direct them to be kept safely locked up, and chained if necessary while the madness lasted: and, if they did not belong to the parish or town in which they were taken, to be sent to their last place of settlement. To my mind the implications of this Act have been slightly misinterpreted. It is said to be the first legislation to deal with pauper lunatics, but in fact it was legislation to deal with dangerous and wandering lunatics – there was a specific provision that they were to be maintained out of their own means, if they had any, and only from the parish funds if not. A similar Act of 1744 carried the additional injunction that the parishes were to be at the expense of curing, as well as keeping and maintaining, lunatics during their restraint, an expedient if optimistic provision, since they were liable to be a drain on the rates so long as they remained uncured.

It is also suggested that because the clause comes in a vagrancy Act, and as it is mentioned that lunatics are not to be whipped as vagrants are, this means that previously such persons had been treated as vagrants and similarly whipped and punished. But the significance of the non-whipping passage seems to be merely a matter of drafting: it is stated that lunatics are to be sent to their place of settlement "as Vagrants by this Act are directed to be sent"; and, since it was directed that vagrants *were* to be whipped before being sent on, this would automatically have become part of the process if not specifically excepted. As to lunatics having previously been treated as vagrants, we have already seen that they were not, at any rate where their lunacy was recognised. The position seems to be that by 1714 it was beginning to be felt that the Common Law did not give sufficient authority for all that the Justices were actually doing – hence the need for legislation.

Protective legislation was originally designed to protect only the paying patients in private madhouses, and particularly to prevent wrongful detention of the sane. It was not only in imaginative literature that a madhouse could provide a handy receptacle for rich uncles, infatuated daughters, supernumerary wives or spendthrift sons. Such cases were not frequent, but were well publicised. In an attempt to prevent this, as also to improve the notoriously bad conditions, the first Act for Regulating Madhouses was passed in 1774, providing for licensing and inspection, and requiring a certificate signed by a physician, surgeon or apothecary before a patient could be admitted, and notification of all admissions. Paupers sent by their parishes were specifically excluded from the provisions. This is not quite so deliberately callous as it appears, since the paupers might be supposed to be already under the supervision of the Justices whose warrant was necessary for their confinement, though of course this meant little in practice.

The Act meant comparatively little in practice either, and increasingly stringent legislation had to be passed throughout the 19th century, covering more and more institutions until even the obdurate Bethlem Hospital, Royal Charter and all, was made subject to inspection by Lunacy Commissioners. The legislation which had begun in 1774 with the very laudable aim of protecting the weak and vulnerable thus culminated in the great Lunacy Act of 1890, which among other things imposed such a rigid system of certification that any real development in the treatment of mental disorder was hamstrung for the next 70 years (until the passing of the Mental Health Act of 1959). And yet it was all intended for the best.

The most important development of the 19th century was, of course, the advance into the 'asylum era', which resulted from a Select Committee appointed in 1807 to inquire into the state of criminal and pauper lunatics in England and Wales. Legislation and provisions relating to the then so-called criminal lunatics, both before and after this date, is a subject of such complexity and current relevancy that it could have made an alternative to this paper (and nearly did) but cannot possibly be accommodated within it. I will confine myself to two observations, from which you may deduce just how new are the problems being faced today in this field. The first is in fact an observation by the Select Committee (1807) itself, that "to confine such persons in a common Gaol, is equally destructive of all possibility of the recovery of the insane, and of the security and comfort of the other prisoners". Secondly, those who are aware of the most up-to-date developments here, arising from the recommendations of the Butler Committee, may or may not be surprised to know that the solution proposed and implemented in 1816 was to build a secure unit in the grounds of Bethlem Hospital. *Plus ça change* . . . .

Regarding pauper lunatics in general the Committee found, as we would by now expect, that those detained under the 1744 Act were mostly in houses of correction, and the rest mostly in poorhouses or workhouses, in conditions "revolting to humanity", with a substantial proportion boarded out in private madhouses.

They concluded that the answer was for each county individually out of its own rates, or by uniting with neighbouring counties, to provide an asylum in which all the pauper lunatics within the district could be received and maintained at the expense of their own parishes, with some accommodation set aside for paying patients; and this was basically what was contained in the Act passed in the following year, 1808. Only 18 counties took action under this permissive legislation, however, and it is under a similar Act of 1845 making the provisions compulsory that the majority of the county asylums were built which are still our psychiatric hospitals today.

There are a number of misconceptions current about the aims and intentions behind the founding of county asylums. One is that they were deliberately planned to be very large and built in isolated country areas, in order to provide custodial care and nothing more for the maximum number behind locked doors and out of sight of respectable people; also, that it is only recently that anyone has noticed what a dreadful state of affairs this is. But no one who has read the 1807 Committee's report can doubt the good faith, indeed, the touchingly naïve faith, of the planners. They really believed that asylums were going to cure insanity. They also emphasised that attention should be paid to "placing the building in such a situation as from its vicinity may ensure the probability of the best medical assistance". As to size, they certainly recommended the maximum accommodation, on economic grounds, but this was not to exceed 300.

In fact the earliest asylums, as the lunatic hospitals and private madhouses before them, were built in towns, and were small; when they soon began to move farther out, this was in response to the by now fashionable belief in the value of good fresh air, and in order to provide exercise and outdoor occupations.

The size factor came eventually to be dictated entirely by economics, and as the century wore on asylums were built ever larger, while the smaller ones were added to instead of being duplicated. The West Riding Asylum at Wakefield, for example, now the Stanley Royd Hospital, was opened in 1818 to hold 150 patients. By the end of the century, it accommodated 1469. This practice was not without vociferous criticism, even at the time. Not unexpectedly, this was voiced by medical men who had to produce the results, against the administrators who provided the conditions in which they must work. Thus the proposal of the Middlesex Justices in 1856 to enlarge the Hanwell and Colney Hatch Asylums, which already accommodated respectively 1000 and 1200 patients, provoked the comment in the *Journal of Mental Science* that "Such Asylums as Colney Hatch and Hanwell might justly be called manufactories of chronic insanity. If a case recover, and few indeed are those that do recover within their walls, it is certainly the result of fortuitous circumstances, and not of any special treatment applied to it".

Hanwell is probably everyone's image of a typical lunatic asylum: and in winding up on what is essentially the great cliché of psychiatric history I am afraid that I risk obscuring the impression which I have been trying to create, of the great variety which has in fact existed in the past. But one must end, as one must begin, somewhere: and by the end of the 19th century there were already in existence nearly all the institutions and the framework within which psychiatry has had, perforce, to be practised until the most recent wave of rethinking. The Maudsley Hospital, a notable exception, is too important to be rushed in at the end here: and I will say no more than that when in 1907 Henry Maudsley finally set in motion the foundation of a *small* specialist mental hospital, in direct reaction against the massive county asylums, he was in fact recycling a model which had previously been used at the end of the 14th century, in 1713, and several times in the second half of the 18th century, and which had already been proposed this time round in 1867 and had been circulating in one form or another ever since.

And on that I will rest my case.

References

ALLDERIDGE, P. (1979) Management and mismanagement at Bedlam, 1547–1633. In *Health, Medicine and Mortality in the Sixteenth Century* (ed. C. Webster). Cambridge: Cambridge University Press.

BATES, E. H. (ed.) (1907) *Quarter Sessions Records for the County of Somerset*. Somerset Record Society.

BICKFORD, J. A. R. & BICKFORD, M. E. (1976) *The Private Lunatic Asylums of the East Riding*. East Yorkshire Local History Society.

BUTCHER, E. E. (1932) *Bristol Corporation of the Poor. Selected Records 1696–1834*. Bristol: Bristol Record Society.

CLAY, R. M. (1909) *The Medieval Hospitals of England*.

COWPER, W. (1816) *Memoir of the Early Life of William Cowper, Esq., Written by Himself*.

DALTON, M. (1618) *The Countrey Iustice, conteyning the Practise of the Iustices of the Peace out of their Sessions*.

FRIZELLE, E. R. & MARTIN, J. D. (1971) *The Leicester Royal Infirmary 1771–1971*. Leicester: No. 1 Hospital Management Committee.

GAIRDNER, J. (ed.) (1876) *The Historical Collections of a Citizen of London in the Fifteenth Century*. III William Gregory's Chronicle of London. London: Camden Society.

HOLLINGSHEAD, J. (1895) *My Lifetime*.

JOHNSON, J. (1826) *Transactions of the Corporation of the Poor*. Bristol.

LAMBARD, W. (1581) *Eirenarcha: or of The Office of the Iustices of the Peace*.

LUCAS, E. V. (ed.) (1905) *The Works of Charles and Mary Lamb, vol. VI, Letters 1796–1820*.

MOORE, N. (ed.) (1923) *The Book of the Foundation of St Bartholomew's Church in London*. London: Early English Text Society.

PARRY-JONES, W. LL. (1972) *The Trade in Lunacy*.

RASTELL, J. (1513) *Liber assisarum & placitorum corone*.

SELECT COMMITTEE (1807) *Report from the Select Committee appointed to Enquire into the State of Lunatics*. London: HMSO.

—— (1815) *First Report. Minutes of Evidence taken before the Select Committee appointed to consider of Provision being made for the Better Regulation of Madhouses, in England*, pp. 43 ff. London: HMSO.

WRIGHT, T. (ed.) (1904) *The Correspondence of William Cowper, vol. I*.

4 'Truth is a point of view': an account of the life of Dr Ernest Jones

THOMAS GRUFFYDD DAVIES

"We", wrote one of the members of the Bloomsbury group, "were the forerunners of a new dispensation, we were not afraid of anything". Dr Ernest Jones, a sympathiser with but never one of that group, and ever-anxious to be among the avant-garde, would surely have found that those words echoed his own experience. After a lifetime spent in defending the Freudian position, he would also have insisted that a description of his life's work should begin with an account of his family background and childhood.

His parents were of working-class origin, with middle-class aspirations. Thomas Jones, his father, was, we are told, an industrious, intelligent and largely self-educated man who started work as a colliery clerk and eventually became director of several concerns. He was radical in his political views and was greatly influenced until middle age by his strong attachment to the nonconformist religious cause. It was by virtue of his church membership in Swansea that he met Mary Ann Lewis, who became his wife. She is described as being a hard-working, wise, Welsh-speaking woman, whose son added an entirely new dimension to the assessment of personality by his curious description of his mother as being both saintly and snobbish.

In 1878, Mary Ann and Thomas Jones moved from Swansea to the hamlet of Ffosfelen (or Gowerton), six miles away, and of their three children, Alfred Ernest, who was born on 1 January 1879, was the oldest and the only son. He found it difficult to forgive his father for having named him Alfred Ernest after Queen Victoria's second son, the Duke of Edinburgh, and would have much preferred his mother's choice of Myrddin. He believed himself to be his parents' favourite child and never heard a cross word between them, although it does not seem to have occurred to him that the second statement might have been a function of the first.

His portrayal of his relationship with them goes (unintentionally perhaps) beyond the more restricted framework demanded by the psycho-analytical formula. It might be said with some justification that as a child he loved his mother and admired his father. Later, because of the

47

intransigent ways that they shared, he distanced himself from his father and, on reflection, he believed that his mother's influence on him had diminished progressively long before he reached adolescence. In spite of that, he continued to recognise the view taken by her (from whose side of the family he claimed he inherited his intelligence) that improvements in the lives of men would more likely be brought about by changes in psychological attitudes than by the alterations in working and social conditions thought so essential by his pragmatic father.

A physically weak infant, he developed rickets (from, he believed, his mother's tendency to overfeed him with patent medicines) and suffered night terrors, and he claimed that his earliest memories dated from the age of two. "Alas for the narcissism of childhood," he said on recalling his first disillusioning experience in life when he realised that the factory hooters that sounded in the distance, on the midnight before his birthday, were not saluting him but were heralding the approach of the New Year. Like Sigmund Freud, he found the devotion of his childhood nurse to her strait-laced, orthodox (but different) religion not to be an inspiring experience. Also, his early years were certainly less happy once his mother's snobbery, triumphing over her saintliness, had insisted he move from the village school to a school in Swansea.

At about 11 years of age, he claims to have had several dreams in which there occurred a sexual contact with his sisters, and he was struck by the contrast between the pleasure that he experienced during the dreams and the feeling of revulsion that came to him on waking and remembering the content of the dreams. He concluded, he says, that the more moral part of the human personality sleeps more deeply than the more primitive part. If this account (Jones, 1959) is to be accepted (and it was written many years later, of course) then he does truly seem to have anticipated an important facet of Freudian theory before ever leaving his childhood home.

At 13 years of age, he won a scholarship to Llandovery College, a public school with a good enough reputation. He never forgave the school authorities for having failed to teach him Welsh, which he felt should have been his first language, and the blow was only partially softened when the Warden at Llanymddyfri referred to him later as being the most brilliant pupil that the school had ever produced. After three years there, he left for University College Cardiff where, despite the opposite impression that he himself gave, he showed no signs of the academic brilliance that came his way later. This was probably because during those adolescent years, he was taken by a series of crises concerning religious matters, that came to an end when he became an atheist at 17 years of age. Three years later, he went on to University College Hospital, London, where he qualified in medicine at the turn of the century with the Conjoint Board diplomas. A year after that he obtained the MB degree, with honours and gold medals in medicine and obstetrics and a University Scholarship in Obstetrics.

During his childhood, his saintly, snobbish mother once asked Jones which of the virtues he would prefer to possess and, to her disappointment, he replied without hesitation "energy". In the early years of this century, that energy was very much in evidence, and within a short time he had obtained a Diploma in Public Health, the Membership of the Royal College of Physicians and the London MD, again with distinction and a gold medal. At that time, it must have seemed that he could have hoped for a distinguished career in any medical specialty of his choice. But that was not to be, because a complex series of events, which are difficult enough to understand and easy enough to misinterpret, changed the whole course of his life. It seems that those occurrences, far from being unconnected, tell a great deal of Jones's whole philosophy of life.

First, in 1903, on a night when his girlfriend was, according to him (Jones, 1959), "seriously ill," he left the Queen Elizabeth Hospital for Children at which he was working in order to be with her, without the permission of the hospital committee. As a result he had to resign. A different account is given in the hospital's minute books (1903), which reinforces the view that the authenticity of parts of his autobiography can be challenged. It seems Jones had left the hospital at night without permission several times previously and his employers found it difficult to accept his account of her illness. Without attempting to defend a system that had such a very restricting effect on the lives of junior hospital medical staff, the point must be made that Jones was well aware of the limitations that being a house officer were likely to make on his lifestyle and it is tempting to speculate that the origin of this whole incident owed as much to his rebellious nature as to any other factors. So, he resigned and took several part-time posts of various kinds, to enable him to continue with his research in neurology.

Apart from Freud himself, the man who had the greatest influence on Jones's life was the surgeon Wilfred Trotter, who became Professor of Surgery at University College Hospital, London, and Jones's brother-in-law by marrying his sister, Elizabeth. Trotter was an unusual surgeon (possibly best remembered by an older generation of psychiatrists as the author of *Instincts of the Herd in Peace and War*) and he helped Jones considerably to broaden his intellectual horizons. In 1905, he suggested that they might both benefit from setting up in Harley Street and Thomas Jones bought the lease of a house there.

A year after moving to Harley Street, the second catastrophe occurred when Jones was accused of having sexually assaulted two mentally handicapped ten-year-old girls at a special school at which he worked. After no less than four court appearances, the case was dismissed. There are those who to this day maintain that he must have been guilty, but the nature of the evidence offered against him suggests that they are ill informed and that he was wrongly and unjustly accused. When the mother of one of the girls said to him in the presence of Dr Kerr, the London County Council's Chief Medical Officer, "I call it disgraceful and disgusting," Jones's reply to her was, "My good woman, if I had done such a thing, I should deserve to be horse-whipped and placed in an asylum". And that came from a man who had decided as early as 1902 that psychiatry as he had seen it practised in England had reached its lowest level ever. On the other hand, from his work with hypnosis, he had become convinced of the existence of what he referred to as "subconscious happenings" and soon after that, Trotter was to introduce him to Freud's early writings. It is worth recalling that on reading the account of the Dora analysis, he was struck by the fact that there was "a man in Vienna who actually listened with attention to every word his patients said to him" – an important sentence in Jones's life and, of course, in the history of psychiatry.

Jones claimed to be the first person outside the German-speaking countries to use Freud's technique in treating patients, and in February 1908, the third disaster occurred when Jones attempted to psychoanalyse a ten-year-old girl, who was in hospital, without her parents' permission. She boasted to her friends that they had been discussing sexual matters, and again Jones had to resign. One can only either marvel at his bravery or wonder at his foolhardiness, and simply say that few people would have recovered from such a series of traumatic events.

By then, it was obvious even to Jones that he could not possibly hope to get an academic post in London and he did seriously consider moving to Cardiff as a neurologist, but in the event he accepted a post as head of a new psychiatric clinic in Toronto. Before going to Canada later in 1908, he spent some months on the continent visiting various centres, and it is apparent that those months were all important in helping him to crystallise his thoughts on those subconscious happenings that had so fired his imagination.

He had already met Jung in 1907, and it was he, Jones, who saw the need for an international meeting to discuss Freud's work. He suggested this to Jung, and as a result the first International Psychoanalytical Congress took place at Salzburg in April 1908. It was there that he met Freud for the first time, and found him to be unaffected and gracious in his ways, with a quiet, rough, unmusical voice, and whose opening remark to Jones was that he could not possibly be English – was he not Welsh? Jones seems to have interpreted this as one of those brilliant flashes of insight which many people associated with Freud, and he was greatly impressed, and equally greatly upset later on discovering that it was Jung who had told the Master of his Welsh origins a few minutes before they were introduced.

Wilfred Trotter was at Salzburg for the Congress, but he left before hearing the first paper because he was rather disillusioned with the company. As he left, his rather scornful parting shot to Jones was: "I console myself with the thought that I am the only one here who could cut off a leg properly". (A remark whose symbolic significance Freud might have found to be of more than ordinary interest coming as it did from a man who was hastily leaving a psychoanalytical meeting where castration anxiety was high on the agenda!) Freud and Trotter only met once after that, when Jones sought Trotter's advice on the treatment of Freud's malignancy in London more than 30 years later.

The Congress started at eight o'clock in the morning and Freud spoke for at least two and a half hours without using notes, and his audience insisted that he should continue for another hour. "I had never been so oblivious of the passage of time," wrote Jones of that morning. According to the minutes of the Vienna Psychoanalytical Society (Federn & Nunberg, 1962) there were 42 people at the Congress (not all of them psychoanalysts), and Freud insisted that there should be no lectures in the afternoon so that they could walk, but the Congress lasted for only a day, and there were eight other papers to listen to. Jones's paper was important in that it contained the first mention of the more well known of the two new terms which he introduced to the psychoanalytical jargon – he spoke on "Rationalisation in everyday life", a concept which he had developed quite independently of Freud.

After the Congress he went to Vienna, and he would have us believe that there he propped up the Wednesday meetings of the Vienna Psychoanalytical Society for a considerable period. The Vienna Society's minutes show that this was not so: in fact, he was an infrequent attender there, but we do know from Dr Melitta Schmideberg (1971) that Dr Hitschmann and the other members were "impressed and cheered" that someone of Jones's stature had visited them at all. His views of the Society's members are intriguing and contradictory: he accuses Jung of antisemitism for having referred to them as a "degenerate, Bohemian crowd", and then he goes on, "I was not highly impressed with the assembly. It seemed an unworthy accompaniment to Sigmund Freud's genius – he has to take what he could get", and then, his *pièce de résistance*, "Coming myself of an oppressed race, it was easy for me to identify myself with the Jewish outlook". It seems likely that the standards of the Vienna Society in those days were not anywhere as low as Jones made them out to be, and this may well be another of the several examples in the autobiography in which he attempts to elevate his own status by denigrating others. Of far greater importance than the question of his connection with the Society was the fact that while he was in Vienna, he spent a great deal of time with Freud discussing their work. This, as might be expected, he found to be a most inspiring experience.

In September 1908, Jones, his sister Elizabeth (the future Mrs Trotter) and his mistress Loe Kann, left for Toronto. In addition to his work at the new clinic there, he soon became responsible for the undergraduate teaching and examinations in psychiatry and was in a position to influence several generations of medical students at a time when no other psychoanalyst, with the possible exception of Ferenczi at Budapest, was allowed to teach in medical schools. However, there is evidence (Greenland, 1966) from one of Jones's former students that he was not an inspiring lecturer at undergraduate level, but that may be because he was not allowed to lecture on psychodynamic topics. It must be said that this description contrasts sharply with the other accounts available of his skill as a lecturer: Edward Glover (1958) said of him that he knew of no one, with the possible exception of Bertrand Russell, who could introduce new ideas with such elegance, clarity and force.

Jones shortly got himself appointed to part-time posts in the Departments of Medicine, Pathology and Physiology at Toronto, where he continued with his research work and writing, and started to accept private patients who came to him, especially from the United States. There is no mention in the autobiography of the fact that he had to be protected by the police after a former patient of his accused him of having sexual intercourse with her and threatened to kill him. Thus what might be politely called his accident proneness persisted. In 1910, Professor Putnam, the Head of the Neurology Department at Harvard, and one of Jones's greatest admirers, tried to get him a post in the Psychology Laboratories there, but failed because it was felt that Jones might corrupt the psychology undergraduates by discussing sexual topics with them. Had he gone there, it might well have delayed the later development of psychoanalysis in London considerably.

Jones's greatest work in Canada was as an archevangelist who travelled the length and breadth of the North American continent spreading the word about Freud; he was often accompanied by Putnam, who would attend his lectures not so much to listen to what Jones had to say, as to defend him from the attacks made on him by his audiences. Jones underwent untold persecution in Canada (and indeed in London later) and he never really got used to life in Toronto. He tended to share Freud's anti-American views, having been influenced possibly by the Master's statement that he did not "hate" America, he merely "regretted" it.

By 1912, Loe Kann's health was deteriorating or, to be more precise, she had become dependent on morphia. Jones decided to ask Freud to undertake her treatment, and they moved to Vienna. Loe's treatment was eminently successful – successful enough for her to leave Jones and to marry a Mr Herbert Jones, with Freud himself being one of their wedding guests.

Throughout their time in Canada, Jones had spent every summer in Europe, and he had hoped to retain his university appointment on that basis, but this was refused, so he resigned in 1913. It was Freud who best summed up Jones's work in Canada by saying that he had conquered that continent in four years.

Jung had already proposed that all future analysts should themselves undergo psychoanalysis, and Jones seems to have been the first to have a training analysis. At Freud's suggestion, he went to Budapest, to Sandor Ferenczi, where he spent an hour twice a day for several months undergoing psychoanalysis. As a result he felt that, on the one hand, he had gained an incomparable degree of self-understanding and personality maturation and that, in the bargain, he had lost all his socialist views.

When Jones returned to London late in 1913, there were still no hopes of his getting a university or hospital post, and for many years he was ostracised and scorned by most of his medical colleagues. But he had decided to establish psychoanalysis in London, and that is exactly what he set about doing. He formed the London Psychoanalytical Society, only to disband it later because several of the members had definite leanings towards Jung.

In 1917, he married a vivacious and brilliant young Welsh musician, Morfydd Llwyn Owen, but 18 months later, while they were on a visit to Swansea, she died, some weeks before her 27th birthday. After her death, Jones spent several months wandering aimlessly, leading a grief-stricken, purposeless existence. But soon the war was over, and that energy of which he had spoken to his mother returned.

Among his papers at the Institute of Psychoanalysis, there is a copy of a letter which he wrote on 29 January, 1919, to Freud, saying "psycho-analysis stands in the forefront of medical, literary and psychological interest" and a week later, he had more important news to send to Vienna: "We [meaning I, of course] intend forming a new Society this month . . . [of] nearly twenty members". Of the first 11 members of the British Psychoanalytical Society, he had psychoanalysed six of them himself, and this time he was unlikely to encounter any anti-Freudian interference.

The early psychoanalysts were not a particularly well organised group, and Jones's skill as an organiser must have been a great boon to the movement. It was he who brought the European psychoanalysts together again after World War I, and in 1919, Hans Sachs, the solicitor turned psychoanalyst, introduced him to a young Austrian lady, Katherine Jokl, and they were married within three weeks of their first meeting. Mrs Katherine Jones was actively able to participate in her husband's interests and work; from that time his energy and enthusiasm for his work as a psychoanalyst knew almost no limits.

In the 1920s, Jones regained a great deal of his interest in Welsh affairs and became very much more aware of his identity as a Welshman. In 1928, Gwenith, their seven-and-a-half-year-old daughter, died, and again he had to face a period of intense grief. He was hurt by Freud's suggestion that he should undertake some research work on a Shakespearean topic to ease his grief and would have preferred some words of comfort, but neither incident had a permanent effect on his zeal as an analyst.

In 1929, as a result of the doubts that existed as to the effectiveness of psychoanalysis as a form of treatment, the British Medical Association set up a committee to consider its relationship to medicine, and it was Jones, with Edward Glover's help, who played the major role in presenting evidence to the committee. His work there was truly phenomenal, and the committee's finding, that psychoanalysis should be regarded as an authentic form of treatment, can only be described as a turning point in the history of psychoanalysis; as Jones himself said, "that was the nearest we ever got to having a charter".

Although it took the Royal College of Physicians 40 years to elect him to their Fellowship, and he had to wait 55 years before being made a Fellow of University College, London, from 1929 onwards, he very gradually became more readily accepted and acclaimed, and in some ways his life history becomes less interesting from there on, in a way that recalls Russell's dictum that "It is the fate of all rebels to create new orthodoxies".

The various descriptions of him that abound are not without interest. Physically he had, to quote a well known Welsh archaeologist out of context, as austere a form as could be found on a deacon's bench in any West Wales chapel next Sunday morning. The "small stature, piercing brown eyes and boundless energy" described admiringly by one colleague became for another "a fiery little man, with a staccato military manner who at his worst was spiteful, jealous and querulous". The man whom Professor Putnam, no mean judge, recognised as the most energetic, enthusiastic and positive personality he had known in many years was, for Morton Price, an "insolent, nervous, highly-strung, self-centred" man who "takes everything one says as personal to himself" – whatever that may mean.

Freud once wrote to Jung saying that "Jones is a very interesting and worthy man, but he gives me a feeling of racial strangeness. He is a fanatic and doesn't eat enough. He almost reminds me of the lean and hungry Cassius". Yet, on Jones's 50th birthday, the Master had this to say to him: "We have reason to be well satisfied with one another . . . I have always looked upon you as a member of my intimate family circle". He was no longer a fanatic – Truth, it seems, in the end, is a point of view and it might be interesting to speculate as to what subtle mental mechanisms were at work when Freud said laughingly of him, "If Jones continues to be this tactful, we will have to send him to the League of Nations".

His complex relationship with Freud deserves a more close examination than is possible in this context. A starting point for such a study might concern itself with the simple fact that Jones, despite his apparent love of attention and his obvious self-importance, never tried to replace Freud as the true head of the psychoanalytical movement. (It might, of course, be argued that, at a practical level, Jones was the undisputed leader, but that argument is simplistic enough to ignore some of the more subtle facets of the bond that drew the two together.)

That there were disagreements between them is beyond doubt and it has been suggested that they were engineered by Jones in order to show the world how tolerant Freud was. There is no valid evidence that corroborates that view and one of his abiding obsessions was describing Freud as the Darwin of the mind. Although he readily accepted his role as being that of playing Huxley to Freud's Darwin, in his lecture "The nature of genius", he quotes Huxley on reading Darwin for the first time, when he said "How extremely stupid of me not to have thought of that".

The differences in their approaches to their work may ultimately prove to be of the greatest interest. In spite of the similarities in their training, with its emphasis on the neurology of the day, they would surely have not totally agreed on the importance of the relationship of the scientific method to psychoanalysis. When Freud was awarded the Geothe Prize in 1930, it was said of him that he was equally a creative writer and a scientist. Jones, although endowed with an enviable literary style and much creative ability, would have preferred to be remembered as a scientist. Freud's view of the unconscious mental mechanisms as being "superb in their indefiniteness" did not appeal to Jones, and as a therapist he was said to be more inflexible than Freud. He seemed to be more certain of what constituted proper technique and would have been prepared to psychoanalyse the neurosurgeon Harvey Cushing on account of a symptom which often troubled Cushing before he started surgical operations. Freud warned him against interfering in such matters but this made little difference to Jones's approach to his work.

Jones's way of dealing with those who defected from Freud showed that he was as capable of rationalising as most other people. Jung, he said (taking his cue from Freud), provided an interesting and rare example of someone who at one stage in his life (namely, at the time when he started to co-operate with Freud) attained massive insight but who later lost it dramatically and suddenly (at the time when he defected). Adler was more fortunate. He merely became pompous and arrogant after defecting. Jones believed that his own analyst, Ferenczi, and Rank had developed intractable paranoid illnesses, for which there is no other evidence at all. Glover and Strachey believed that Jones never forgave Ferenczi for having analysed him in the first place and, of course, for having been so close to Freud. Some new evidence suggests another reason for Jones's later hatred of Ferenczi. This is to be found in a letter (in the collection at the Institute of Psychoanalysis), written by Ferenczi to Jones in the 1920s, in which he offers to re-start Jones's analysis. Without doubt, the inference from Ferenczi was that Jones's first analysis had been incomplete, and this was being suggested at a time when Jones was President of the International Psychoanalytical Association.

As an administrator and organiser, he accomplished the most unparalleled feats: he founded two of the most important psychoanalytical societies in the world. Not only did he found the American Society in 1911, he also played the major part in converting the USA into the country with the largest number of psychoanalysts in the world; and as a sideline, at the same time, he helped form the American Psychopathological Association and was Assistant Editor to the *Journal of Abnormal Psychology*, at a time when editors of such journals were not always prepared to accept psychoanalytical material. After forming the British Psychoanalytical Society, he remained its President for 25 years, and ruled over its affairs like a dictator. He refused membership to well qualified applicants who did not appeal to him, and from time to time he used a technique, beloved by many species, of eliminating powerful male rivals. He was a strict disciplinarian and once threatened to deprive a niece of Bertrand Russell's of her membership of the Society because she undertook a series of lectures on psychoanalysis without his consent.

He founded the first psychoanalytical clinic in Britain and created the Institute of Psychoanalysis and its training programme, but his most spectacular administrative feat must have been to bring over Melanie Klein to London to work as a child analyst and to psychoanalyse his own children, without actually losing the friendship of the Freud family.

It was Jones who saw the need for the first International Psychoanalytical Congress, and he became the leader of the international movement for many years. He was the only one who was President for more than four years – and he was President for 25 years (1920–24 and 1932–49). He saw the need for and founded the *International Journal*, and saw the first 50 volumes (which included some of the great classics of psychoanalysis) through the press.

However, the hallmark of his status as an international leader must surely be that it was he who, in 1933, was asked to chair the last free meeting of the Berlin Psychoanalytical Society before the Nazis virtually destroyed it. He warned Freud of the dangers that were certain to follow Hitler's ascension, but Freud refused to consider leaving Austria then. (When Freud was told that his books were being burned publicly, his laconic reply was: "Things are improving – in the Middle Ages, they would have burned me – now they're only burning my books".)

Jones was one of the few prominent followers of Freud who remained faithful, and after Jung, Adler, and Stekel had defected, it was Jones who conceived of the idea of the famous Komittee whose main function was to defend Freud from having to face any further public criticisms. They were to function secretly, and Freud presented each of the members with an antique Greek intaglio from his collection, and these were then mounted in gold rings. Jones was the only member of the Komittee to lose his ring. It was actually stolen from the boot of his car, but as Professor Roazen (1975) remarked, "That was indeed a curious place in which to store a sacred object!"

Jones established himself as an author of repute early in his career. Trotter once said to him, "Jones, your idea of bliss is for the Almighty to despatch the Archangel Gabriel for one of your re-prints". And there were reprints galore because he wrote 300 or so papers and several books. He has been praised for his clarity of expression and blamed for his lack of originality as an author, but he never set out to do anything other than interpret Freud's views. His 1500-page biography of Freud is a curious work: it has been widely acclaimed and severely criticised. The many deficiencies in it were best summarised by an anonymous reviewer (Anonymous, 1977) who referred to Jones's work as an exercise in applied hagiography.

In spite of that, it seems that no one else could have written such a sensitive account of the last 18 months of Freud's life, and the work remains as Jones's last great crusade on behalf of psychoanalysis. It is fitting to remember that not only did he save Freud and his family from the Nazis, but that he was also able to help in the removal of nearly 50 other psychoanalysts and their families to safety and that they included among their number the late Professor Stengel. Two other facts that are not well known about him are that because of his opposition to the Nazi regime from the chair of the International Psychoanalytical Association a few years earlier, his name was included on a list of people who were quickly to be exterminated by the Nazis if they ever reached London. He was, in fact, arrested in Vienna in 1938 and was fortunate to escape with his life.

Neither is it generally appreciated that he suffered greatly for many years from persistent pain due to an ear infection and from what he referred to as rheumatism, which was really Gaucher's disease which he had inherited (along with his intelligence, it seems) from his mother's side of the family. He was unique even in the illnesses suffered by him in that his was the first recorded example of that condition recorded in the absence of splenomegaly.

After retiring in 1944 he suffered a heart attack, and within weeks of having treatment for a bladder tumour, in 1956, he was on his way to America to lead the Freud Centenary celebrations, to lecture, and to impress everyone with that never-absent energy. He then returned to London to perform the same feats there and to unveil the plaque on the Freud family house. Two years later he died of carcinoma of the liver, on 11 February 1958.

It is rumoured that Ernest Jones, ever ready to take a kick at the devout during his lifetime, became a Christian on his deathbed.

It would scarcely be possible to do justice to Alfred Ernest Jones without enlarging greatly on his many accomplishments. It hardly seems enough to say of him that his life's work had a great influence on psychoanalysis, because of his standing as a clinician, a teacher of clinicians, a lecturer of international repute, an organiser and founder of psychoanalytical societies, an editor and driving force, and particularly as someone who was prepared to lay down his own life in order to save that of a disillusioned old Jewish gentleman who believed that the world had forgotten about him. Nietzsche once wrote to a friend saying: "If you should ever come around to writing about me, be sensible enough, as no one has been until now, to characterise me, to describe but not to evaluate". And that might be best achieved in this case by quoting those sterling words that were once spoken about the Lord Protector of England (himself of Welsh origin) by his servant who simply said, "A larger soul hath seldom dwelt in a house of clay".

Acknowledgements

I am grateful to the National Library of Wales and the Glamorgan Record Office for permission to include material from their collections.

The late Mrs Katherine Jones, Mrs Kitty Idwal Jones, Miss Anna Freud, Dr Melitta Schmideberg and Dr W. H. Gillespie and Mr Aled Vaughan helped to provide me with a clearer picture of Ernest Jones during their conversations with me. I am grateful to my secretary Mrs Cynthia Jenkins, BA, for typing the manuscript.

Appendix

A copy of one of the examination papers which Dr Ernest Jones sat during his MD examination.

University of London MD and MS examinations, 1903

Mental Physiology
Examiners: William McDougall, Esq MB, MA
            G. H. Savage, MD

No more than three questions in either section are to be answered.

A: 1. Describe the forms of mental disorder most commonly associated with Epilepsy

2. Contrast the symptoms met with in Hysteria and Hypochondriasis.

3. Describe the forms of mental disorder and their course met with as the result of alcoholism.

4. What are the most common forms of Delusional Insanity? Give the probable course and termination of such cases.

B: 1. It has been said that "Man has more instincts than any other animal". Discuss the meaning and validity of this statement.

2. Describe the more important phenomena of "post hypnotic suggestion" and the hypotheses that have been proposed for the explanation of them.

3. What is the theory of psychological disintegration. Contrast briefly the forms of anaesthesia due to lesion with those symptomatic of Hysteria.

4. State and discuss the doctrine of mental elements and the doctrine of the specific energies of sensory nerves, exhibiting the relation between them. Distinguish carefully between Sensation and Perception.

References

ANONYMOUS (1977) Book review. *Psychological Medicine*, **7**, 355.
FEDERN, E. & NUNBERG, H. (eds) (1962) *Minutes of the Vienna Psychoanalytical Society, vol. 1*, p. 389. New York.
GLOVER, E. (1958) Obituary notice. *British Journal of Medical Psychology*, **31**, 71–73.
GREENLAND, C. (1966) Ernest Jones in Toronto, Part 1. *Canadian Psychiatric Association Journal*, **11**, 519.

JONES, E. (1953–57) *Sigmund Freud: His Life and Work*. London.
—— (1959) *Free Associations*, pp. 112–113. London.
ROAZEN, P. (1975) *Freud and his Followers*, p. 352. New York.
SCHMIDEBERG, M. (1971) A contribution to the history of the psychoanalytical movement Great Britain. *British Journal of Psychiatry*, **118**, 61–68.

Further reading

DAVIES, T. G. (1979) *Ernest Jones 1879–1958*. Cardiff.
GLAMORGAN COUNTY COUNCIL, Reports of Organising Agent to the Technical Instruction Committee, 1895–97. Glamorgan Record Office.
HALE, JR, H. G. (ed.) (1968) *James Jackson Putnam and Psychoanalysis*. Cambridge, Massachusetts. pp. 252–255.
MAYNARD KEYNES, J. (1949) *Two Memoirs*, p. 82. London.
TRITSCHLER, G. (1963) *Morfydd Owen – a Biography*. National Library of Wales, unpublished manuscript.

...d the realities of
early modern England

MacDONALD

In a recent issue of *The New York Review of Books*, Owen Chadwick grumbled: "Insanity is not a matter for the historian, whose business is the reality of the past" (Chadwick, 1979). The aim of this paper is to show that insanity is very much a matter for the historian, because the history of insanity mirrors wider transformations in society. To demonstrate this claim I have chosen to explore some of the ways in which the history of madness and healing in England between about 1600 and 1800 was affected by precisely those aspects of historical reality which are Professor Chadwick's personal preoccupations: religious controversy and secularisation. Early modern England would not, at first glance, seem to be promising territory in which to search for evidence that changes in beliefs about mental disorder were shaped by events outside the sphere of scientific investigation and discovery. Historians of psychiatry depict the period in heroic terms, celebrating the achievements of a small band of physicians and scientists who led the people of Europe out of the darkness of superstition and credulity into the light of reason and observation. "The Renaissance," according to one standard text, "marked Western man's reorientation toward reality. Although the battle against superstition was not won during the period, the turning point was reached: Western man was committed to seeking the truth about himself" (Alexander & Selesnick, 1967). From this perspective the history of psychiatry, like the history of science generally, follows the high road of progress during the 17th and 18th centuries, moving inexorably away from magic and religion towards medical science.

Yet even the most cursory survey of the rise of medical psychology in early modern England casts doubt on the standard interpretations of the period. The simple maps sketched by historians of psychiatry are as fabulous as the parchment fantasies of Elizabethan cartographers, filling in the blank spaces between Constantinople and Cathay. Further exploration reveals that the passage from superstition to rationality resembled the mazy wanderings of refugees more than the purposeful march of a conquering army. Educated men and women followed the lead of physicians and scientists largely because traditional religious and magical beliefs about insanity had been discredited by political events, and not because new psychological theories and medical treatments provided superior explanations and treatments for insanity. The rise of medical psychology reflected a change in the outlook of the ruling élite in England, and it did not greatly affect the beliefs of ordinary people until the 19th century. The secularisation of ideas about insanity and of psychological healing was an aspect of the governing classes' response to the political and religious conflicts of the 17th century. This is an audacious hypothesis, and I would need more space and time than the compass of this essay to prove it. The best I can achieve here is to demonstrate its plausibility by retracing one major theme in the history of mental disorder in early modern England: the effect that the upper classes' aversion to religious radicalism after 1660 had on their views about how insanity ought to be explained and treated.

This paper has three parts. I shall begin by discussing the century-long attack on religious enthusiasm, a campaign waged by Anglicans to discredit popular religious radicalism by claiming that it was a form of mental disease. I shall then present an assessment of the effects that the attack on enthusiasm had on upper-class attitudes towards insanity and healing. I shall conclude with a consideration of the most obvious objection to my argument and an assessment of some of the implications of this approach to the history of mental disorder.

Two preliminary matters call for comment. Firstly, throughout this essay I have employed terms for mental illness, words such as 'insanity', 'madness' and 'melancholy', more or less as they (or their archaic equivalents) were understood by laymen in the 17th and 18th centuries and much as they are understood today. Since my purpose is to discuss changes in the governing élite's beliefs about mental disorder, it would be inappropriate to adopt present-day definitions of psychiatric illnesses and project them backwards into the past. Nor would it be appropriate to describe those beliefs in a specialised terminology unlike the words laymen use now. The changing meaning of the popular language of madness presents complex and illuminating problems which are touched upon only briefly here. Secondly, the argument of this paper necessarily ignores important variations in the views of the governing élite, and it fuses together very disparate individuals into phrases like 'the upper classes' and 'the educated élite'. I have in mind the members of the landed, commercial, and professional classes, who possessed sufficient education to expose them to Anglican propaganda and the new fashions in science and philosophy, and who were in a position to influence public policy towards the insane by acting as magistrates, coroners, physicians, madhouse proprietors, preachers, and pamphleteers. It is notoriously difficult to formulate a precise definition of social class in early modern England, or to demonstrate its significance. A historian of mental disorder cannot simply ignore the matter, because until the 19th century the central government played a relatively small part in providing for the care and treatment of the insane. The practices which prevailed in earlier periods were those which were encouraged by the actions of men of authority and property, and one is obliged to seek the reasons for changes in those practices in the forces which shaped their attitudes and behaviour. Contemporaries recognised a rough, but significant, division between the upper and lower orders of society and, in spite of the sharp differences in religious and political opinion among the members of the governing classes, I believe that it is legitimate to treat them as a single social group, sharing a common set of beliefs and prejudices.

The attack on enthusiasm

In 1762 William Hogarth published an etching attacking "Credulity, Superstition, and Fanaticism" (Paulson, 1970). The print (Fig. 1) is a violent satire of Methodist preaching, and it epitomises ruling-class prejudices towards popular religious enthusiasm. In it we see a fabulous congregation assembled in a Methodist meeting hall. High above the worshippers a preacher is whipping up the crowd. Thrusting himself out of the pulpit, he dangles puppets of a witch and a devil, embodiments of the satanic rhetoric allegedly favoured by Whitefield and Wesley. His periwig has tumbled behind, revealing the tonsured skull of a secret papist beneath his orthodox garb. Below, the congregation lolls in states of ecstasy, torment, and mystical affliction. A Jew kills lice between his thumbs; his gaze is directed at the preacher, but the Bible before him is open at the bloody passages of the Old Testament. Across from him, a man is shoving a religious icon down the dress of a swooning girl. Two spurious miracles are occurring in the foreground: a woman is giving birth to a litter of rabbits, and a boy is bent forward vomiting hobnails and iron staples, a reference to the symptoms of the famous 'Boy of Bilson' and subsequent victims of demonic possession. George Whitefield himself stands as a clerk in the vortex of this busy scene, a stricken look on his face and the decapitated heads of two cherubs hovering beside him.

The Anglican opponents of Methodism relied heavily upon two lines of argument to discredit the sect, both of which are embodied in Hogarth's etching. First, they claimed that Methodism was a form of religious enthusiasm, a religion based on spurious claims of divine revelation, and that Methodist beliefs and behaviour were signs of madness. Their leaders were stricken with the insane delusion that they were directly inspired by God, and their followers were maddened by fiery preaching. In his *History of Modern Enthusiasm*, for instance, Theophilus Evans (1757) charged that the Methodists

> "have been looked upon as mad (on account of their wild and frantic
> actions) by friends and relations, by indifferent persons, by regular

Fig. 1. Hogarth's print "Credulity, Superstition and Fanaticism", 1762

physicians (the most proper judges), by the world in general, and have been sent to Bedlam, and adjudged there to be persons distracted."

A notable 18th-century mad-doctor, William Pargeter, claimed that all the maniacs he had treated were religious fanatics, and that Methodism was the most pernicious form of enthusiasm (Pargeter, 1792). Although he certainly exaggerated the number of insane Methodists he encountered in his practice and in the asylums of the age, Pargeter's views were shared by other physicians. Almost every important medical book about mental disorder printed in the 18th-century repeated the assertion that religious enthusiasm often caused insanity, and some early Methodists were actually incarcerated in asylums on their doctors' orders (Whitefield, 1960; Wesley, 1842). Bishop Lavington, echoing the words of earlier figures as diverse as Addison, Bolingbroke, Swift, and Shaftesbury, concluded aphoristically: "enthusiasm and madness are but the same thing in different words" (Lavington, 1757; De Porte, 1974).

Hogarth handled this theme more amusingly. His preacher's text is "I speak as a fool", and, in place of the traditional church hour-glass, he has inserted a thermometer calibrated to measure the degree of insanity the congregation achieves. The instrument thrusts upwards out of a Methodist's disembodied brain, which rests on copies of Wesley's sermons and Glanvill's defence of the existence of witches. It is calibrated with a scale which runs from 'suicide' through 'madness', 'despair', 'settled grief', 'agony', 'sorrow', 'low spirits', 'lukewarm', 'love heat', 'lust', 'ecstasy', 'convulsion fits', to 'madness' (again) and, finally, all the way up to 'raving'. The mercury shows that the congregation is still just lukewarm: there are wilder scenes to come.

The second line of argument commonly followed by the Anglican critics of Methodism attacked their continued belief in demonic possession and witchcraft, and especially Wesley's claim that these spiritual maladies could be relieved by prayer and fasting (Wesley, 1842). Thus the eponymous Thomas Church addressed Wesley directly in a sermon: "You would have these cases considered as those of the demoniacs in the New Testament, in order, I suppose, to parallel your supposed cures of them with those of the highest miracles of Christ and his disciples" (Church, 1745). Hogarth's etching is jammed with references to Methodist beliefs in possession, witchcraft, and supernatural apparitions. We have already noted the puppets of a witch and the Devil brandished by the preacher, the Boy-of-Bilson figure, and Glanvil's treatise, but there are more. A basket containing Whitefield's journals rests on a copy of King James' *Daemonology*, and on top of the thermometer of enthusiastic madness is a figure representing the Drummer of Tedworth, a famous poltergeist credited by both Glanvill and Wesley (Glanvill, 1681; Wesley, 1842).

By the time Hogarth published his etching in 1762 the idea that religious enthusiasm was a form of insanity had become a ruling-class shibboleth. Individual prophets and mystics had for centuries been denounced as madmen, but the equation of intense religious experience and madness became a forceful polemical device only during the mid-17th century. Writing early in the reaction against Calvinist zeal before the Civil War, Robert Burton argued, in his famous *Anatomy of Melancholy*, that English Puritans were both the victims and the carriers of a mental disease he named religious melancholy. Some of them were deluded by the disease into believing themselves to be divinely inspired; other, more sober Puritans cultivated pathological religious anxiety, because they believed that emotional turmoil was the necessary prelude to regeneration. Stiff doses of orthodoxy and physic were necessary to cure the commonwealth of this infestation of religious melancholy (Burton, 1968). Burton's argument was an effective and enduring polemical weapon because it contained a kernel of truth. Historians of puritanism have long noted the preoccupation of godly preachers with anxiety and despair. Puritans such as Greenham and Sibbes emphasised the spiritual significance of inner turmoil. They used the traditional allegorical imagery of spiritual warfare to describe psychological distress, and they preached that the only sure means to strengthen one's self against emotional disturbance was to experience moral and spiritual regeneration through conversion and self-discipline (Haller, 1958; MacDonald, 1979).

Burton's emphasis was on the emotional effects of religious melancholy: the uncompromising doctrines of the Puritans drove melancholy men and women to despair and even to suicide. During the Interregnum, the rise of the radical sects prompted Henry More to write an influential pamphlet which stressed the *delusive* effects of religious insanity. In *Enthusiasmus Triumphatus*, published in 1656, More asserted that sectarians who claimed divine revelation or prophetic powers were suffering from diseased imaginations. Elaborating Burton's scientific arguments. More explained that melancholy can cause fabulous delusions when the victim's brain became polluted by the poisonous fumes of the melancholy humour, boiling in his overheated body (More, 1656). More's pamphlet became the basis for most subsequent attacks on extreme religious sects, including the Quakers, the French Prophets, and, of course, the Methodists (Sena, 1973; Schwartz, 1978). Its views were recast by Locke and echoed by a host of famous writers and obscure sermonisers. Johnson, for example, defined enthusiasm in his *Dictionary* as "a vain belief in private revelation", and he quoted Locke's view that it "rises from the conceits of a warmed or overweening imagination" (Johnson, 1755; Locke, 1959). The decline of humoural psychology did not daunt this crew of propagandists, who tended more and more during the 18th century to follow Swift in labelling enthusiasm as a variety of madness instead of melancholy (Harth, 1961).

Hogarth's print implies that credulous beliefs in demons and witches were also a product of enthusiastic madness. The notion that many apparently supernatural perceptions and diseases were actually caused by mental disorders was venerable by 1762, but it was also controversial. The opponents of witchcraft trials since the late 16th century had argued that the confessions of accused witches were nothing but the ravings of poor old women deluded by melancholy. Elizabethan and Jacobean physicians, jealous of the intrusion of clerical doctors and folk magicians into medical practice, had maintained that most of the symptoms popularly attributed to possession were the tokens of mental and physical diseases. At the turn of the 16th century the church hierarchy lent its support to this view as part of its efforts to discredit the exorcisms performed both by the Jesuits and by the Puritan, John Darrell, who practised a method of casting out devils by prayer and fasting that was compatible with rigorous Protestant scruples about popish rituals (Kocher, 1953; Thomas, 1978). The arguments against witchcraft and possession gained ground among the eduated élite after the Restoration, and some very bold writers, including the most famous 18th-century physician, Richard Mead, even applied them to the witches and demoniacs in the Bible (Mead, 1775). Such arguments were, notoriously, also championed by Hobbes and by the deists. Those associations were too much for many Anglicans and Old Dissenters, who were alarmed that materialist explanations for supernatural phenomena might undermine the central revelations and miracles of the Christian church as easily as they demolished the enthusiasts' pretensions to divine inspiration and miraculous powers. Yet, in spite of the reservations of churchmen wary of associating themselves with Hobbists and deists, scepticism prevailed among the governing classes during the 18th century. Exorcism was abandoned, the witchcraft statute was repealed, and the Nonconformists who continued to cater to popular beliefs in witches and demons were denounced as the carriers of madness and delusion (Tourney, 1972; Thomas, 1978).

Changing beliefs about madness and healing

The reaction against religious enthusiasm and the much more fitful spread of scepticism about other supernatural phenomena among the educated élite have often been discussed before. Literary scholars have shown that hatred for religious passion was an integral aspect of Restoration and Augustan high culture (Williamson, 1933; Steffan, 1941; Harth, 1961). Religious historians have long recognised that the antagonism to enthusiasm contributed to the creation of a style of Anglican devotion in which emotion was so effectively cooled by reason that signs of life in the main body of the church were hard to detect (Abbey & Overton, 1878; Walsh, 1966). Historians of science have argued that the replacement of the Puritan zeal for a new order with the latitudinarian longing for social stability contributed to the upper-class receptiveness to scientific, and especially Newtonian, interpretations of the natural world (Hill, 1975; Jacob, 1976). The idea that religious enthusiasts were madmen was enormously attractive to a ruling élite weary of religious strife and seeking new cultural and intellectual pursuits free from the political perils of theological controversy. Commending the study of science as a vocation suitable for Restoration gentlemen, for example, Thomas Sprat remarked that the natural philosopher was the antithesis of the religious enthusiast, because he was "truly acquainted with the tempers of men's bodies, the composition of their blood, and the power of fancy, and so better understands the differences between diseases and inspirations" (Sprat, 1959).

What has not been widely remarked upon, however, is that the century-long attack on enthusiasm contributed to a change in the educated élite's beliefs about insanity itself. The ruling classes altered both their conception of what the nature and significance of insane behaviour were and also their notions of how madness ought to be managed and treated. The most significant changes in the definition of insane behaviour all reflect a secularisation of the mental world of the upper orders of society. The most important of these were the addition of delusions and hallucinations to the signs of acute insanity, the spread of the view that suicide was a symptom of mental disease, and the rejection of witchcraft and demonism as explanations for actual cases of mental disorder.

Prior to the English revolution, popular stereotypes of mad behaviour emphasised the irrational violence and furious ravings of lunatics. The worst kinds of insanity, which were usually referred to as 'madness', 'lunacy', or 'distraction', were characterised by two patterns of behaviour, one of which likened madmen to criminals, the other to the mortally ill (MacDonald, 1979). Both physicians and laymen described lunatics as wild, incoherent creatures, who were either bent on senseless destruction or clamoured deliriously, like the victims of deadly fevers. Extravagant delusions and hallucinations are seldom found in descriptions of men and women who were believed to be mad; they were taken instead to be symptoms of melancholy, a milder form of insanity than madness (MacDonald, 1979). During the century following the Restoration, however, these stereotypes of insanity changed. Philosophers, physicians, and fashionable scribblers focused their attention on the *ideas* of madmen, and they stressed that delusions and hallucinations were the very essence of utter madness. The famous anatomist Thomas Willis stressed that insanity was caused by violent and unrestrained imagination (Willis, 1683). John Locke developed this idea in what was to become one of the most often repeated remarks about insanity. Madmen, according to Locke (1959),

> "do not appear to have lost the faculty of reasoning, but having joined together some ideas very wrongly, they mistake them for truths; and they err as men do that argue rightly from wrong principles. For by the violence of their imaginations, having taken their fancies for realities, they make right deductions from them."

Grub Street hacks and literary geniuses alike took up the notion that lunacy was characterised by deluded ideas and imaginary perceptions. Writing soon after the turn of the century, the 'London spy', Ned Ward, described a visit to Bedlam. Perambulating the asylum, "to see what whimsical figaries their wandering fancies would move them to entertain us withal," Ward and his companion encounter among the inmates a counterfeit king with a moonshine crown and an army of eagles at his command, a love-sick melancholy fiddler, and a religious fanatic, intently trampling his conscience down, lest it rise up and fly in his face (Ward, 1706).

The notion that deluded beliefs were a cardinal symptom of severe insanity had become so general by 1758 that William Battie could claim in his famous *Treatise on Madness* that they were the defining characteristic of the disease. "All mankind as well as the physician," Battie observed, agreed that false perceptions are "a certain sign of madness". "Therefore," he concluded, "deluded imagination . . . is not only an indisputable but an essential character of madness" (Battie, 1962). Some physicians naturally objected that there was more to madness than mistaken opinions and false perceptions, but the emphasis early-19th-century writers placed on delusions and hallucinations reflected the general conviction among the educated élite that they were indeed the certain signs of madness (Smollet, 1758, 1759; Monro, 1962). Witnesses who testified to the insanity of 19 lunatics whose cases came before the Court of Chancery between 1719 and 1733 described them as people who, in the words of one observer, had "wild fancies, as distracted persons are used to do". These deluded creatures included six imaginary noblemen, a man who dressed and acted as the Archbishop of York, two people who saw visions of Satan and devils, and one person who received miraculous revelations (PRO, C. 217/55). The conviction that delusions and hallucinations were symptoms of grave mental disorder also found its way into most of the medical books about insanity written in the late 18th century. For instance, a physician of the Manchester Infirmary and Lunatic Asylum, John Ferriar, endorsed the substance of Battie's definition of madness in 1795 and added that when melancholics appeared to have false perceptions, their disease was unusually intense, and consisted in many cases of a mixture of melancholy and mania (Ferriar, 1795).

The elevation of delusions and hallucinations from symptoms of melancholy to emblems of madness was one consequence of the governing élite's growing scepticism about supernatural phenomena. Before the middle of the 17th century most men and women believed that perfectly rational people could receive inspiration from God or have intercourse with the Devil. Godly Protestants read in the pages of John Foxe that the heroes of the Church of England, like medieval saints and martyrs, sometimes received prophetic visions and communications; King James I himself was among the writers who popularised the notion that the Devil appeared to malevolent hags and recruited them as witches (Thomas, 1978). So long as educated people continued to believe in the potent presence of an invisible world of supernatural beings, few authorities were willing to classify apparent delusions and hallucinations, many of which were religious in character, as the sure tokens of stark madness. Some doubt always remained that such experiences might be genuine contacts with good or evil spirits. It is hardly surprising, therefore, that prior to the Civil War eccentric beliefs and strange perceptions were typically attributed to melancholy, a disease which lacked the pejorative connotations of madness and was even supposed to enhance the mental powers of some people (Babb, 1951; Bamborough, 1951).

The secularisation of the ruling classes' ideas about mental disorder also affected the definition of suicide and the official reaction to it. Until the later 17th century, suicide was regarded as a religious and civil crime by almost all Englishmen. Self-murder was the embodiment of a heinous sin against the Holy Ghost, despair, and thus it was an act of apostasy. The suicide succumbed to the temptations of the Devil, and many suicidal men and women reported that they had actually seen or heard an evil spirit urge them to despair and self-destruction. The Fiend or his dark servants appeared to many of the suicidal patients of an early-17th-century astrological physician named Richard Napier (MacDonald, 1977, 1979). Describing the circumstances of her mother's suicide in 1690, an 11-year-old girl told investigators this story:

> "The day before the fact was done, there was a strange man in black with her mother, and had discourse with her, but she knew not what it was. But when he went away, she heard her mother say to him, 'But what will become of my poor children'? To whom he replied, 'Take you no care of them, they will be provided for." (Historical Manuscripts Commission, 1876)

The constable who heard this child's tale believed her, for the ancient stereotype of self-murder declared that the crime was the Devil's own handiwork. Encounters with the Tempter reported by despairing men and women did not suggest that suicides were mad visionaries, but quite the contrary: successful suicides were classified by the authorities as fully rational criminals who had committed premeditated murder, rather than as innocent lunatics suffering from morbid gloom and hallucinations. The savage religious and civil penalties against suicide were based on the assumption that suicides were sane, and that like other felons they committed their crime "at the instigation of the Devil," a phrase which appears in every felony indictment and inquest on a suicide's body. The suicide's corpse was buried secretly, profanely, denied the rites of a Christian's funeral; his property was confiscated by the Crown, and only his landed estate passed to his heirs (MacDonald, 1977).

These terrible sanctions were widely enforced before the English revolution. Very few suicides were officially forgiven for their deed, judged by coroners' juries to have been mad at the time of their deaths and so not responsible for their actions. During the later part of the 17th century, however, verdicts of *non compos mentis* became increasingly common as the governing classes abandoned their belief in demonism (Murphy, 1981). Throughout the 18th century, clerical traditionalists complained about the rapid disappearance of the old penalties. Predictably, Wesley was one of these. In 1790 he proposed gibbeting the bodies of suicides as a mark of their infamy and lamented that by that time everybody who slew himself was supposed to be a lunatic; the act itself was construed as a sign of mental disease (Wesley, 1842). He was right: by the latter half of the 18th century almost every suicide reported by the county coroners was declared to have been insane (Hair, 1971; Hunnisett, 1981). John Adams insisted that it was the coroners, and not the humble folk who composed their juries, who were to blame for this shift in the official response to suicide. The coroner summoned whomever he pleased to serve on the panel; he gave them whatever charge he wished; he examined the witnesses; he summed up the evidence at the conclusion of the inquest. "Tis his fault chiefly," Adams concluded, "if the laws which provide against self-murder are eluded" (Adams, 1700). As the idea of the immanent Devil was cast out of the world-view of the ruling élite, they turned to medical interpretations of the meaning of suicide and viewed it as a symptom of lunacy rather than the criminal manifestation of a satanic compact (MacDonald, 1977).

We have already briefly considered the most obvious manifestation of the educated élite's increasingly secular attitude towards mental disorders, their growing scepticism that they could be caused by witches and demons. The decline of faith in witchcraft and demonism among the upper classes was a complex event; even Keith Thomas' magnificent book makes it seem simpler and faster than it was (Thomas, 1978). The plainest manifestations of scepticism, the repeal of the laws against witchcraft and the refusal of physicians to validate cases of possession, show that educated laymen had lost confidence in these old beliefs by the mid-18th century. Their faith in supernatural malevolence was partially corroded by their hostility towards the visionary claims of the enthusiasts. Was it not unreasonable to suppose that the Devil was permitted to enter the minds and bodies of men and to confer miraculous powers on witches while God Himself no longer inspired prophets and granted his followers the gift of healing? The deist, Charles Blount, made this point with characteristic directness: "How can it be admitted with reference to divine nature," he asked, "that prophecy should cease and witches so abound?" (Blount, 1695). On the other hand, many Anglicans, and particularly churchmen, were reluctant to fall into step with Hobbists and deists and repudiate witchcraft and demonism altogether, since materialist objections to those beliefs cast doubt upon the validity of scripture, which contains numerous tales of witches and demons and depicts Christ and his apostles as exorcists. Writing a century after Blount, and from the antithetical theological stance, Wesley (1842) raised this problem in his characteristic way:

> "they well know . . . that giving up witchcraft is, in effect, giving up the Bible; and they know . . . that if but one account of the intercourse of men with separate spirits be admitted, their whole castle in the air (Deism, Atheism, Materialism) falls to the ground. I know no reason, therefore, why we should suffer even this weapon to be wrested out of our hands."

Throughout the 18th century clerical polemicists and philosophers battled between these two extreme positions. Among Anglicans faith in the central miracles of the Christian religion was at odds with hatred for the miraculous claims of papists and enthusiasts, and the result was a highly selective type of scepticism. Many orthodox writers concluded that, although divine providence had the power to permit demonic possession and miraculous cures, as God had done in Biblical times, He would not allow them to occur in circumstances which would imperil the authority of the Anglican establishment. To Samuel Clarke's mind it was "infinitely certain" that God restrains evil spirits "from imposing upon men's minds and understandings in all such cases where wise and honest and virtuous men would have no possible way left, by which they could discover the imposition" (Clarke, 1706). The attack on enthusiasm therefore helped to create a climate of opinion in which scientism flourished, and in which medical and mechanical explanations for mental disorders were encouraged, so long as they were not employed to question the legitimacy of the Church of England's own claims to possess authority ultimately based on miraculous revelation.

The governing élite's long and intense hostility towards radical religion also encouraged them to repudiate methods of psychological healing which were based on popular religious and magical beliefs and to advance medical therapies as the only proper means to relieve mental illnesses. Before the Civil War, an insane or troubled person might seek help from practitioners offering spiritual counsel, communal prayer, exorcism, natural magic, or physic. Although clergymen, physicians, and astrologers often championed the effectiveness of one form of therapy, reputable healers frequently combined them; and many educated people saw no irreconcilable conflicts between the religious, magical, and scientific theories on which they were based (MacDonald, 1979). During the century after the revolution, Anglican clergymen not only refused to perform exorcisms, they also grew increasingly reluctant to provide the kind of spiritual counsel which had been a popular aspect of pre-Civil War divinity. Probing the emotions of distressed sinners and bringing them to a heightened realisation of their spiritual condition was regarded with extreme suspicion, and the sufferings of people tormented by religious doubt and guilt were explained as the signs of mental illness. Anglican propagandists declared that the spiritual pangs which accompanied the new births of Methodists and Calvinist dissenters were caused by hypochondriacal passions, melancholy, or some other mental disease. Methodists, like the Puritans before them, described their emotional turmoil as "conflicts and combats with Satan", but, trumpeted writers such as Bishop Lavington, "the greatest part of these strange feelings and sufferings, dejections of mind and dreadful apprehensions, &c, proceed from disease" (Lavington, 1757). The orthodox élite's hostility towards popular religious radicalism probably contributed less to their rejection of magical therapies, such as astrological amulets, than it did to their

Fig. 2. Hogarth's print "A Rake's Progress, Plate VIII", 1735

repudiation of religious healing. Nevertheless, Christopher Hill and Bernard Capp have remarked that the most prominent astrologers were Parliamentarians, and the gradual disenchantment with medical astrology after the Restoration may have owed something to the unsavoury political connotations it had acquired during the revolution (Hill, 1975; Capp, 1979). In the 18th century, patients who craved astrological evaluations of their maladies and astral amulets to protect them had to turn to popular healers whom the educated regarded as quacks. The triumph of secular therapies among the upper orders was embodied in the regimens of private and public madhouses, which appear to have concentrated on medical treatments almost exclusively (Parry-Jones, 1972; Scull, 1979). As the number of asylums rapidly increased during the 18th century, more and more insane people were subjected to medical treatments which stressed flogging or physical restraint, purging, vomiting, and bleeding. The age of therapeutic eclecticism gave way to the age of medical psychology and the asylum.

Hogarth documented the spirit of the new era in a picture much more well known than "Credulity, Superstition, and Fanaticism". In the last stage of the Rake's Progress, the ruined Rakewell is pictured lying in

Bedlam (Fig. 2) (Paulson, 1970). He has just suffered a fit, and an attendant is attaching chains to his legs to restrain him; his head has been shaved to permit his overheated brain to cool, the least painful and unpleasant of the medical treatments for insanity. He is surrounded by the victims of extravagant delusion, the hallmark of the new view of lunacy. A religious fanatic prays in one cell, a madman mimics a king in another, a man masquerades as the Pope near the stairs. The picture's caption declares madness to be:

> "Tyranny of Fancy's reign.
> Mechanic Fancy; that can build
> Vast Labyrinths, & Mazes Wild."

An objection and some implications

My argument has been that the attack on religious enthusiasm, sustained by the ruling élite for over a century, prompted the governing classes to embrace secular explanations of the nature of insanity and to repudiate treatments which were based on religious and magical beliefs. I want now to discuss briefly one of the possible objections to this argument and some of its implications. The objection is that the secularisation of beliefs about insanity was simply a consequence of the rise of new science, and that all over Europe educated men and women rejected irrational beliefs in favour of scientific materialism during the 18th century. This is the interpretation of the period enshrined in the standard textbooks in the history of psychiatry, and there is much to be said in its favour (Zilboorg, 1941; Alexander & Selesnick, 1967). The influence of Enlightenment philosophy certainly contributed to the growth of scepticism about magic and miracles. The discoveries in astronomy undermined the ancient principles of astrological medicine. Advances in physics and anatomy no doubt encouraged the optimistic view that apparently supernatural apparitions and diseases would eventually be found to have natural causes (Thomas, 1978). The existence of a long and authoritative tradition of medical psychology provided a ready set of naturalistic theories about the causes and cure of mental diseases.

But the diffusion of scientific thought beyond the small circle of physicians and natural philosophers who fully understood it cannot adequately be explained simply by conjuring up the rationalistic spirit of the Enlightenment. The relevance of scientific assumptions and methods to matters beyond the classic concerns of the physical sciences was far from self-evident, and many of the theories propounded to explain occult phenomena were frankly just as fabulous as the beliefs they were meant to replace. Even the most ardent champions of medical psychology admitted that very little was actually known about madness, and that medical therapies often did

not work (Wagstaffe, 1669; Battie, 1962; Thomas, 1978). The new discoveries in anatomy actually undermined the ancient authorities on whom
traditional theories of mental illness had been based; experiments to prove
that insanity was caused by physical lesions in the brain failed (Hunter &
Macalpine, 1963). There were at least three new systems of abnormal
psychology in circulation after 1660, and none of them commanded general
confidence (De Porte, 1974). Even more damaging to the case for a strictly
medical view of insanity was the fact that medical treatments, which had
been justified by the obsolete humoural physiology, did not change at all
until the end of the 18th century. These treatments were repeatedly denounced as brutal, painful, dangerous, and ineffective. A popular quip
attributed to Pope Adrian declared that doctors covered up their mistakes
with earth, and the poetaster, Flecknoe, added sarcastically that "another
reason why never physician yet held up his hand at the bar for killing
patient[s] is because coroners' quest have found it self-murder in those who
take physic of them; certainly they do more harm than good" (Flecknoe,
1665; Howell, 1890; Tilley, 1950). Even the patron saint of scientific
rationalism, Sir Francis Bacon, provided scant comfort for the medical
fraternity, for had he not written this about their craft? "Medicine is a
science which hath been . . . more professed than laboured, and yet more
laboured than advanced; the labour having been, in my judgment, rather
in circle than in progression" (Bacon, 1969).

Many people believed that religious therapies cured the maladies of the
mind more effectively than medical remedies alone. Nonconformist divines,
dissenting sects, and Catholic priests exploited the popular demand for faith
healing and exorcism after the Restoration to win adherents to their creeds
(Thomas, 1978). The dissenters' methods of psychological healing are
particularly interesting. They practised three kinds of treatments, all of
which were non-violent and supportive: spiritual counsel, charismatic
healing, and prayer and fasting. Prominent clergymen preserved the
Puritan tradition of practical divinity, visiting the homes of sick and
unhappy people and offering them counsel and consolation. "Another part
of our work," Richard Baxter explained, "is to comfort the disconsolate and
settle the peace of our people's souls" (Baxter, 1656). Some of the leaders
of dissenting sects possessed special powers of persuasion and healing.
George Fox, in particular, enjoyed an extraordinary gift for calming raging
lunatics and people who were thought to be possessed or bewitched. The
remarkable narratives of his dealings with the insane show that he could,
through patient and intense attention, somehow establish a bond between
himself and mad people. The key to healing the insane, in Fox's view, lay
in communicating the Quaker conviction that the innerlight resided in all
men, and his followers sought to sustain his tradition of concern for the
mentally disturbed (McKenzie, 1935; Fox, 1948). Finally, all of the dissenting groups seen to have comforted mad and melancholy people by congregational prayer and fasting. The practice evidently began as a method

for helping the victims of demonic possession, and such meetings retained a strong element of psychomachy, the dramatic struggle between the supernatural forces of good and evil for the possession of a man's soul. The author of a dramatic account of a congregation of Bristol Baptists' efforts to restore a madman to sanity, for example, makes use of demonological language to describe the stages of his affliction and recovery, and concludes that the Lord cast "as it were, three spirits, visible, to be seen, out of him" (Hayden, 1974). These healing techniques were immensely attractive to villagers indifferent to the ruling élite's brand of rational religion, and John Wesley employed all of them with great success during the next century.

Although thaumaturgy was rejected by orthodox physicians and clergymen during the 18th century, the dissenting tradition of psychological healing may have been more influential than has been generally recognised. When the treatment of lunatics finally began to be reformed in the 1790s, Quakers were conspicuous among the leaders of the 'moral therapy movement'. Moral therapy, to be sure, owed a great deal to Pinel, whose methods were first publicised in 1808, but the system had much in common with the practices of the dissenters. The new therapy was first practised in England at the Quaker asylum, the York Retreat, founded in 1792 , where it was apparently developed without any knowledge of Pinel's work (Tuke, 1964). Testifying before a parliamentary committee in 1815, the prominent reformer Edward Wakefield contrasted the Quaker and the medical traditions of healing: "There are Quakers who are neither medical men nor of any professional class, who are conspicuous for the extraordinary treatment of insane persons, by the attention and kindness which they pay to them" (Bynum, 1974). The rejection of religious therapies by the leaders of English society between 1660 and 1790 owed nothing to the intrinsic superiority of medical theories and treatments; it was instead a consequence of their aversion to practices long associated with religious enthusiasm.

From the point of view of historians of medicine, the implication of this argument is that social and political forces had a profound influence on the acceptance of scientific explanations for mental disorders. Both the subject matter and the methods of medicine were shaped by religious controversies and professional rivalries. The distinction between magical beliefs and treatments and scientific ones, for example, did not arise as the result of the articulation of scientific principles which plainly separated bad magic from good science. The concept of magic was greatly reformulated by Protestant controversialists, as Keith Thomas has pointed out, and the practices which were denounced as magical in early modern England were selected by the church (Thomas, 1978). The specific contents of the category 'magic' were thus determined largely by religious strife, and by extension the legitimate objects of scientific study were also determined partly by the same sectarian conflicts. The range of medical theories and therapeutic techniques acceptable to the governing classes was limited by the lingering effects of the tumultuous religious politics of the mid-17th century. Physicians advanced their claim to be the proper healers of the mind and repudiated religious psychology and magical methods of curing mental disorders in the century following the English revolution. They clung to ineffective medical methods of healing the insane because those practices provided them with a professional identity which set them apart from their rivals, especially the dissenting thaumaturgists and folk magicians. If this hypothesis is correct, then the history of psychiatry, and more broadly the history of medicine, will have to be rewritten to account for the influence of religious and political events on the theory and practice of medicine. We should discard simple and misleading models of inexorable scientific progress and place the development of modern medicine in its changing historical context; only in that way will we be able truly to understand the forces which contributed to the gradual triumph of scientific medicine over its ancient rivals.

From the point of view of the social historian, the argument presented here has two important implications. The first is that the definition and interpretation of social actions were transformed by political and religious conflict. The types of deviant behaviour were not immutable, and the amount of deviance discovered by laymen and officials depended both on the number of people who violated specific social norms and on the way in which their actions were interpreted. The incidence of suicide, for example, is determined both by the number of people who kill themselves and how suicide is identified: what contemporaries think suicide is and how they decide it has been committed. The meaning of the act varies from time to time and place to place, and according to the perspective of the person who records a suicide. We have seen that the interpretation of suicide was different in the late 18th century from that which prevailed in the 16th century. This change in attitudes towards suicide affected its recorded incidence as much as or more than changes in the social and economic environment. The educated élite of 18th-century England believed that suicide was the outcome of mental disease, and that melancholy sickness was epidemic in their rapidly changing society. Suicide was therefore presumed to be a common-place, secular phenomenon rather than a rare religious catastrophe. A study which sought to measure the health of English society by gauging the rate of suicide between the late Middle Ages and the Industrial Revolution would be futile unless it took into account the governing classes' changing beliefs about self-murder, for it was they who actually controlled the registration of such deaths (MacDonald, 1977). The point of this example is that social historians must treat the records of actions in the past as complex products of the *interpretation* of behaviour. To understand the significance even of actions as apparently timeless as suicide, we must comprehend contemporary definitions of deviance and the religious and scientific beliefs on which they were based.

The second implication of this argument for social historians is closely related to this point. As sketchy and incomplete as it is, this essay strongly suggests that the history of insanity was profoundly influenced by a growing divergence between the mental worlds of the upper and lower orders of society. During the 16th century, most people shared a common assessment of what the most destructive kinds of insanity were, and they often employed traditional religious and demonological symbolism to describe abnormal thoughts and actions. This popular mentality was based on an almost Manichaean dichotomy between good and evil, normal and abnormal, and it served to reinforce ancient conceptions of the proper relationship between the individual and his social environment, the physical universe, and the world of God and the Devil (Thomas, 1978; MacDonald, 1979). Because competing religious beliefs became matters of political controversy during the late 16th and 17th centuries, the governing élite rejected those aspects of popular religion and demonology which had become politically charged. The rise of sectarianism, the extraordinary resurgence of magical and demonological beliefs, and the threat of social revolution during the Interregnum vastly accelerated this process. The 18th-century élite succeeded in restoring political stability and in creating an upper-class culture, based on rational religion, natural science, and neoclassicism, which was free from the divisive potentialities of sectarian religion. The result was a society divided not merely by differences in wealth and status, but also by differences in *mentalité*: the educated classes and the mass of the rural poor possessed two different, often antagonistic, mental outlooks, each with its own cosmology. There is strong evidence that traditional beliefs about the causes and significance of misfortune, and in particular of mental disorders, survived among the lower orders of society well into the 19th century (Naylor, 1795; Ward, 1972; Obelkevich, 1976; Thomas, 1978; Harrison, 1979).

The relationship between these ideological changes and the asylum movement, the most well known aspect of the history of insanity during this period, is still obscure. The asylum movement began with the establishment of private madhouses in increasing numbers during the late 17th and 18th centuries. Andrew Scull's argument that it was a consequence of industrial capitalism seems improbable simply because there were already many asylums in England before the social effects of industrialisation were widely felt in the first half of the 19th century (Parry-Jones, 1972; Scull, 1979). Michel Foucault's efforts to discover the origin of the asylum in the intellectual changes Europe experienced in the late 17th century is more promising, but he fails to clarify the causes of the changes he describes and makes many questionable assertions (Foucault, 1972). A great deal of research remains to be done before a truly satisfactory history of insanity in England, or elsewhere in Europe, can be written. Historians who undertake that challenging task will not be neglecting "the reality of the past".

Acknowledgements

I am grateful to the Dean, Dr J. L. T. Birley, for inviting me to address the Institute, and to Professor Michael Shepherd for sponsoring my semester as a visiting colleague there. For trenchant criticisms and other assistance with an earlier version of this lecture, I am indebted to Carol W. Dickerman, Terry Parssenin, and Charles Webster. The Society for the Humanities, Cornell University, provided financial support and a stimulating setting in which to work while I was writing the first draft of this essay.

References

ABBEY, C. J. & OVERTON, J. H. (1878) *The English Church in the Eighteenth Century* (2 vols). London.

ADAMS, J. (1700) *An Essay Concerning Self-Murder*, pp. 120–121. London.

ALEXANDER, F. G. & SELESNICK, S. T. (1967) *The History of Psychiatry*, p. 88. London: George Allen & Unwin.

BABB, L. (1951) *The Elizabethan Malady*. East Lansing: Michigan State University Press.

BACON, F. (1969) *The Advancement of Learning and New Atlantis* (ed. T. Case), p. 130. London: Oxford University Press.

BAMBOROUGH, J. B. (1951) *The Little World of Man*. London: Longman.

BATTIE, W. (1962). *A Treatise on Madness* (eds R. Hunter & I. Macalpine), pp. 5–6. London: Dawsons.

BAXTER, R. (1656). *Gildas Salvianus: The First Part. i.e. The Reformed Pastor*, pp. 77, 94. London.

BLOUNT, C. (1695) *Anima Mundi*. In *Miscellaneous Works*, p. 53. London.

BURTON, R. (1968) *Anatomy of Melancholy* (ed. H. Jackson). London: Everyman.

BYNUM, W. F. (1974) Rationales for therapy in British psychiatry, 1780–1835. *Medical History*, **18**, 318–328.

CAPP, B. S. (1979) *Astrology and the Popular Press: English Almanacs, 1500–1800*. London: Faber.

CHADWICK, O. C. (1979) Prophetess. *The New York Review of Books*, 12 September, p. 31.

CHURCH, T. (1745) *Remarks on the Reverend Mr John Wesley's Last Journal* , pp. 68–69. London.

CLARKE, S. (1706) *A Discourse Concerning the Unchangeable Obligations of Natural Religion*, p. 366. London.

DE PORTE, M. V. (1974) *Nightmares and Hobbyhorses: Swift, Sterne, and Augustan Ideas of Madness*. San Marino: Huntington Library.

EVANS, T. (1757) *The History of Modern Enthusiasm* (2nd edn), p. 127. London.

FERRIAR, J. (1795) *Medical Histories and Reflections*, vol. 2. London.

FLECKNOE, R. (1665) *Sixtynine Enigmatical Characters*, p. 101. London.

FOUCAULT, M. (1972) *Histoire de la folie à l'âge classique* (rev. edn). Paris: Gallimard.

FOX, G. (1948) *George Fox's 'Book of Miracles'* (ed. H. J. Cadbury). Cambridge: Cambridge University Press.

GLANVILL, J. (1681) *Saducismus Triumphatus*. London.

HAIR, P. E. H. (1971) Deaths from violence in Britain: a tentative secular survey. *Population Studies*, **25**, 5–24.

HALLER, W. (1958) *The Rise of Puritanism*. New York: Harper & Row.

HARRISON, J. F. C. (1979) *The Second Coming: Popular Millenarianism. 1780–1850*. New Brunswick: Rutgers University Press.

HARTH, P. (1961) *Swift and Anglican Rationalism*. Chicago: University of Chicago Press.

HAYDEN, R. (ed.) (1974) *Records of a Church of Christ in Bristol, 1640–1687*. Bristol Record Society Publications no. 27.

HEYWOOD, O. (1882–1885) *His Autobiography, Diaries, Anecdote and Event Books* (4 vols) (ed. J. Horsfall Turner). Bingley & Brighthouse.

HILL, J. E. C. (1975) *The World Turned Upside Down*. Harmondsworth: Penguin.

HMC, REPORT V (1876) *Historical Manuscripts Commission, Report V.*

HOWELL, J. (1890) *Epistolae Ho-Elianae* (ed. J. James). London.

HUNNISETT, R. F. (1981) *Wiltshire Coroners' Bills, 1752–1796.* Wiltshire Record Society, no. 37.

HUNTER, R. & MACALPINE, I. (1963) *Three Hundred Years of Psychiatry.* London: Oxford University Press.

JACOB, M. C. (1976) *The Newtonians and the English Revolution. 1689–1720.* Ithaca: Cornell University Press.

JOHNSON, S. (1755) *A Dictionary of the English Language,* s.v. 'Enthusiasm'. London.

KOCHER, P. H. (1953) *Science and Religion in Elizabethan England.* San Marino: Huntington Library.

LAVINGTON, G. (1757) *The Enthusiasm of Methodists and Papists Compared* (2 pts in 3 vols), pt II, p. 39; pt III, p. 16 London.

LOCKE, J. (1959) *An Essay Concerning Human Understanding* (2nd edn) (2 vols) (ed. A. C. Fraser), vol. 1, pp. 209–210. New York: Dover.

MACDONALD, M.(1977) The inner side of wisdom: suicide in early modern England. *Psychological Medicine,* **7,** 565–582.

—— (1979) *Madness and healing in seventeenth century England.* PhD Thesis: Stamford University.

MCKENZIE, I. (1935) *The Social Activities of the English Friends in the First Half of the Nineteenth Century.* Privately printed: New York.

MEAD, R. (1775) *The Works of Richard Mead.* Edinburgh.

MONRO, J. (1962) Remarks on Dr Battie's Treatise on Madness. In *Treatise on Madness* (ed. R. Hunter & I. Macalpine). London: Dawsons.

MORE, H. (1656) *Enthusiasmus Triumphatus.* London.

MURPHY, T. R. (1981) Suicide and madness in early modern England: a Szaszian perspective. (To be published.)

NAYLOR, M. J. (1795) *The Insanity and Mischief of Vulgar Superstitions.* Cambridge.

OBELKEVICH, J. (1976) *Religion and Rural Society: South Lindsey, 1825–1875.* Oxford: Clarendon Press.

PARGETER, W. (1792) *Observations on Maniacal Disorders.* Reading.

PARRY-JONES, W. L. (1972) *The Trade in Lunacy.* London: Routledge & Kegan Paul.

PAULSON, R. (1970) *Hogarth's Graphic Works* (2 vols) (rev. edn). New Haven: Yale University Press.

PRO, C. 217/55. Public Record Office, Chancery 217/55, Parts I and II. Unpublished manuscripts.

SCHWARTZ, H. (1978) *Knaves, Fools, Madmen, and that Subtile Effuvium.* Gainesville: University of Florida.

SCULL, A. T. (1979) *Museums of Madness.* London: Allen Lane.

SENA, J. F. (1973) Melancholic madness and the Puritans. *Harvard Theological Review,* **66,** 294–309.

SMOLLET, T. (1758, 1759) [Untitled reviews of the Battie-Monro controversy.] *Critical Review,* **4,** 509–516; **5,** 224–228.

SPRAT, T. (1959) *History of the Royal Society* (ed. J. I. Cope), p. 359. St Louis: Washington University Press.

STEFFAN, T. G. (1941) *The Social Argument against Enthusiasm, 1650–1660.* Studies in English, no. 21. Texas: Austin.

THOMAS, K. (1978) *Religion and the Decline of Magic* (2nd edn). Harmondsworth: Penguin.

TILLEY, M. P. (1950) *A Dictionary of Proverbs in the Sixteenth and Seventeenth Centuries.* Ann Arbor: University of Michigan.

TOURNEY, G. (1972) The physician and witchcraft in Restoration England. *Medical History,* **16,** 143–155.

TUKE, S. (1964) *Description of the Retreat* (ed. R. Hunter & I. Macalpine). London: Dawsons.

WAGSTAFFE, J. (1669) *The Question of Witchcraft Debated.* London.

WALSH, J. (1966) Origins of the Evangelical revival. In *Essays in Modern Church History* (eds G. V. Vennett & J. D. W. Walsh), pp. 132–162. London: Adam & Charles Black.

WARD, E. (1706) *The London Spy* (3rd edn), pp. 62–67. London.

WARD, W. R. (1972) *Religion and Society in England, 1790–1850.* London: Batsford.

WESLEY, J. (1842) *The Works of John Wesley* (4th edn) (14 vols), vol. 3, pp. 308–309. London.

WHITEFIELD, G. (1960) *Journals*. The Banner Trust.
WILLIAMSON, G. (1933) The Restoration revolt against enthusiasm. *Studies in Philology*, **30**, 571–603.
WILLIS, T. (1683) *Two Discourses Concerning the Soul of Brutes*. In *Dr Willis's Practice of Physick* (trans. S. Pordage). London.
ZILBOORG, G. with the collaboration of Henry, G. W. (1941) *A History of Medical Psychology*. New York: Norton.

Further reading

ACADEMICUS (1761) *The Principles and Practices of the Methodists Further Considered*. London.
ARNOLD, T. (1806) *Observations on the Nature, Kinds, Causes and Prevention of Insanity* (2nd edn) (2 vols). London.
AYSCOUGH, F. (1755) *A Discourse against Self-Murder*. London.
BARTEL, R. (1959–60) Suicide in eighteenth-century England: the myth of a reputation. *Huntington Library Quarterly*, **23**, 145–158.
BAXTER, R. (1716) *The Signs and Causes of Melancholy* (ed. S. Clifford). London.
BOWEN, M. E. (1974) *The Scientific Revolution in Astrology: the English Reformers, 1558–1686*. PhD thesis, Yale University.
BROWN, T. M. (1970) The College of Physicians and the acceptance of iatromechanism in England, 1665–1695. *Bulletin of the History of Medicine*, **64**, 12–30.
BYRD, M. (1974) *Visits to Bedlam: Madness and Literature in the Eighteenth Century*. Columbia: University of South Carolina Press.
CASAUBON, M. (1970) *A Treatise Concerning Enthusiasme* (ed. P. J. Korshin). Gainesville, Fla: Scholars' Facsimiles.
CHARDLER, S. (1763) *An Answer to the Rev. Mr John Wesley's Letter to William, Lord Bishop of Gloucester*. London.
CHRITTON, A. (1798) *An Inquiry into the Nature and Origin of Mental Derangement*. London.
CLARKE, B. (1975) *Mental Disorder in Earlier Britain*. Cardiff: University of Wales.
COPE, J. I. (1956) *Joseph Glanvill, Anglican Apologist*. St Louis: Washington University Press.
CULLEN, W. (1829) *First Lines in the Practice of Physic* (2 vols) (ed. J. C. Gregory). Edinburgh.
Enthusiasm Explained: Or, a Discourse on the Nature, Kind and Cause of Enthusiasm (1739). London.
FLEETWOOD, W. (1705) *The Relative Duties of Parents and Children, Husbands and Wives, Masters and Servants*. London.
ANONYMOUS (1762) *The Gentleman's Magazine*, **33**, 20–21.
GIBSON, E. (?1778) *A Caution against Enthusiasm*. In *Political Tracts*. London.
GREEN, T. (1755) *A Dissertation on Enthusiasm*. London.
HARPER, A. (1789) *A Treatise on the Real Cause and Cure of Insanity*. London.
HASLAM, J. (1798) *Observations on Insanity*. London.
—— (1809) *Observations on Madness and Melancholy* (2nd edn). London.
HAZARD, P. (1973) *The European Mind, 1680–1750* (trans. J. Lewis May). Harmondsworth: Penguin.
HICKES, G. (1680) *The Spirit of Enthusiasm Exorcised*. London.
LEIGH, D. (1961) *The Historical Development of British Psychiatry*, vol. 1: *18th and 19th Century*. New York: Pergamon.
MACDONALD, M. (1981) *Mystical Bedlam: Madness, Anxiety, and Healing in Seventeenth-Century England*. Cambridge: Cambridge University Press.
MOORE, C. (1790) *A Full Inquiry into the Subject of Suicide*. (2 vols). London.
NEWCOME, H. (1849) *The Diary of the Rev. Henry Newcome* (ed. T. Heywood). Chetham Society, no. 28.
PERFECT, W. (n.d.) *Cases of Insanity* (2nd edn). London.
ROSEN, G. (1968) Enthusiasm: 'a dark lanthorn of the spirit'. *Bulletin of the History of Medicine*, **42**, 393–421.
ROWLEY, W. (1788) *Treatise on Female, Nervous, Hysterical, Hypochondriacal, Bilious, Convulsive Diseases*. London.

SCHMITT, J.-C. (1976) Le suicide au moyen âge. *Annales: économies, sociétés, civilisations*, **31**, 2–28.

SCOT, R. (1584) *The Discoverie of Witchcraft*. London.

SPROTT, S. E. (1961) *The English Debate on Suicide: From Donne to Hume*. La Salle, Ill: Open Court.

SWIFT, J. (1975) *A Tale of a Tub and Other Satires* (ed. K. Williams). London: Everday.

THOMSON, E. P. (1974) Patrician society, Plebian culture. *Journal of Social History*, **7**, 382–405.

THOMPSON, E. P. (1978) Eighteenth-century English society: class struggle without class? *Social History*, **3**, 133–165.

TROSSE, G. (1974) *The Life of the Reverend Mr George Trosse* (ed. A. W. Brink). Montreal: McGill University Press.

WALSH, J. (1972) Methodism and the mob in the eighteenth century. In *Popular Belief and Practice* (eds G. J. Cuming & D. Baker), pp. 213–227. Studies in Church History, no. 8. Cambridge: Cambridge University Press.

WARBURTON, W. (1763) *The Doctrine of Grace*. London.

WILDER, J. (1739) *The Trial of the Spirits: Or, a Caution against Enthusiasm, or Religious Delusion*. Oxford.

6 Old familiar faces: some aspects of the asylum era in Britain

EDWARD HARE

There are some minor medical disorders which affected patients in British asylums and mental hospitals during a period of about 100 years, from 1850 to 1950, and which, to all intents and purposes, are no longer seen today. The most rapid change in British psychiatry during these 100 years occurred, I think, soon after World War II, in the decade centred on 1950. It was then that many of the old asylum disorders, which had long been declining, finally disappeared. The present generation of psychiatrists will hardly have known them. But the distress they occasioned to patients, and the worry they caused the staff, will still be clear in the memories of those who, like myself, were working in mental hospitals throughout the critical post-war decade. Such memories may recall the refrain from a poem of Charles Lamb: "All, all are gone, the old familiar faces".

Asylum pellagra

A condition which began to cause concern in British asylums just before World War I was pellagra. Pellagra is characterised by redness and roughness of the exposed skin, by diarrhoea and loss of weight, by paralysis and by mental disturbance. The condition was first recognised in Spain about 1740, and by the early 19th century was a frequent cause of admissions to the asylums in north Italy. For an early, and for a recent, historical review, see Peacock (1863) and Roe (1973).

By the mid-19th century pellagra, or a condition like it, was being found in southern France. An asylum officer there, Billod (1859), reported 66 cases of a disorder which he described as "very like pellagra" and for which he proposed the name "asylum pellagra". Pellagrous insanity was found in the asylums of the southern United States soon after 1900, and the number of cases there grew rapidly until the researches of Goldberger and his colleagues led to an improvement in asylum diet (see Terris, 1964).

In Britain, if we exclude one or two isolated reports (see Stannus &

Gibson, 1934), the first case series was reported in 1912 (Sambon & Chalmers, 1912) and included two asylum cases from Scotland. This was followed by a spate of reports in the *British Medical Journal* and the *Lancet*, including 11 cases from Napsbury asylum (Blandby, 1913) and three from Holloway Sanatorium (Johnston, 1913). Whether these represented a new phenomenon here, or whether attention had been alerted by the accounts given in British journals to the increasing problem of pellagra in the United States, is uncertain, but during the next ten years, 66 deaths from pellagra were reported in the asylums of England and Wales. Although the mortality declined thereafter, pellagra continued to figure in the reports of the Board of Control and the Ministry of Health right up to 1952, the last year in which such statistics were published, when there were four cases with one death. In 1948 I myself saw a mental hospital case, diagnosed by a dermatologist as "probably pellagra", but I doubt if any cases have been reported in mental hospitals here during the last 20 years.

Many authorities considered asylum pellagra to be a syndrome rather than a specific disease, and it would seem that the classic pellagra associated with a diet of maize may have differed in some ways from the British asylum pellagra, where maize was not a factor, where the diet seems to have been adequate, and where vitamin supplements apparently did not necessarily effect a cure (White & Taylor, 1932). Of asylum pellagra it was often asked (see for example Parfitt, 1939), which came first, the pellagra or the insanity? But the question was never really answered. Thus McCowan (1924) described four cases of pellagra at Cane Hill asylum. The patients had all been malnourished, from their refusal to eat enough, before signs of pellagra appeared; but whether their refusal was due to an unrelated mental illness, or to the early stages of pellagra, could not be said.

The type of mental disorder associated with pellagra was variously reported. McCowan perhaps voiced a common opinion in saying that "pellagra may be the exciting cause of most of the recognized forms of insanity". But at the St Hans Hospital in Copenhagen (Guttmann, 1936), schizophrenia was the psychosis most often associated with pellagra; and, in a smaller series, the same was found by Leigh (1952). It was of course the clinical association of these two disorders which played a part in the hypothesis that a deficiency of nicotinic acid was a factor in the cause of schizophrenia. That hypothesis would have had a stronger basis if asylum pellagra could have been equated with maize-diet pellagra. But, at least in Britain, the nature and causes of asylum pellagra, like the reasons for its appearance and disappearance, remain unclear.

Erysipelas

There was another asylum condition where the skin of the patient presented the most obvious sign of disease – erysipelas. Erysipelas (the word simply means red skin) has been known to medicine for centuries. It was called St Anthony's fire, and was a frightening condition because the associated toxaemia carried a high mortality – Charles Lamb died of erysipelas.

During the second half of the 19th century, epidemics of erysipelas began to occur in the asylums of this country. Such outbreaks might involve up to 50 cases, and the death rate from erysipelas in asylums was ten times that in the general population. A typical case is described in the *Journal of Mental Science* of 1858 from the Dorsetshire Asylum (Symes, 1858): a female patient aged 49, who had been washing clothes,

> "rubbed with her wet hand a small boil on her forehead. The next morning she complained of headache, and stiffness over the eyes, with a sense of itching. On the third day, erysipelas appeared all over the scalp, eyes and face, of great severity, and rapidly extended downwards to the throat. She speedily got worse and died on the ninth day after the appearance of the inflammation."

From the Reports of the Commissioners in Lunacy, we learn that outbreaks occurred in about half of all asylums and that the disease was more than twice as common in females as in males.

There was much argument about the cause. Dirty floors were at one time held to blame, but the best way to keep them clean posed a problem. For, said John Bucknill (1859), when the floors were "dry-rubbed" there was dysentery, but when "in the attempt to preserve extreme cleanliness" the floors were frequently scoured, erysipelas appeared. This led Bucknill to observe that "dysentery and erysipelas are the Scylla and Charybdis of ward management".

Another theory, upheld by Dr Phillimore (1877, 1878) of the Nottinghamshire County Asylum, blamed the many post-mortem examinations made in asylums. He drew a parallel between erysipelas and puerperal fever and showed that epidemics of erysipelas had become common only since the Lunacy Commissioners had stressed the importance of post-mortems. But the preferred view sprang from the observation that outbreaks of erysipelas tended to occur in the same hospitals as outbreaks of diarrhoea. Dr McDowall (1878), of the South Yorkshire Asylum, wrote to the *Journal of Mental Science* saying that all medical men, "with the exception of Dr. Phillimore", agree that erysipelas, typhoid and dysentery "are due to over-crowding, sewage gas, deficient and impure water supply, and like causes".

Until the bacterial cause of erysipelas was established, the sewer gas theory was firmly held both by doctors and also, it seems, by the public. At the inquest on a female patient in the Somerset and Bath Asylum in 1879 (Commissioners in Lunacy, 1880, p. 85), the coroner's verdict was that she "died from erysipelas, caused by sewer-gas emerging from the water closets of the infirmary"; and the jury added a rider that "they were unanimous in their conviction of the absolute necessity of immediate and thorough inspection, by a competent man, of the sewerage and ventilation of the Asylum". The inspection was made and various defects remedied. But the erysipelas continued, and the Commissioners concluded that the inspection could not have been sufficiently thorough, for (they said in their 1880 report) "we are strongly of opinion that defective drains permitting the escape of sewer gas will be found to be the cause", and they recommended "that the services of a sanitary engineer of eminence and practical experience should, without delay, be secured". Perhaps the hospital authorities were reluctant to incur further expense; for "it then appeared that at this asylum there was no general plan of the whole of the drains"; and the Commissioners had to content themselves with the barbed remark that, in the absence of such a plan, they "could express no opinion as to the probable efficacy of the means proposed".

Elsewhere, however, such measures might be rewarded. Outbreaks of erysipelas had occurred at the Midlothian and Peebles Asylum; and on examining the drains, wrote the Superintendent, Dr Mitchell (1892), "it was found that a water closet, abolished a good many years ago, had had its soil pipe led into a branch drain near the windows of the north-east wing, and that this pipe had never been disconnected or sealed. It contained a large quantity of foul matter, and it appears most probable that this was the cause of the epidemic. The defect was thoroughly remedied by our own workmen, and since then the health of the inmates has remained good".

There are no references to erysipelas in the *Journal of Mental Science* later than 1902, but it continued to be a cause of morbidity and death in mental hospitals until quite recently. From the reports of the Board of Control, we learn (for example) that there were 179 cases during 1925, with 16 deaths – and a further three deaths among the nursing staff. It was not until after World War II that the yearly number of deaths from erysipelas fell below 20, and non-fatal cases continued to figure in the reports of the Ministry of Health up until 1952. Even at that time, when most young doctors would have regarded an attack of erysipelas as a relatively trivial matter, older staff remembered it as an epidemic disease and one likely to be taken as reflecting adversely on nursing efficiency, and they might still feel a sense of anxiety and alarm when a case of 'ERY' was discovered.

We do not know why erysipelas became an asylum disease in the 1850s. Overcrowding, by increasing the chance of cross-infection, may have played a part, but 90 years later, during World War II, when the overcrowding was probably worse, erysipelas was less common and much less severe. We do not know why it became a milder disease, rarely seen in mental hospitals after 1940. The virulence of the infecting organism may have declined, as has been supposed in the parallel case of scarlet fever. But there was probably another factor. During much of the last century, the general state of health of patients admitted to Bethlem Hospital was recorded (it should be noted that because of its policy of taking recoverable cases, patients admitted to Bethlem were likely to be in better health than those admitted to county asylums). Of 200 patients admitted to Bethlem Hospital in 1854 and 1874, the physical health on admission was described as weak, feeble or bad in 25%, and as indifferent in a further 12%. That certainly could not be said of present-day admissions, and this evidence supports the view that, during the past 100 years, the general health of mental patients improved greatly, and with it, presumably, their resistance to infection.

Insane ear

I now describe a condition which came and went long before my time. Haematoma auris (Fig. 1) was a relatively minor ailment. Because it was almost confined to asylum patients it was commonly called 'insane ear'. The ear was affected by a blood-stained effusion, often developing rapidly over a day or two. In the acute stage, the swelling was red, tense and painful. But in the course of a few weeks, the fluid was replaced by granulation tissue which then became fibrosed, leaving the ear thickened, scarred and mis-shapen. For a historical review, see Robertson (1896).

Insane ear was first reported in 1833 from an asylum in Germany, and one of the earliest British accounts was that of Stiff (1857). The condition was commoner in the left ear and in males, and particularly affected patients with mania or with general paralysis (the disorder which Americans, with greater logic, call general paresis and continental Europeans used to call dementia paralytica).

Several writers were able to collect series of more than a 100 cases, and in the average asylum during the mid-19th century there might be three or four cases a year. Gradually, however, the numbers diminished. In 1896, the President, William Mickle, observed that the condition was rarer than formerly (Mickle, 1896), and there are no references to haematoma auris in the *Journal of Mental Science* after 1907.

Although it was never very common and although it was relatively trivial in its effects, insane ear was a subject of considerable medical attention – five whole pages are devoted to it in Hack Tuke's *Dictionary of Psychological Medicine* (Tuke, 1892, p. 557) – and this was because of the belief that it was caused by trauma and in particular by a blow from an attendant or nurse. Why did the condition occur only in the insane? Because (said those who held this belief) the insane cannot protect themselves from assault. Why did it occur more in men? Because men are more likely to be struck, and because women are protected by their hair and their caps. Why did it occur more in the left ear? Because that ear would be struck by a right-handed person facing the patient. And according to the superintendent of a German asylum, when the attendants were held responsible and "appropriately disciplined", the condition practically disappeared.

But not everyone thought the attendants were to blame. One

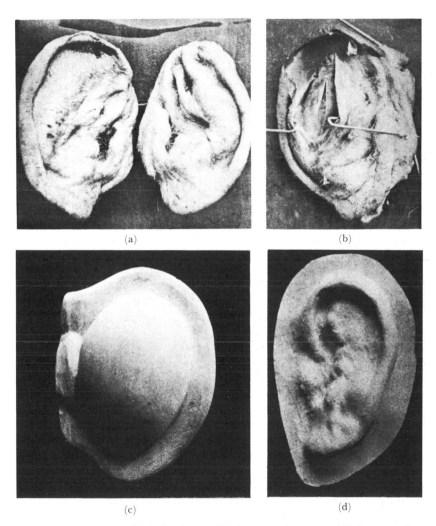

Fig. 1. Haematoma auris: (a, b) the chronic stage; (c) plaster cast of acute stage; (d) plaster cast of same ear after rupture and contraction. From Hun (1870)

superintendent reported that insane ear continued to occur even after the attendants had been warned; and others (Stiff, 1863) pointed out that the patient's ear might have been struck by another patient rather than an attendant, or might have been injured in a fall. And there were arguments against any idea of trauma (Hun, 1870). Thus insane ear was rare in epileptics who had frequent falls; it might occur spontaneously in quiet and docile patients; an actual blow on the ear led to an entirely different sequence of events; and, most significantly, insane ear was a bad prognostic sign for it occurred only in cases which proved to be incurable – as Maudsley (1867, p. 349) characteristically remarked, it was "ever of evil augury". The most commonly held theory was of poor local nutrition. This, it was supposed, led to degenerative changes in the cartilage of the ear and so to a cyst which became lined with fragile blood vessels; these then ruptured either spontaneously or from a minor trauma. Treatment, which does not seem to have influenced the course of the disorder, was by incision or blistering.

So insane ear came – and went. The question of trauma was never really resolved; and as late as the 1880s one authority (Pieterson, 1892) maintained that asylum officers played down the role of trauma from fear that they or their staff might be censured for ill treatment in the reports of the Lunacy Commissioners. We do not know whether it was a new condition when it was first described, we do not know what really caused it, and we do not know why it went away when it did.

Insane ear seems to have been commonest in general paralytics, and its disappearance, from the literature at least, coincided with the decline of general paralysis. Yet general paralysis continued to be a common disorder for decades after insane ear had apparently gone.

Fractured ribs

The concern of asylum staff, and of the public, that insane ear might be the result of ill treatment, was as nothing compared with the furore over fractured ribs. The death of an asylum patient, where post-mortem examination revealed fractured bones or any other sign suggestive of violence, was a matter of particular concern to the Commissioners of Lunacy, that body of independent asylum inspectors, set up by Parliament under the Lunatics' Act of 1845. For 40 years under the Chairmanship of the great Lord Shaftesbury, the Commissioners were untiring in their determination to detect and expose instances of harshness, mismanagement or neglect. (Lord Shaftesbury was certainly a great man: but he was also an eccentric one. Florence Nightingale said of him that "he would have been *in* a lunatic asylum if he had not devoted himself to reforming lunatic asylums" (Smith, 1950, p. 589).)

In August 1861, a patient with advanced general paralysis was admitted to the Durham County Asylum. He died the following January, and the Medical Officer gave the cause of death as "pleuro-pneumonia". But at the inquest it was revealed that the post-mortem examination had shown fractures of "16 or 17" ribs and a rupture of the bladder. An attendant, Metcalfe, was implicated by the coroner, but the jury acquitted him of manslaughter and found the cause of death to be – pleuro-pneumonia. On learning of these events, the Commissioners in Lunacy (1863, p. 32) set up their own inquiry (they were empowered to take evidence on oath). It transpired that about two weeks before the death, Metcalfe had had "a personal altercation with the patient in the airing court, and they fell together, Metcalfe uppermost, and that the latter – as it is believed – to extricate himself from the patient's grasp, knelt upon his chest". For this, and for certain other instances of harshness, Metcalfe was dismissed. The Commissioners then instituted proceedings against the Medical Officer for he, in certifying the cause of death, had omitted all mention of the post-mortem results. But the Justices of the Petty Sessions dismissed the case, and the Commissioners, who wished to appeal, found themselves frustrated by a legal technicality.

Between about 1850 and 1890, the yearly reports of the Lunacy Commissioners are replete with such cases. Strangely, as it might seem, the Commissioners often found themselves at variance with the hospital's Committee of Visitors and with the local justices: where the Commissioners sought to prosecute, the justices tended to block proceedings and the Visitors were often content with a dismissal or simply a censure. But sometimes the Commissioners gained their point. A notorious case occurred at Lancaster Asylum in 1869 (Lunacy Commissioners, 1870, p. 17). On the death of a patient with general paralysis, post-mortem revealed 12 broken ribs, three of them broken in two places. Two attendants were implicated but both denied the charge. They were convicted however on the sole evidence of another patient, and were each sentenced to seven years' penal servitude. It was this case which established the admissibility of evidence by a lunatic.

Such stories naturally got into the newspapers and caused public concern. The novelist Charles Reade wrote to the *Pall Mall Gazette*, denouncing the brutalities of asylum practice (see Sankey, 1870). And yet, as time went on, the clamour died down and the accusations became rarer. One reason for this was the growing evidence that factors other than violence might be responsible. Sankey (1870) observed that cases of fractured rib were too common, and the numbers of ribs fractured were too many, for it to be likely that the blame always lay with the attendants. Nor could the fractures be caused simply by falls, since epileptic patients often fell but did not fracture their ribs. Fractured ribs occurred most commonly in patients with general paralysis; and the cause, Sankey suggested, was the furious behaviour of such patients together with a lack of reflex muscular protection. Another idea was that the ribs of general paralytics were unusually brittle, a suggestion which some saw simply as an attempt to excuse the asylum staff. In a paper to the *Lancet*, the Superintendent of the Sussex Asylum, Williams (1870), described two cases of fractured ribs where neither patient had at any time been violent. Although in each case the coroner's verdict was that death had been due to natural causes and to disease of the bone, Williams commented that, for his part, he "could not for a moment subscribe to the absurd hypothesis that lunatics' ribs are more brittle than other people's".

Yet it was this 'absurd' hypothesis that gained ground. In 1873, post-mortem examination of a manic patient showed fractures of 12 ribs, some of them fractured in "2 or 3 places", together with a transverse fracture of the breast bone, although no wound of the pleura or lungs was detected. There was evidence of a struggle, but the Hospital Visitors found "that if the attendants did in fact inflict the injury, they did not intend to do so, and that the fatal result was entirely owing to the abnormal condition of the patient". The Lunacy Commissioners (1874, p. 30) reported without comment that the ribs of this patient "were stated to be unnaturally brittle". Another patient, dying from general paralysis in 1890, was found at post-mortem to have four fractured ribs. This patient had never been excited and had never required coercion, and the post-mortem report stated that "the bones were in a very fragile state". The coroner's jury concluded that "how the said ribs were fractured there is no evidence to show"; and the Commissioners (1891, p. 61) said only that "no doubt it was due to a fall, probably from the edge of his bed".

By the early years of the present century it seems to have become accepted that patients with general paralysis were very liable to fractured bones and that this was due, not to muscular weakness or inadequate reflexes, but to the bones (with the exception of the cranial bones) being porous, light and fragile.

Although the evidence strongly suggests that in general paralysis the rib bones *were* unduly fragile, we have no satisfactory explanation of the cause. The subject attracted little attention after 1900, and I cannot determine how long fractured ribs continued to occur. In the 1940s, I dealt with many cases of general paralysis, but I never met one with fractured ribs and I do not recall reading or being told that this was a complication to be looked for. It seems likely then that at some stage patients with general paralysis ceased to have fragile ribs, just as they ceased to have insane ears. But if so, we do not know why that was.

I think this story of fractured ribs has an enduring relevance for psychiatry. To the Commissioners in Lunacy, humanely concerned to expose maltreatment in asylums, it was obvious in the 1860s that fractured ribs meant violence. As a result, a number of medical officers were severely censured and a number of attendants dismissed and prosecuted; and if those numbers were not as many as the Commissioners wanted, this was perhaps because the Hospital Visitors and local justices, closer to the grass roots of the matter, sensed that things were not always as bad as they might seem. Even so, in all probability some asylum staff were wrongly censured and wrongly dismissed. There is a deeply rooted tendency in human nature to believe that unexplained misfortunes are the result of someone's sins. In just the same way as it was believed that dementia praecox was due to the patient's masturbatory habits (Hare, 1962), and general paralysis to his sexual excesses (Hare, 1959), so it was believed that erysipelas was due to the carelessness, and insane ear and fractured ribs to the wickedness, of the asylum staff. We now know that all these beliefs were almost certainly incorrect; but the story may remind us that one may be overzealous in the search for evil, and that where illness, and particularly where mental illness is concerned, cause and effect may not be as simple as they seem.

Physiognomy

Physiognomy is the art of judging character and disposition from the features of the face or (more generally) of the body form. This is something we do all the time, but in the 19th century it was considered an important diagnostic aid. "There is no class of diseases," wrote Alexander Morison (1840), "in which the study of physiognomy is so necessary, as that of mental disease. It not only enables us to distinguish the characteristic features of different varieties, but also gives warning of the approach of the disease . . . as well as confirms our opinion of convalescence." John Charles Bucknill (1856) considered that no physician could practise his art satisfactorily or successfully unless he were a good physiognomist: "In a great number of cases, a remarkable peculiarity is observable in the physiognomy of the insane." In chronic mania, for example, "the hair becomes harsh and bristling"; and in secondary dementia, it is the varying enfeeblement of the mental faculties that "renders the facial expression of so many chronic lunatics at once stupid and vicious".

But during the second half of the century, these abnormalities of feature seemed to fade away. Bucknill & Tuke (1874, pp. 411–421) wrote that the peculiarity in the physiognomy of secondary dementia "is infinitely less frequent and less pronounced than we remember to have seen it, from 10 to 15 years ago; or than is delineated in the engravings of Morison or Esquirol, and to a still greater extent in the paintings of Hogarth and Fuseli." And Cibber, whose "well-known statue of Dementia . . . reported to have been copied from the actual condition of a lunatic in the wards of Bethlem, a man who had been Oliver Cromwell's porter, . . . would not at the present day find it easy to procure such a model, faithfully and painfully expressing not only the effects of disease but those of cruel and brutal treatment" (see Appendix, and Fig. 2).

Psychiatric interest in physiognomy waned rapidly during the 1890s and has not been revived. If we ask why the interest arose and why it declined, there are, broadly, two different answers.

One answer comes from the fact that psychiatry is a branch of medicine largely dependent on subjective assessment and is always emotionally loaded. Before photography, portrayal of the features of madmen or criminals had to be made by a drawing, sculpture or written description, and so carried the risk that the portrayer would exaggerate for the sake of dramatic effect or, from the same motive, would search for especially striking examples. Now as Bucknill & Tuke (1874) remarked, "the idea entertained of a madman by the public is more frequently taken from such descriptions than from personal observation"; and from such descriptions,

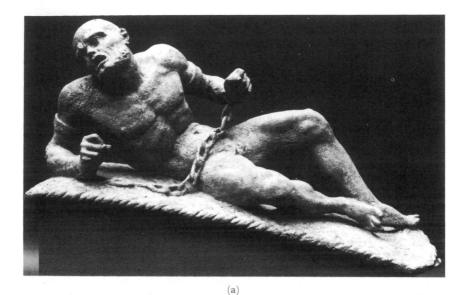

(a)

(b)

Fig. 2. Cibber's statues of 'raving madness' (a) and 'melancholy madness' (b)

just as from textbook descriptions, observers may be biased into distorting what they actually see into what they believe they ought to be seeing, and it may take many years for such distortion to yield to common sense or new techniques. One such new technique was photography, and the decline in physiognomy was doubtless due in part to the objective and permanent record provided by a photograph. Another technique, perhaps, was that of statistical comparison: the old idea that ears of abnormal shape indicated an insane or criminal tendency was countered by Professor Schwalbe (1895), of Strasbourg, who compared the ears of 467 criminals, 800 lunatics and 25 000 normal persons.

But we ought not to suppose that experienced men such as Bucknill and Tuke would have been liable to much subjective distortion. They had been in no doubt there was a characteristic physiognomy in the insane, and they also had no doubts of why this was becoming less marked: "The most undubitable testimony with which we are acquainted of the immense change which has taken place in the condition of lunatics, is afforded in the entirely different *facial expression* of lunatics as they are painted and described by our forefathers and as they are observed by ourselves." And the change, they believed, was due to improvements in care and treatment, for "the old treatment converted the insane patient into a ferocious, malevolent and repulsive being," but "under the humane and judicious treatment which now prevails in lunatic asylums" these exaggerated passions no longer occurred (Bucknill & Tuke, 1874).

With regard to the changes in physiognomy, we do not know the truth of the matter. It seems reasonable to suppose, on the evidence, that many chronic asylum patients did show characteristic peculiarities of appearance during the first half of the 19th century, and that these gradually became less marked. But as to the cause of the change, I think there is no simple answer. It is an understandable prejudice of medical men to suppose that any improvement in the outcome of a disease is due to improvements in medical treatment. But the supposition is not necessarily true. Treatments change of course, but so do diseases, and it may not be easy, over a short span of time, to say which change came first.

Incontinence

There are two conditions which were not strictly disorders but which caused difficult ethical problems of mental hospital management right up until the 1950s, although I think they are much rarer nowadays. These are incontinence and destructive behaviour.

Incontinence of urine and faeces seems to have been common in asylum patients in the last century. Where the patient suffered from an evident organic disorder, such as general paralysis, no doubt it was accepted that he could not be held responsible. But where there was no such evidence, as in cases of what we would now call chronic schizophrenia, the patient's responsibility was harder to assess. An incontinent patient was a source of unpleasantness on the ward and of trouble to the attendants. Was there a treatment for incontinence?

The cold shower, or douche, had been introduced as a purely medical treatment. "It is used," said Hack Tuke (Commissioners in Lunacy, 1857, pp. 24–33), "in the form of a continued stream of cold or iced water poured on the head from a sponge or hand shower-bath, for from 2 to 6 minutes, as a revulsive in cases of congestion of the brain;" and he added that "the pain attending its application beyond a certain time is severe and becomes intense if prolonged."

In 1857, a notorious case of misuse, which resulted in the death of a patient at the Surrey County Asylum, led the Lunacy Commissioners to make a general inquiry of its value among medical superintendents; and, as might be expected, the replies were diverse (Commissioners in Lunacy, 1857, p. 119). "I prescribe the douche," said Dr Sutherland of St Luke's Hospital, "in cases of acute dementia, the effects of which are something marvellous. *Before* the douche, the patient is like a statue; he never speaks, he is apparently unconscious of all that passes around him, his movements are automatic, the limbs fixed as in catalepsy in the position in which they are placed. . . . *After* the douche, the patient's energies of mind and body are roused into activity. He appears like someone waking out of sleep." Mr Millar, of the Buckinghamshire Asylum, employed the cold shower "as a remedial agent in its moral character. . . . As a last resort with patients of excited, mischievous, destructive, dirty or immoral habits, I have used the bath for the purpose of stimulating the power of self-control, which I believe them to possess but which, from indolence or perversion of the moral feeling, they are unwilling of their own account to exert;" and at two licensed houses, the cold bath was used particularly "in the cases of patients who are dirty in their habits." With regard to the duration or number of such treatments, Dr Palmer of the Lincolnshire County Asylum found that in the majority of cases one or two showers were sufficient, "but still, with reference to time, I think they should always be given *ad effectum*, on the same principle as jalap, opium or any other therapeutic agent is employed."

Others were more guarded or more sceptical. "The utmost caution is needed," said Mr Hill of the North East Riding Asylum, "to avoid the semblance of punishment, and great pains are invariably taken to explain the nature of the remedy before its application so as to prevent the recipient from suspecting foul play." And according to Dr Burnett of Westbrook House, "the use of such baths does not apply to the insane; and my impression is that their application in a cold state to the bodies of the insane is quite as cruel as the most objectionable form of mechanical restraint."

The Commissioners caustically summed up the supposed medical virtues of the shower-bath: "It is stated to act according to the mode of its administration, as a stimulant in cases of cerebral inaction and depressed nervous power, invigorating and giving tone to the system generally; and as a sedative in cases of maniacal excitement . . . relieving congestion of the circulation, and producing sleep." They concluded that "an agent which is always regarded by the patient, and admits of being used as, a punishment should be administered only in the presence of the Medical Officer – a full record being inserted by him into the case book." Yet the Commissioners' strictures did not lead to the total demise of the cold shower. As late as 1920, the Board of Control, which, by comparison with the old Lunacy Commissioners, were very restrained in their comments, reported "undesirable practices" at an asylum where, on medical orders, the cold douche had been given "as a correctional treatment" to certain patients who exhibited filthy and destructive habits and were believed to know better." The report adds that whereas the Board "entirely deprecate any form of correctional treatment," they "of course entirely approve of the considered use of hot and cold baths or douches as purely medical treatment" (Board of Control, 1920, p. 17).

The cold shower or cold plunge was an example of those 'shocking' treatments which are common in the history of psychiatry, and which reflect the widespread belief that a sudden shock may bring a deranged person to his senses. Then, as now, the medical officer faced a dilemma in the prescription of such treatment. If he believed in its efficacy but gave too much, or gave it *ad effectum*, he might be accused of using it as a punishment. If he was sceptical and gave too little, or none at all, he might be accused of failing to provide treatment or stimulation for his patients, with the consequence, as one Commissioner put it, of their "drifting pleasantly into dementia". Granville (1877, pp. 131, 210, 211), who agreed with this Commissioner, observed that Connolly's system of non-restraint had been followed not merely by the absence of any improvement in outcome, but on the contrary by a diminution in the proportion of cures. He favoured the use of shocking treatments such as the cold pack, even if these carried the risk of abuse, and he deplored the fact that public outcry had led to their being used less often: "the penalty we have to pay for the unreasonable, and I fear unreasoning, criticism sometimes hurled at medical superintendents by censors less familiar with the phenomena of insanity than skilled in the art of fine and fierce writing." In fact, the prognosis of insanity seemed to worsen during much of the second half of the 19th century, in America as well as Britain (Hare, 1982) and in so far as this was so, it was probably quite unrelated to any method of management or treatment then available.

Destructive behaviour

Another problem of management in asylums was presented by habits of destructiveness. The patient, usually a woman, would persist in tearing, or tearing off, her own clothing and during the 19th century the attempt to control such behaviour was commonly by use of the canvas dress (or 'strong clothes'). A canvas dress was made of heavy, coarse, untearable material, often in one-piece-like combinations, fastening at the back and sometimes with blind sleeves so that the patient could not use her fingers.

We learn about the ethics of its use from the reports of the Lunacy

Commissioners. Their statutory visit to Colney Hatch Asylum in 1873 led them to censure its superintendent, Dr Sheppard, for the degree of mechanical restraint and particularly for the free use of canvas dresses. The Superintendent defended his practice. Canvas dresses, he said, are "as pinafores for children. If a patient persistently undresses himself, or destroys ordinary clothing, I should be no more justified in *withholding* from him a canvas suit, than in *giving* a knife to a suicidal patient. . . . It is an utter misuse of terms to call any treatment humane and philanthropic which violates the first principles of decency and safety". The Commissioners disagreed. Canvas dresses, they said, were unsightly and must be uncomfortable to wear; but they "are mainly objectionable because they lead to the permanent degradation of the patient, by tending to confirm bad habits and by accepting such habits as incurable, instead of attempting their improvement by correction. . . . Experience has shown that good results follow the persistent efforts of treating or curing, patients of a destructive or dirty character" (Commissioners in Lunacy, 1873, p. 1).

The ethical problems – the distinctions between medical treatment, moral treatment and correctional treatment – were very difficult. The use of a canvas dress could be seen as too degrading to justify its undoubted practical value, but it could also be seen as a form of moral treatment, rather like a dunce's cap. As for the persistent efforts at treatment which the Commissioners recommended, the superintendent at Colney Hatch might have replied that such efforts had already been made in the case of incontinence, by the use of the cold shower, without marked success.

The habit of tearing clothes, and the use of canvas dresses, certainly continued, although with diminishing frequency. I can remember seeing a patient in a canvas dress at Brentwood Mental Hospital in 1947, but I am sure it is never used now. One reason for the change seems probable enough. "The fact," said the Board of Control (1932, p. 8), "that women commissioners can now take part in statutory visits has resulted in greater attention being paid to the clothing of female patients;" and I expect it was a woman commissioner who made the sensible comments that, "clothing which no sane person would ever wear except under compulsion ought not to be inflicted on convalescent or other well behaved persons;" and that such patients should wear attractive clothes, not only because "in these days such clothes can be produced very cheaply," but also because "anything which helps to restore the patient's self-respect is an aid to recovery." Even the men benefited, for "though the use of pyjamas cannot be encouraged since the cords might offer too great a temptation in suicidal cases, it is satisfactory to note the increasing adoption of night shirts for male patients" (Board of Control, 1933, p. 17). One may further presume that once patients were in a position to wear their own clothes, that constituted a powerful reason for not tearing them.

The use of the cold shower, whether for medical or correctional purposes, was abandoned at least 50 years ago. What then replaced it, as a means of

treating incontinence, I am not sure. But when I joined the staff of Warlingham Park Hospital in 1955, there was still a special ward for incontinent
male patients, where treatment was by a mixture of methods which would
now be known as token therapy or behaviour therapy. The scheme had
worked well, and the numbers of such patients diminished until a special
ward was no longer needed – and all this was substantially before the
introduction of neuroleptic drugs. Nowadays, as far as I know, patients are
very rarely incontinent simply from chronic schizophrenia, just as they very
rarely display persistent destructiveness. But it remains a matter of opinion
how far these changes were the result of new drugs, or of the kind of moral
treatment practised at Warlingham, or of an amelioration in the schizophrenic process (in the sense that schizophrenia in this country does not
now progress to the profound dementia which Kraepelin thought to be
characteristic).

Conclusion

I have said nothing of the *major* disorders of asylum patients, the disorders
which were the principal causes of death and morbidity during most of the
years 1850–1950 and which have now disappeared or greatly decreased:
dysentery, tuberculosis, Bright's disease, epilepsy. Most notable of all,
perhaps, has been the disappearance of general paralysis. It was probably
this disease, above all others, which contributed to the popular fear of
asylums and to a sense of pessimism among asylum staff. General paralysis
was a mental disorder which, in the words of Maudsley (1867, p. 360)
selects "those who seem to be buoyant in health and at the height of their
energy." Its course was almost invariable: progressive dementia, with death
in a very few years. During most of the second half of the 19th century, it
was responsible for about one in seven male admissions and for some 1500
asylum deaths a year. Its cause was then quite unknown and there was no
useful treatment. General paralysis was first described around 1820, and its
prevalence seems steadily to have increased throughout the 19th century,
but began to decline from about 1900. The causes of this increase and
decline, and the question whether the disorder was present before 1820 but
unrecognised, are still matters of opinion (Jacobowsky, 1965; Martin,
1972).

When a disease appears abruptly and then disappears within a few years,
as happened with encephalitis lethargica, it will be thought of as a passing
epidemic, but once a chronic disease has been recognised for a century or
more, like general paralysis, it is apt to be thought of as one which must
always have afflicted mankind and which will continue to do so until
conquered by the advance of medical science. Yet it seems to me more
reasonable to suppose that all diseases are continually changing, more or
less rapidly, in their manifestations, prevalence and severity, and that new

diseases continually appear and old ones continually disappear in response to changing environments, mutations, or (rarely) prevention.

The present account of some relatively minor disorders which have now practically disappeared from British mental hospitals may illustrate this theme of change in the pattern of disease. Two further points may be noted. In most cases we do not know what caused the changes, and the medical and ethical problems presented by the management of the disorders were never solved – the problems simply disappeared when the disorders themselves disappeared.

We should not forget, though, that during 100 years when the nature of asylum insanity was continually changing and when the various attempts at curative treatment were at best unavailing (and at worst of a kind which later generations, faced with quite different problems, too easily see as having been harmful to the cause of medicine), one thing remained constant – the need to provide care and comfort for the patients. The manner in which the services of mental hospital staff have been acknowledged has varied with the times. Dr Forbes Winslow (1858) concluded his Presidential Address to the Medico-Psychological Association with words which might raise a smile today: "Oh! what a holy, honourable and sacred occupation is that in which we have the privilege to be engaged. The angels in Heaven might well envy us the nobling and exalted pleasures incidental to our mission of love and charity." The mode of expression has changed, but the sentiment, I think, has not. Thirty years after Winslow, the Commissioners in Lunacy (1891, p. 39), always grudging in these matters, observed that the work of the asylum staff was "wearing and not free from danger" and that it called for "the exercise of qualities of intelligence, tact and patience which are by no means too common". Forty years later, the Board of Control (1926, p. 1) took the opportunity of paying tribute "to the skill, devotion and self-sacrifice of the nursing staff who, in circumstances peculiarly exacting, are rendering great service to suffering humanity." And those are words which today we might still accept unchanged.

Appendix

Cibber's statue of 'dementia'

The two well known statues by Cibber (1630–1700), originally on the gates of the 17th-century Bethlem at Moorfields and now in the museum of Bethlem Hospital at Beckenham, Kent, have generally been held to represent 'raving madness' and 'melancholy madness' (Fig. 2). Morison (1840), however, considered that the statue of melancholy madness properly represented dementia because the features displayed a "total absence of mind" and a "want of emotion"; and of the statue of raving madness (which he considered to represent mania) he says: "This is supposed to represent the porter of Oliver Cromwell, who, it is said, was a patient in the Bethlem Hospital of his time". Bucknill and Tuke, in using Morison's title of Dementia, seem mistakenly to have applied it to the statue of raving madness.

We should note that Thomas Arnold (1806, p. 224), in his *Observations on Insanity*, refers to a patient Daniel, a porter of Oliver Cromwell, "whose brain was supposed to have turned by his plodding in mystical books of divinity", and who was confined for many years in Bethlem. But his treatment there is particularly noted to have been humane, and he was permitted to continue his preaching from a window, below which his audience "would often sit for many hours . . . with great signs of devotion". The possibility that Daniel was the same patient as Cibber's model must raise a doubt about Bucknill and Tuke's belief that the patient's ferocious appearance, as reflected in the statue, was the consequence of brutal treatment.

References

ARNOLD, T. (1806). *Observations on the Nature, Kinds, Causes and Prevention of Insanity, Lunacy or Madness* (2nd edn). Leicester: Robinson and Cadell.

BILLOD, E. (1859) D'une variete de pellagre propre aux alienes. *Annales Medico-psychogiques*, **5**, 161–216.

BLANDBY, G. S. (1913) Contributions to the study of pellagra in England. *Lancet*, ii, 713–717.

BOARD OF CONTROL (1920) *7th Report*. London: HMSO.

—— (1926) *13th Report*. London: HMSO.

—— (1932) *19th Report*. London: HMSO.

—— (1933) *20th Report*. London: HMSO.

BUCKNILL, J. C. (1856) The diagnosis of insanity. *Journal of Mental Science*, **2**, 433–455.

—— (1859) Reports of lunatic asylums. *Journal of Mental Science*, **5**, 166.

—— & TUKE, D. H. (1874) *A Manual of Psychological Medicine* (3rd edn). London: Churchill.

COMMISSIONERS IN LUNACY (1857) *11th Report*. London: HMSO.

—— (1863) *17th Report*. London: HMSO.

—— (1870) *24th Report*. London: HMSO.

—— (1873) *27th Report*. London: HMSO.

—— (1874) *28th Report*. London: HMSO.

—— (1880) *34th Report*. London: HMSO.

—— (1891) *45th Report*. London: HMSO.

GRANVILLE, J. M. (1877) *The Care and Cure of the Insane*, vol. 2. London: Harwicke and Bogue.

GUTTMANN, E. (1936) Review of *Pellagoide Dermatosen an Geisteskranken* (by Reiter P L and Jakobsen J J. Copenhagen, Levin and Munksgaard 1935). *Journal of Mental Science*, **82**, 74.

HARE, E. H. (1959) The origin and spread of dementia paralytica. *Journal of Mental Science*, **105**, 594–626.

—— (1962) Masturbatory insanity; the history of an idea. *Journal of Mental Society*, **108**, 1–25.

—— (1982) Was insanity increasing? *British Journal of Psychiatry*, **142**, 439–455.

HUN, E. R. (1870) Haematoma auris. *American Journal of Insanity*, **27**, 13–28.

JACOBOWSKY, B. (1965) General paralysis and civilization. *Acta Psychiatrica Scandinavica*, **41**, 267–273.

JOHNSTON, E. M. (1913) Note on a case of pellagra. *Lancet*, ii, 1114

LEIGH, D. (1952) Pellagra and the nutritional neuropathies: a neuro-pathological review. *Journal of Mental Science*, **98**, 130–142.

MARTIN, J. (1972) The conquest of general paralysis. *British Medical Journal*, iii, 159–160.

MAUDSLEY, H. (1867) *The Physiology and Pathology of the Mind*. London, Macmillan.

McCOWAN, P. K. (1924) Pellagra. A report of 4 cases. *Journal of Mental Science*, **70**, 410–422.

McDOWALL, J. (1878) *Journal of Mental Science*, **24**, 328–333.

MICKLE, W. J. (1896) Haematoma auris. *Journal of Mental Science*, **42**, 888.

MITCHELL, R. B. (1892) Asylum reports. *Journal of Mental Science*, **38**, 289

MORISON, A. (1840) *The Physiognomy of Mental Diseases* (2nd edn). London: (no publisher cited).

PARFITT, D. N. (1939) Pellagra in recent psychoses. *Journal of Mental Science*, **82**, 440–444.

PEACOCK, T. B. (1836) Notes on hospitals in northern Italy and on pellagra. *Medico-chirurgical Review*, **31**, 210–224.

PHILLIMORE, W. P. (1877) Post-mortem examinations in lunatic asylums. *British Medical Journal*, *ii*, 908–909.

—— (1878) Erysipelas in county asylums. *Journal of Mental Science*, **24**, 506–508.

PIETERSON, J. F. C. (1892) In *Dictionary of Psychological Medicine* (D.H. Tuke), p. 561. London: Churchill.

ROBERTSON, W. F. (1896) On morbid changes in the ear-cartilages, with special reference to the pathology of haematoma auris. *Edinburgh Hospital Reports*, **4**, 407–422.

ROE, D. A. (1973) *A Plague of Corn: The Social History of Pellagra*. London: Cornell University Press.

SAMBON, L. W. & CHALMERS A. J. (1912) Pellagra in the British Isles. *British Medical Journal*, *ii*, 1093–1096.

SANKEY, W. H. O. (1870) Ribs fractured in asylums. *Journal of Mental Science*, **16**, 135–142.

SCHWALBE, G. (1895) Zur Methodik statisticher Untersuchungen uber die Ohrformen von Geisteskranken und Verbrechern. *Archiven fur Psychiatrie*, **27**, 633–644 (reviewed in *Journal of Mental Science* (1896), **42**, 401–402).

SMITH, W. C. (1950) *Florence Nightingale*. London: Constable.

STANNUS, H. S. & GIBSON, C. R. (1934) Pellagra in Great Britain. *Quarterly Journal of Medicine*, **27**, 211–236.

STIFF, W. P. (1857) On simple sanguineous cyst of the ear in lunatics. *British and Foreign Medico-chirurgical Review*, **21**, 222–227.

—— (1863) Notes on haematoma of the external ear in the insane. *British Medical Journal*, *ii*, 115.

SYMES, J. G. (1858) Treatment of erysipelas by the Tr. Ferri Sesquichloridi externally and internally. *Journal of Mental Science*, **4**, 587–588.

TERRIS, M. (1964) *Goldberger on Pellagra*. Baton Rouge: Louisiana State University Press.

TUKE, D.H. (1892) Article on Haematoma auris. In *Dictionary of Psychological Medicine*, p. 557. London: Churchill.

WHITE, E. B. & TAYLOR, A. L. (1932) A case of pellagra at the Bristol Mental Hospitals. *Journal of Mental Science*, **78**, 929–934.

WILLIAMS, S. W. D. (1870) On fractured ribs in the insane. *Lancet*, *ii*, 323–324.

WINSLOW, F. (1858) Presidential address. *Journal of Mental Science*, **4**, 4–16.

7 Opium and the doctors: disease theory and policy

VIRGINIA BERRIDGE

What is now popularly termed 'addiction' has existed in all societies, even if the addicts were often unrecognised as such at the time. The terminology in English society has varied and has reflected the underlying perceptions of the time. The relatively uncondemnatory, or at most morally disapproving, 'opium eater' and 'opium drunkard' of the early 19th century had been replaced by 'morphinist' or 'morphinomaniac', more medical terms, by its end. Even 'opium inebriate', then in use, signified the medical shift to a disease view of addiction. 'Addiction' itself as a commonly used word made its appearance around the time of World War I, along with further developments in disease theory.

In the 1960s and '70s, in line with thinking within the World Health Organization, the term 'dependence' was favoured as the official discourse and as a substitute for 'drug addiction'. Addiction was seen as conveying too limited a sense of what the condition might be about, emphasising only its physical dimension. The incorporation of psychological imperatives within the medical model was reinforced by a form of official terminology more related to behavioural models: hence the Institute for the Study of Drug Dependence, dating from that period, and the World Health Organization's expert advisory committee on the subject. In the late 1970s and '80s the official paradigm has again shifted. The attempt to relate drug taking – and drinking, where similar conceptual developments can also be noted – to some form of social context and social process, has led to the emergence of a new way of writing and talking about 'drug misuse' or 'problem drug users'.

There is a tendency for such shifts in official language to be set within a model of progress. This discarding of one way of talking for another has usually been accompanied by criticism of what went before, and this has aided a process which is still all too common in many forms of medical history. Yet, as Harry Levine has pointed out in his analysis of the "vocabulary of drunkenness", it is not as simple as that (Levine, 1984). Disease views had moral links with temperance perceptions; the 'problem drug use' and 'drug misuse' paradigm of today, while denying the fully fledged disease model, masks assumptions, concepts and ideologies no less than its predecessors.

Our present assumptions about addiction and the language we use are as historically and socially specific as the words in use 100 years ago. What I would like to do here is to sketch in some of the historical beginnings of the process, turning back firstly to the 19th century, to the initial emergence of this view of a separate medically defined condition, to the way disease views developed, and were placed in the 1920s to practical effect, at the heart of British drug control policy.

The 19th century, in particular its early decades, presents a radically different picture so far as opium is concerned. For much of the century, there was what can be termed a social rather than a medical culture of opium use, and the distinction between what we would now call medical and non-medical use is difficult to make. The use of opium among the small circle of Romantic writers and poets has always attracted the lion's share of attention. But De Quincey and Coleridge and their opium eating were only particularly notable examples of what was a common enough practice at all levels of society (Hayter, 1968; Lefebure, 1974). The range of opium preparations was enormous – from laudanum, the tincture of opium, opium pills, paregoric, the camphorated tincture, through to Dover's powder and Battley's sedative solution. There were patent medicines based on opium, such as Dr Collis Browne's Chlorodyne, and children's quieteners, such as Godfrey's cordial and Street's Infants Quietness. There were also a whole host of local 'home-made' preparations whose names and uses are now being discovered by detailed local research. The number of preparations was, in short, very large; there were even 14 'official' opium preparations in the first *British Pharmacopoeia* (1858).

Such preparations were used freely at all levels of society. Even after 1868, when the Pharmacy Act of that year restricted sales of opium preparations to qualified pharmacists, legal restrictions remained lax and the drug was almost as easily available as before. It is perhaps unfair to quote by way of illustration an example from the Fens, since this area was noted as one of particularly high opium consumption, but the encounter here related in a Wisbech chemist's shop on an evening in 1870 was typical of many such (Berridge, 1979). The writer:

> "went into a chemist's shop, laid a penny on the counter. The chemist said – 'the best?' I nodded. He gave me a pill box and took up the penny, and so the purchase was completed without my having uttered a syllable. You offer money and get opium as a matter of course. This may show how familiar the custom is." (Anonymous, 1873)

Going for opium was often a child's errand like any other small family purchase. The scene in Wisbech could be repeated in many other areas, in the industrial towns in particular.

Given the availability of opium and the high level of usage (home consumption between the 1820s and 1860 varied between 1.3 lb and 3.61 lb per 1000 population, or 127 therapeutic doses of opium for everyone in a year), what would, at a later stage, be termed 'addiction' or 'dependence' on opium must have been widespread. However, the drug was readily available, and it was only in exceptional circumstances that the extent of reliance became obvious. During the Lancashire cotton famine of the 1860s, many families in the mill towns fell on extreme hard times. Robert Harvey, who was then house surgeon at Stockport Infirmary, noted one strange effect of this: "Many applications were made at the infirmary for supplies of opium, the applicants being then too poor to buy it. . . . I was much struck by the fact that the use of the drug was much more common than I had any idea of, and that habitual consumers of ten and fifteen grains a day seemed none the worse for it, and would never have been suspected of using it" (Royal Commission on Opium, 1894).

Such a lack of knowledge of the extent of the condition was matched by the lack of a developed concept of addiction. There was a substantial medical literature on opium as far back as Sydenham in the 17th century, and many of the writers recognised phenomena such as dependence, physiological tolerance, and particularly withdrawal symptoms, Samuel Crumpe (1793), in his *Inquiry into the Nature and Properties of Opium*, noted that regular opium users, when deprived of the drug "for a single day, became languid, dejected, and uneasy at the customary hours of taking it, and could only be roused from this state by the usual quantity of opium, or by a large draught of wine". Opium eating was seen as a type of bad habit rather than a fully developed disease, and the terminology used to describe it was that of moral reform. Here is an anonymous correspondent, 'Medicus', writing in the *Lancet* in 1851, trying to seek some clarification about the condition.

> "Is it possible to reform a person who has long been addicted to the practice of taking opium? . . . Since the crusade of teetotallers against spirit-drinking, there is a great reason to believe that the practice of taking opium is on the increase; and when one of the first of our physicians describes it as a virtuous and comparatively harmless species of excitement, compared with gin-drinking, I cannot but think that he treats it with undue levity and may unintentionally contribute to the extension of the vice." (Medicus, 1851)

The language here is notably that of moral failing, not of disease.

Nor was the condition, as so defined, specifically the province of the medical profession. Medicus's request for advice came in the 1850s, but one of the earliest texts to treat on the condition, the anonymous *Advice to Opium Eaters* of 1823, was written by an ex-addict, not a doctor. With its chapters on "the pleasant effect of opium taken internally" and its "directions for the choice of opium", its avowed purpose, to warn possible imitators of De

Quincey away from use of the drug, may be regarded with some scepticism, but the book, nevertheless, dealt in detail with methods of leaving off opium and what it termed the "ill effects of a long and lavish use of opium" (Anonymous, 1823). Such extensive consideration was notably absent in the medical literature of the period. Some doctors reported cases of quite huge doses of opium taken regularly without considering it their duty to intervene. Where treatment was given, decisions were not always in the doctor's hands. The case of a Bradford woman, taking a quart of laudanum a week and a gallon of whisky a month, provides illustration. Her whisky was stopped by her doctor and the laudanum decreased with the intention of stopping it altogether. However, he reported that her relatives told him that "it was their intention to allow her the laudanum, but in smaller doses, they being infatuated with the idea that to discontinue its use entirely would be to endanger her life" (Whalley, 1866). The balance of power in the doctor–patient relationship still inclined to the latter, and maintenance doses were continued.

The most significant development in medical thinking about addiction came, not in discussions about treatment, but in consideration of the question of opium eating and longevity – whether or not an opium eater could live to a ripe old age. The question first arose in connection with a life insurance case involving the Earl of Mar. The Earl, who died in 1828, was revealed posthumously to have been a confirmed opium eater. His insurance company refused to pay out on his policy, arguing that his opium eating, as a life-shortening condition, should have been declared to them. Medical men were called in to give 'expert' evidence. The main witness was Sir Robert Christison, Professor of Medical Jurisprudence at Edinburgh, a noted pioneer of toxicology, and later, in his old age, a strong advocate of the virtues of the coca leaf (Christison, 1832*a*,*b*, 1876). He collected a number of case histories for examination, in the first attempt at what might be termed an epidemiological approach to the condition – previous examples had largely been culled from books of travellers' tales in the East. Despite Christison's initial prejudice against the condition, these indeed demonstrated that opium eating was not incompatible with longevity. The best summing up of the most generally adopted position appeared in Jonathan Pereira's well known textbook in 1842:

> "some doubt has recently begun to be entertained as to the alleged injurious effects of opium eating on the health, and its tendency to shorten life . . . we should be . . . careful not to assume that, because opium in large doses, when taken by the mouth, is a powerful poison, and when smoked in excess is injurious to health, therefore the moderate enjoyment of it is necessarily detrimental. . . ." (Pereira, 1842)

Various semi-medical views were common in the earlier years of the 19th century. In the second half of the century, a disease theory of addiction emerged out of the medical debates. The earlier medical discussions had approached opium eating less as an autonomous condition, more in relation to its effects on the consumer. The concern about the effects of opium eating was paralleled by medical discussions of the effects and treatment of opium poisoning and the accidental deaths which occurred as the result of the open availability of the drug. The context in which medical discussion took place in the earlier part of the century was, hence, a public health one. But in the last quarter of the century a different medical view of opium eating emerged, a disease theory of addiction which had an essentially individual emphasis. Opium eating and morphine habituation were established as a sickness or a form of insanity.

Much medical discussion of addiction centred on the question of hypo-dermic morphine. Early limited use of this newly discovered alkaloid of opium in the 1820s and '30s was given considerable impetus by a change to the new, hypodermic technique of administration, devised by Rynd and Alexander Wood in the mid-1850s and developed and refined by Dr Charles Hunter at the end of the decade (Howard-Jones, 1947). The method was at first carefully used. When Sir Clifford Allbutt, later Regius Professor of Physic at Oxford, was a young physician at Leeds Infirmary in 1864, the senior physician had called his colleagues together to see whether a physician should give the injection himself or should call in a surgeon. Such extreme care was succeeded by more wide-ranging recommendation, notably in the pages of the newly established *Practitioner*, which prided itself on pushing the newer, more 'scientific' medical treatments.

But it was in the *Practitioner* that Allbutt first described the progress of his own doubts about the method. He witnessed several of his patients appar-ently finding relief in injecting for its own sake. "Gradually," he wrote, "the conviction began to force itself upon my notice, that injections of morphia, though free from the ordinary evils of opium-eating, might, nevertheless, create the same artificial want and gain credit for assuaging a restlessness and depression of which it was itself the cause" (Allbutt, 1870). Allbutt's article led to some discussion in the pages of the journal. Dr Anstie, its editor, made a spirited defence of moderate and controlled addiction, "granting fully that we have here a fully-formed morphia-habit, difficult or impossible to abandon, it does not appear that this is any evil, under the circumstances" (Anstie, 1871).

The most developed account of the new disease was given in a German text, Edward Levinstein's *Die Morphiumsucht*, translated as *Morbid Craving for Morphia* and published in England in 1878 (Levinstein, 1878). Levinstein was not simply warning colleagues about the possible dangers of a new form of drug treatment; he was describing a new disease: "the uncontrollable desire of a person to use morphia as a stimulant and a tonic, and the diseased state of the system caused by the injudicious use of the same remedy". The book was based on Levinstein's own experiences in the institutional treatment of addiction in Berlin; it was instrumental in defining 'morphinism' as a separate condition, a disease with a similarity to dipsomania, although not a mental illness. Despite his mechanical model of disease, Levinstein still saw addiction as a human passion "such as smoking, gambling, greediness for profit, sexual excesses etc." Levinstein's distinction between the 'morphinist', who wished to be cured, and the 'morphino-maniac', who was irredeemably enslaved and who wished to spread the condition to others, was widely adopted in both the English and American literature on the subject. It continued to influence thinking, as in the later model of addiction as a communicable disease, the public health and epidemiological model.

There were also English experts, most notably Dr Norman Kerr. Through his work with a new expert body, the Society for the Study of Inebriety (SSI), Kerr, who was at one stage chairman of the British Medical Association's Inebriates Legislation Committee, was closely involved in moves to secure the compulsory detention of alcoholic inebri-ates, moves which achieved success when the 1878 Habitual Drunkards Act was extended into the Inebriates Act of 1888. His interest in narcotic addiction was an offshoot of this main concern, and his writings on the subject, *Inebriety or Narcomania* for instance, were important in defining disease views. Kerr also founded, in 1884, the Society for the Study and Cure of Inebriety – from 1887, less optimistically, simply the Society for the Study of Inebriety. Its journal, later the *British Journal of Inebriety* and now the *British Journal of Addiction*, provided the arena for debate and for elaboration of the theory. Its central message was that addiction was indeed a disease. Kerr claimed that inebriety "is for the most part the issue of certain physical conditions . . . the natural product of a depraved, de-bilitated, or defective nervous organisation . . . as unmistakeably a disease as is gout, or epilepsy, or insanity" (Kerr, 1888). Kerr and his colleagues were primarily concerned with alcohol, and the concept of inebriety was originally formulated with drink in mind. However, Kerr claimed that the "opium habit" was a "true inebriety", although he saw it as a "functional neurosis" in which "organic lesions were comparatively rare". Opiomania, morphino-mania, chloralomania and chlorodynomania were, Kerr told the Colonial and International Congress on Inebriety in 1887, all variants of this disease.

Kerr's addition of a psychological element to disease theory was widely accepted. The 'morphine disease' was indeed a medical growth area at the turn of the century. No textbook of medicine was complete without its section on the 'morphia habit'. Specialist texts were produced and there was a strong American influence, as for example in T. D. Crothers' *Morphinism and Narcomanias from other Drugs* (1902) and J. B. Mattison's *The Mattison Method in Morphinism: A Modern and Humane Treatment of the Morphin Disease* (1902). The tendency to look at American examples is thus long established. In the 1920s, when British drug control policy was being formulated, the focus was again on the evolution of policy in the US; and even today both the history of policy and also current practice continue to be of reciprocal interest, with the debate on the 'Minnesota Method' as one example.

In Britain, doctors such as Seymour Sharkey and Benjamin Ward Richardson were among the first to write about the condition from English experience. Sharkey's popular treatment in his article "Morphinomania", published in 1887, helped set a style of writing easily recognisable in its present-day versions in the popular press:

> "the evil is in our midst, often where least suspected, though it has not assumed the proportions which it appears to have assumed among the French. But, once introduced, the danger of rapid growth is great and so relentless is the habit, when it has once established itself, that few of its victims succeed in releasing themselves from it by their own unaided efforts." (Sharkey, 1887)

It is only by close attention to the article that one realises that Sharkey actually conceded that there was really little morphine addiction in England! Sir Clifford Allbutt, one-time advocate of hypodermic morphine, also contributed to the elaboration of disease perceptions. Dr Thomas Clouston of the West Riding Lunatic Asylum, who had made his medical reputation in part through his experiments with cannabis and the bromides to replace opium as a treatment for insanity (Clouston, 1870, 1871, 1890), also wrote about the new disease.

Morphinomania, morphinism, whatever term was used, had clearly become the prerogative of the profession. But what did this disease theory comprise and why did it emerge when it did? A few answers can briefly be given. The British version of disease theory did emphasise the physical components of addiction; but there was a stronger emphasis on disease in terms of deviation from the normal. A theory emerged in which the older 'vice' view of opium eating was reformulated in apparently scientific form, where social factors were largely ignored in favour of explanations in terms of individual personality and biological determination. The public health perceptions of the earlier part of the century had little influence. According to Norman Kerr, the medical profession wished to move away from those dark ages when inebriates were "vicious depraved sinners", but the medical theories still had their moral basis. They found it difficult to accommodate the element of free will, for the condition appeared to be to a great extent self-induced. What emerged was a formula whereby addiction, clearly not simply a physical disease, became a 'disease of the will'. It was disease *and* vice. The moral weakness of the patient was an important factor in causation. According to Dr Clouston, both morphine addiction and alcoholism were the product of "diseased cravings and paralysed control". A paralysed control over a craving for drink or opium or cocaine could be a disease as much as suicidal melancholia, he wrote. The aetiology of the disease, through its stress on the individual constitution, with predisposing and exciting causes, emphasised this notion of personal responsibility. However, the condition was also the proper province for medical intervention.

This British version of disease theory was also much affected by the parallel moves to define a disease theory of alcoholism. The concept of inebriety included both alcohol and opium, morphine and other drugs; consideration of these latter was usually subsidiary to consideration of alcohol. This meant that opium, as much as alcohol, was viewed in the context of the temperance views which informed the work of many medical men in this area. As Brian Harrison (1971) has pointed out in his *Drink and the Victorians*, the temperance movement in England so advertised the moral dimensions of the drink problem that in the 19th century scientific studies of alcoholism took place only on the continent (Bynum, 1968; Harrison, 1971). There were certainly strong organisational links between the medical specialists in inebriety and morphinomania and the temperance movement. Norman Kerr was a strong temperance supporter. Many of the medical men involved in the SSI were also active in the anti-opium movement, and in particular in the Society for the Suppression of the Opium Trade (SSOT), which campaigned against Britain's involvement in the Indian opium trade with China. Benjamin Richardson, for instance, was a vice-president of the SSOT and in 1892 organised for it a conference on the medical aspects of the opium question. The medical declaration which followed this conference significantly saw the habit as morally as well as physically debasing.

Addiction was a disease of 'modern civilisation', yet its application was somewhat exclusive, for the theory was formulated and applied always to those middle-class addicts whom doctors were likely to treat. Disease was reserved for this class, whereas consumption by working-class purchasers, who mostly bought their opium and laudanum over the counter, rather than having it prescribed and administered to them, was viewed largely as a matter of limitation of availability. Crothers' (1902) view was typical. He saw physical and nervous exhaustion among "hard working physicians, clergymen, active business men, lawyers, teachers," who "early become neurasthenic and cerebrasthenic". This was likely to lead to a generation of children who become morphine addicts. Physiological theories of brain functioning, the belief that insanity and addiction had their source in localised brain lesions, gave added force to this approach. Sir Ronald Armstrong-Jones of Claybury Asylum gave one of the clearest expositions of this class approach. He argued that morphine addicts were more commonly to be found in the private class, whom, by happy coincidence, he treated at Claybury. He went on,

> "there is generally a physical difference between the brains of those in the private and rate-aided class . . . not only is the brain-weight heavier, but there is also in the private class an added complexity of convolutional pattern, and these differences, of necessity, carry with them psychological and physiological concomitants, which mean a higher sensitiveness and greater vulnerability." (Armstrong-Jones, 1914)

Disease theory was certainly not formulated with the "rate-aided" patient in mind; it is notable in the last 20 years or so how disease perceptions have · given way to an emphasis on control as the circle of addicts has widened (Stimson & Oppenheimer, 1981).

At the turn of the century, too, there was increasing emphasis on the possible hereditary nature of the condition. The imperial concern about 'national efficiency' and race also affected perceptions of domestic drug use. Allbutt & Rolleston's *System of Medicine* (1906), for instance, emphasised heredity, which is particularly significant in this case as Sir Humphrey Rolleston was to be chairman of the 1924–26 Committee on Morphine and Heroin Addiction, which established the medical basis of British narcotic policy (Allbutt & Rolleston, 1906). Under the influence of Sir William Collins, President of the Society for the Study of Inebriety between 1916 and 1919, and a noted temperance and anti-opium supporter as well a Liberal MP, the notion of addiction (the word was now in use) as a 'disease of the will' was more strongly asserted: "Alcohol and drug addictions are . . . to be regarded as examples of the surrender of self control in favour of self indulgence" (Collins, 1915; see also Collins, 1919).

There has been a tendency to see this development within some sort of model of progress, whereby a pure 'scientific' condition existed, only awaiting its discoverer. Such an analysis is given by Glenn Sonnedecker in his 'Emergence of the concept of opiate addiction'. Addiction, in this interpretation, is a clinically defined disease, not an historically specific concept; medical writers of the time are praised or criticised depending on the proximity of their views to present understanding (Sonnedecker, 1962, 1963). Even a more recent article by Dolores Peters is not immune to this approach, despite its greater sophistication in other respects. Here, "The disease model of addiction and the program of treatment associated with it, are characteristic features of an interim period in the development of a modern concept of addiction" (Peters, 1981). This type of analysis shows scant comprehension that 'modern' and by implication 'better' concepts are no less rooted in the perceptions and social situations of the present as were their historical predecessors. Doubtless 'drug dependence' and 'problem drug use' will take their place as similar interim concepts in some 'neo-Whig' version of medical history.

This 'march of progress' approach is inadequate – but what can be put in its place? A limited explanation can be found in the particular circumstances of morphine administration. Subcutaneous injection had indeed made it possible for the patient to take a much larger dose than normally taken by means of laudanum, and injection meant that a higher proportion of the drug reached the nervous system. But it also brought, for the first time, the medical profession into close contact with a regular morphine-using group of patients, something never the case with opium users.

But an explanation must also be sought in the changing role, status, and self-confidence of the medical profession itself. By the last quarter of the 19th century, the profession was at a strong point organisationally and its theoretical basis was sounder. Disease entities were established in more directly physical conditions – typhoid, tuberculosis, and cholera, for instance. The legislative successes of the public health movement in the 1860s and 1870s encouraged extension of the scope of public health concerns – and disease theories, in the same process of medical self-affirmation, were also being extended to conditions such as homosexuality, alcoholism and criminality, where, as with addiction, the social and cultural basis went largely unrecognised.

Disease theories were then a particular manifestation of the progress of the medical profession rather than of 'medical progress' as a whole, and such theories naturally represented the particular class prejudices of that section of the middle class of which the profession formed part. Hence came the emphasis on morphine injection and the particular emphasis of disease theory. But disease theory was not simply a theoretical nicety or another example of the extension of medical hegemony. It was also of practical policy significance; disease theory became the cornerstone of British drug control policy in the 1920s. This was not an automatic process, even though Roy MacLeod, in his study of the Society for the Study of Inebriety, has characterised it and the activities of its medical members as an example of developing links between medical 'experts' and bureaucracy (MacLeod, 1967). The medical view underwent a diminution of influence during World War I and initially during the 1920s it seemed as though policy with a penal emphasis would prevail.

Britain had already, before that time, been committed to a more extensive system of narcotic control as a result of the largely American-inspired international narcotic control movement. The movement was originally conceived as a means of controlling the Far Eastern, and especially the Chinese, opium problem, but the 1912 Convention signed at the Hague extended control to morphine and cocaine, thereby envisaging a domestic system of narcotic control which would be of world-wide application. However, discussion between government departments in Britain prior to the outbreak of war in 1914 had envisaged little more than an extension of the existing pharmacy laws; no challenge was offered either to professional control or to disease conceptions.

The impact of war conditions gave addiction the appearance of a pressing social problem, which, if not controlled, could lead to serious deficiencies in the war effort. In an apparent state of emergency, the disease conception was seriously undermined. The problem was twofold: smuggling of opium and morphine to the Far East, much of it on British ships; and evidence at home that the recreational use of cocaine was spreading among soldiers on leave in London. On to the stage at this point came Sir Malcolm Delevingne, Assistant Under-Secretary at the Home Office, and the man later responsible for the penal direction of drug policy. It was at his insistence, supported by the police and army, that Regulation 40B was promulgated under the 1916 Defence of the Realm Act. Cocaine and opium (but not morphine) were strictly controlled – the first legislative attempts to control the addict as well as the sale of the drug.

A Commons Select Committee reported in 1917 that addiction, at least to cocaine, was very limited indeed, confined, as the report put it, to a number of "broken-down medical men". But this did not accord with official preconceptions (the report, like others since, was not published) and the penal and prohibitive attitude of 1916 was extended into the 1920s (Berridge, 1978). The 1920 Dangerous Drugs Act laid the foundation for wholesale restriction of morphine as well as opium and cocaine. Home Office regulations in 1921 and 1922 implied that doctors as well as addicts were to be strictly controlled. The basis of official policy took little account of disease views; doctors not in actual practice were prohibited from prescribing, and doctors were forbidden to write prescriptions of dangerous drugs for themselves. The 1923 Amended Act imposed heavier penalties; the police had increased powers of search. There was considerable Home Office disapproval of doctors who continued to write regular prescriptions for addicts who could not otherwise function, and a move to secure official confirmation that abrupt and not gradual withdrawal should be standard practice (Berridge, 1984).

The disease concept of addiction and all that it entailed was under attack. A prohibitionist policy under which doctors and addicts would both incur penalties, as in the US under the Harrison Narcotics Act at the same time, was being established. That this did not happen owed much to intense opposition from many sections of the profession, most obviously the addiction specialists. Dr W. E. Dixon, Reader in Pharmacology at Cambridge, gave the firmest defence of medical control. In a letter to *The Times* in 1923, he commented,

> "We do not seem to have learned anything from the experience of our American brethren. . . . Cannot our legislators understand that our only hope of stamping out the drug addict is through the doctors, that legislation above the doctors' heads is likely to prove our undoing, and that we can no more stamp out addiction by prohibition than we can stamp out insanity?" (Dixon, 1923)

Here, in essence, was the disease basis of the case for medical control. In 1924, the Home Office persuaded the Ministry of Health to set up a committee chaired by Sir Humphrey Rolleston, President of the Royal College of Physicians, as a medical committee on addiction. The Home Office had found that in actual practice it could not exclude doctors. This was a recognition that official policy could proceed only in alliance with medical premises. What resulted, in the Rolleston report of 1926, was the legitimisation of much of the medical discussion of the previous half century as the basis of drug control policy. Addiction was firmly defined as a disease and a fit subject for medical intervention:

"there was general agreement that in most well-established cases, the condition must be regarded as a manifestation of disease and not as a mere form of vicious indulgence. In other words, the drug is taken in such cases not for the purpose of obtaining positive pleasure, but in order to relieve a morbid and overpowering craving. The actual need for the drug in extreme cases is in fact so great that, if it be not administered, great physical distress, culminating in actual collapse and even death, may result unless special precautions are taken such as can only be carried out under close medical supervision, and with careful nursing." (Rolleston, 1926)

Regular maintenance doses were allowed, and the system, with compulsory notification rejected and a medical tribunal to deal with 'rogue' doctors and the doctor-addict, was to be policed by the profession itself. The 'medical model' of addiction, with its roots in the 'disease of the will' approach, emerged as the dominant feature of official drug control policy.

This report, and the 'system' of drug control it fostered, has been of enduring political significance. In the 1960s critics of the American penal system looked to British medically based policy as the cause of Britain's limited addict population (Schur, 1963). In the 1980s, there has been a move to restore elements of the old 'British system' through advocacy of the restoration of heroin prescribing in general (and private) practice (Trebach, 1982). It is therefore important to establish what disease theory in relation to policy did represent. One can conclude that the penal/medical dichotomy is inadequate as an explanatory framework. Rolleston and the approach it enshrined was medically biased – but within a system based on the Dangerous Drugs Acts which had penal provisions and which came under the control of the Home Office, not the Ministry of Health. Medical 'experts' certainly did not defeat the penal tendencies of civil servants; drug control policy was established more as the result of struggles and the combinations between competing medical and bureaucratic sources of power. The medical emphasis was sustained in part because of the prestige of the medical profession by this period and its role as a medical bureaucracy within the Ministry of Health; it proved impossible to disentangle doctors from addiction, much as the Home Office might initially have liked to. It was sustained also because the addict population was small and mostly middle class, iatrogenic in origin; doctors had no wish to lose control of their respectable addict clientele. It was notable that the prison doctors who gave evidence before the Rolleston Committee favoured a much harsher approach, including opposition to maintenance and support for abrupt withdrawal. The medical approach was dependent on the type of clientele. The 'British system' then was not as exclusively medical as it seemed; nor can it be held responsible for the small addict population at its inception, or for the continuance of a fairly stable number of addicts over the next thirty years (Edwards, 1978). Nevertheless, the establishment of disease theories had their policy impact. Medical experts were to control policies decided in conjunction with the Civil Service in an area still overtly designated as medical. The disease of addiction became the basis of drug control policy; a further stage began in a still developing relationship between medicine and the state.

Acknowledgements

I am grateful to Professor Griffith Edwards for the calculations of opium dosage. My thanks are also due to Danielle Bassry for secretarial assistance.

References

ANONYMOUS (1823) *Advice to Opium Eaters*. London: W. R. Goodluck.
—— (1873) Notes on Madras as a winter residence. . . . *Medical Times & Gazette*, **2**, 73–74.
ALLBUTT, T. C. (1870) On the abuse of hypodermic injections of morphia. *Practitioner*, **5**, 327–331.
—— & ROLLESTON, H. D. (eds) (1906) *A System of Medicine*, vol. 2. London: Macmillan.
ANSTIE, F. E. (1871) On the effects of the prolonged use of morphia by subcutaneous injection. *Practitioner*, **6**, 148–187.
ARMSTRONG-JONES, R. (1902) Notes on some cases of morphinomania. *Journal of Mental Science*, **48**, 478–495.
—— (1914) Drugs of addiction. *Morning Post*, 10 June.
BERRIDGE, V. (1978) War conditions and narcotics control: the passing of Defence of the Realm Act Regulation 40B. *Journal of Social Policy*, **7**, 285–304.
—— (1979) Opium in the Fens in nineteenth century England. *Journal of the History of Medicine and Allied Sciences*, **34**, 293–313.
—— (1984) Drugs and social policy: the establishment of drug control in Britain, 1900–30. *British Journal of Addiction*, **79**, 17–29.
British Pharmacopoeia (1858) London: Spottiswoode.
BYNUM, W. F. (1968) Chronic alcoholism in the first half of the nineteenth century. *Bulletin of the History of Medicine*, **42**, 160–185.
CHRISTISON, R. (1832a) *Treatise on Poisons* (2nd edn). Edinburgh: Adam Black.
—— (1832b) On the effect of opium eating on health and longevity. *Edinburgh Medical and Surgical Journal*, **37**, 123–135.
—— (1850) Supplement to the preceding paper (by Little) on the habitual use of opium, more especially the mode of cure. *Monthly Journal of Medicine Science*, **10**, 531–538.
—— (1876) Observations on the effect of the leaves of erythroxylon coca. *British Medical Journal*, **i**, 527–531.
CLOUSTON, T. S. (1870) Observations and experiments on the use of opium, bromide of potassium and cannabis indica in insanity. *British and Foreign Medico-Chirurgical Review*, **46**, 493–511.
—— (1871) Observations and experiments on the use of opium, bromide of potassium and cannabis indica in insanity. *British and Foreign Medico-Chirurgical Review*, **47**, 203–220.
—— (1890) Diseased cravings and paralysed control. *Edinburgh Medical Journal*, **35**, 308–521, 689–705, 793–809, 985–996.
COLLINS, W. J. (1915) The ethics and law of drug and alcohol addiction. *British Journal of Inebriety*, **13**, 131–154.
—— (1919) The aims and future work of the Society for the Study of Inebriety. *British Journal of Inebriety*, **17**, 1–7.
CROTHERS, T. D. (1902) *Morphinism and Narcomanias from other Drugs. Their Etiology, Treatment and Medico-Legal Relations*. Philadelphia and London: W. B. Saunders.

CRUMPE, S. (1793) *An Inquiry into the Nature and Properties of Opium*. London: G. G. and J. Robinson.

DIXON, W. E. (1923) *The Times*, 21 March.

EDWARDS, G. (1978) Some years on: evolutions in the 'British System'. In *Problems of Drug Abuse in Britain* (ed. D. J. West). Cambridge: Institute of Criminology.

HARRISON, B. (1971) *Drink and the Victorians*. London: Faber and Faber.

HAYTER, A. (1968) *Opium and the Romantic Imagination*. London: Faber and Faber.

HOWARD-JONES, N. (1947) A critical study of the origins and early development of hypodermic medication. *Journal of the History of Medicine and Allied Sciences*, 2, 201–249.

KERR, N. (1888) *Inebriety, its Etiology, Pathology, Treatment and Jurisprudence*. London: H. K. Lewis.

LEFEBURE, M. (1974) *Samuel Taylor Coleridge: A Bondage of Opium*. London: Victor Gollancz.

LEVINE, H. G. (1984) What is an alcohol-related problem? (or, what are people talking about when they refer to alcohol problems?). *Journal of Drug Issues*, winter, 45–60.

LEVINSTEIN, E. (1878) *Morbid Craving for Morphia*. London: Smith, Elder.

MACLEOD, R. M. (1967) The edge of hope: social policy and chronic alcoholism, 1870–1900. *Journal of the History of Medicine and Allied Sciences*, 22, 215–245.

MATTISON, J. B. (1902) *The Mattison Method in Morphinism: A Modern and Humane Treatment of the Morphin Disease*. New York.

MEDICUS (1851) Opium taking. *Lancet*, ii, 45.

PEREIRA, J. (1842) *Elements of Materia Medica* (2nd edn). London: Longman, Orme, Browne, Green and Longmans.

PETERS, D. (1981) The British medical response to opiate addiction in the nineteenth century. *Journal of the History of Medicine and Allied Sciences*, 36, 455–488.

ROLLESTON, H. D. (1926) *Report of the Departmental Committee on Morphine and Heroin Addiction*. London: HMSO.

ROYAL COMMISSION ON OPIUM (1894) Minutes of evidence, LXI, q. 3387. *Parliamentary Papers*. London: HMSO.

SCHUR, T.M. (1963) *Narcotic Addiction in Britain and America*. London: Tavistock.

SHARKEY, S. J. (1887) Morphinomania. *Nineteenth Century*, 22, 335–342.

SONNEDECKER, G. (1962, 1963) Emergence of the concept of opiate addiction. *Journal Mondiale Pharmacie*, 3, 275–290; 1, 27–34.

STIMSON, G. V. & OPPENHEIMER, E. (1981) *Heroin Addiction. Treatment and Control in Britain*. London: Tavistock.

TREBACH, A. (1982) *The Heroin Solution*. New Haven and London: Yale University Press.

WHALLEY, W. (1866) Confessions of a laudanum drinker. *Lancet*, ii, 35.

8 The nervous patient in 18th- and 19th-century Britain: the psychiatric origins of British neurology

WILLIAM F. BYNUM

"The more marked the mental disturbance the fewer the neurological signs, and vice versa. Psychiatrically noisy, neurologically silent, is no bad adage." (Hunter, 1973)

My epigram comes from the late Richard Hunter. It was one of Hunter's firm professional and historical convictions that psychiatric disorders are at bottom physical, and that psychiatry and neurology developed as separate specialties because of the curious fact that patients can suffer substantial impairments of their nervous systems without signs of mental derangement, and that individuals with bizarre affects, mental states, or behavioural characteristics can die with brains which stubbornly refuse to yield evidence of abnormality to the dissecting scalpel or chemical analyst. However, a more astute diagnostician than many psychiatrists, Hunter could often find evidence of neurological deficit where more casual observers had found only psychiatric disorder. For instance, he suggested that the earliest picture of a patient in Bethlem (or Bedlam) taken from the title page of Robert Burton's *Anatomy of Melancholy*, showing a patient with 'mania', actually depicts an abnormal arm and hand posture associated with choreoathetosis. (The patient depicting 'Maniacus' was engraved on the title page of the fourth edition of Burton (1632), and has been reproduced in Hunter (1973).)

The historical relationships between psychiatry and neurology have been markedly different in different national contexts. In the German-speaking lands, they merged in the middle of the 19th century to form the rich neuropsychiatric tradition of Griesinger, Wernicke, Krafft-Ebing, Meynert, and Korsakoff. These German and Austrian neuropsychiatrists made no real distinction between diseases of the brain and diseases of the mind, for they held that mental processes were always the unvarying result of underlying brain functions; Meynert (1884) subtitled his psychiatric textbook "A Treatise on Diseases of the Forebrain". Not surprisingly, they were more interested in scientific research than in practice, and although psychopharmacology came within their ken, they were little concerned with psychotherapy, and the tradition made little concession to psychoanalysis, even if, ironically, the tradition actually nourished the young Sigmund Freud. The German neuropsychiatric approach was taken up in many parts of Europe – Italy, Greece, and Spain, for instance – and is still alive and well in places like Japan (Ackerknecht, 1968; Howells, 1975; Okada, 1982).

In the English-speaking world, however, the pattern was different. In both the United States and Britain, a formal psychiatric profession developed in the first half of the 19th century, decades before medical specialties such as cardiology, gastroenterology, or neurology. In both countries, the psychiatric profession coalesced around specialised hospitals, the insane asylums, whose medical superintendents became, for the most part, administrators and overlords of vast establishments filled with chronically incapacitated patients. Richard Hunter and Ida Macalpine's history of one such establishment, at Colney Hatch in North London, has reminded us that these institutions were not simply museums of madness: they were also museums of neuropathology, where unwanted patients with neurosyphilis, epilepsy, ataxias, and many other organic diseases of the nervous system spent their monotonous lives (Hunter & Macalpine, 1974). But neuropsychiatry never really flourished in Britain or America, despite continued lip-service paid to the notion of the organic nature of insanity (see Clarke, 1981, 1982). In America, neurology, as a clinical specialty, developed largely in the private sector associated, above all, with men such as William Hammond, Silas Weir Mitchell, and George Beard (see Rosenberg, 1962; Blustein, 1979). Early on American neurology was identified with neurasthenia and the rest cure. The tensions between American psychiatrists and neurologists have recently been explored by Bonnie Blustein, and Russell Dejong has looked at more traditional features of American neurology (Blustein, 1981; Dejong, 1982).

But what of the nervous British patient? I should like here to consider briefly some of the traits of patients suffering from nervous diseases from the early 18th to the early 20th century. These nervous diseases were a class in which physical symptoms predominated, but for which the evidence for structural derangement was lacking. Historians have been particularly intrigued by these 'functional' diseases, as they have come to be called, for they seem to show most clearly the cultural, social, and ideological factors which influence definitions and perceptions of disease and constrain the behaviour of both patients and their doctors (Fischer-Homberger, 1970; Krohn, 1978; Trimble, 1981). Hysteria is perhaps the best known of these disorders, all the more famous since it played such a crucial role in Freud's elaboration of the principles of psychoanalysis. But of course hysteria was only one of a cluster of these functional disorders. As Thomas Trotter (1807) wrote in his *View of the Nervous Temperament*: "They have been designated in common language, by the terms NERVOUS; SPASMODIC; BILIOUS;

INDIGESTION; STOMACH COMPLAINTS; LOW SPIRITS; VAPOURS etc." (Trotter, 1807, p. xv). Earlier, George Cheyne, in his treatise on the *English Malady* (1733) had identified the spleen, vapours, lowness of spirits, hypochondriacal and hysterical distempers as constituting the cluster of nervous diseases to which he believed the English were especially prone (see Rousseau, 1980; Porter, 1983).

It was, in fact, only in the 18th century that it became possible to suffer from the 'nerves'. If a patient had gone to his doctor in Hippocratic times and complained of being 'nervous', his doctor would have expected to see a sinewy fellow, strong and vigorous. (The *Oxford English Dictionary*, while noting that by the late 19th century the usage was 'rare', gives the original definition of 'nervous' as "Sinewy, muscular; vigorous, strong".) Shakespeare never used the word 'nervous', but he used the cognate adjective, 'nervy', to describe the arm of a strong warrior in *Coriolanus*:

"Death, that dark spirit, in's nervy arm doth lie,
Which, being advanc'd, declines, and then men die." (II. i, 177–78)

Thomas Willis, whose English translator Samuel Pordage gave us the word 'neurologie', as the 'doctrine of the nerves', occasionally described patients without, as he said, "any notable sickness", but his vocabulary for these functional disorders was traditional, even if he helped dismantle the old notion that hysteria is a disease of the uterus (see Spillane, 1981; Dewhurst, 1982a).

Half a century after Willis's death, however, George Cheyne put the nerves on the map. His popular treatise, which went through five quick editions, described a personality type found in those with "weak, loose, and feeble or relax'd nerves", the result of which was extreme sensitivity to hot and cold, weak digestion, a tendency to alternative diarrhoea and costiveness, and other signs of valetudinarianism. This English disease, affecting, he insisted, as many as one-third of all people of quality in England, was the result of the high living, prosperity, and progress unique on such a wide scale in early 18th-century England. Cheyne flattered his patients: only those of quick and lively dispositions and good breeding suffered from the nerves. "We *Hypochondriacks*," James Boswell mused to himself, "may console ourselves in the hour of gloomy distress, by thinking that our sufferings make our superiority" (see Porter, 1985). With Cheyne, 'nervous' acquired some of its modern connotations, although Dr Johnson, with his firm sense of historical etymology, lamented its new and trendier meaning. He described in a letter to Mrs Thrale a person with "a tender, irritable, and as it is not very properly called, a nervous constitution". In his *Dictionary*, Johnson (1983) gave as the first meaning of 'nervous' the older one: "well strung; strong; vigorous". Its second meaning was also acceptable to him: "Relating to the nerves; having the seat in the nerves". Finally, with Cheyne as his authority, Johnson recorded a third meaning of 'nervous':

"Having weak or diseased nerves", indicating his disapproval by the stern caveat that this usage was *"medical cant"*.

In the meantime, Cheyne's Scottish colleagues, Robert Whytt and William Cullen, elevated the nervous system to a prime position within physiology, pathology, and nosology. "In my opinion," wrote Whytt (1768, p. 487), "the generality of morbid affections so depend on the nervous system, that almost every disease might be called nervous" (see also Lawrence, 1984). To Cullen, we owe the invention of the term, and the original elaboration of the concept, of neurosis (see López Piñero & Morales Meseguer, 1970; López Piñero, 1983). Cullen's lectures on physiology were about two-thirds devoted to the nervous system; his *First Lines of the Practice of Physic*, which became a textbook for a whole generation of British and American medical students, included as one of his major classes of diseases the neuroses, defined by him as affections of sense and motion, without fever or evidence of local disease. Cullen further divided the neuroses into four orders, the *comata* (apoplexy, paralysis); *adynamiae* (syncope, hypochondriasis, chlorosis), *spasmi* (convulsions, chorea, hysteria, hydrophobia), and *vesaniae* (melancholia, mania, and other diseases of impaired judgement) (see Thomson, 1827, 1859; Lawrence, 1984). It was, of course, a classification which did not stand the test of time, but its *functional* orientation, its division of diseases of the nervous system essentially into those of sensation and those of motion, continued to dictate neurological nosology throughout the 19th century, particularly through the *locus classicus* of modern neurology, Moritz Romberg's *Manual of the Nervous Diseases of Man*, published in parts between 1840 and 1846, and translated, from its second edition, into English in 1853. The title was significant: Romberg wrote about nervous diseases, rather than diseases of the nervous system – a functional rather than structural outlook (Romberg, 1853). Earlier, John Cooke's *Treatise of Nervous Diseases* had quietly adopted the same approach (Cooke, 1820–23; see Spillane, 1981, for an assessment).

This functional orientation is one of the common strands of 19th-century neurology and psychiatry, and continues to be a soft spot in modern psychiatric diagnoses. Initially, for neither specialty did the anatomico-pathological thrust so successfully cultivated by the French school seem to be of much systematic use. John Cooke devoted 150 pages to general considerations of the functions of the nervous system, and only about 10% of that amount to post-mortem dissections. He knew that apoplexies could be correlated with contralateral lesions in the brain, but the range of post-mortem appearances, and the absence of precise correlations with clinical symptoms, led him to devalue this avenue to medical knowledge. Likewise, his contemporaries who were primarily intrigued with psychiatric disorders such as melancholia and mania, sometimes puzzled over their inability to discover those footsteps of disease which Francis Bacon long before had suggested were the tangible legacies of suffering and sickness, and whose precise elaboration offered the surest hope of an efficacious medical science. James Cowles Prichard (1835), for instance, used an appendix to his *Treatise on Insanity* to consider the French alienists' attempts to apply the methods of clinicopathological correlation to the mad. The result, Prichard insisted, was a failure: there were simply too many instances where overt insanity could not be correlated with structural abnormalities of the brain and nervous system.

One consequence of this common functional mould was the mixture of moral and medical language so emphasised by recent historians. Many of the characteristics of the nervous patient as he (or, increasingly in the 19th century, she) was described by Enlightenment doctors and moralists were pulled together in the view of the nervous temperament, elaborated by one of Cullen's pupils, Thomas Trotter. Trotter's nervous patient has such persistence throughout the 19th century that he deserves a closer look. For this nervous patient, in Trotter's opinion, was extremely easy to find. As he wrote (1807, p. xvii):

> "Sydenham at the conclusion of the seventeenth century, computed fevers
> to constitute two thirds of the diseases of mankind. But, at the beginning
> of the nineteenth century, we do not hesitate to affirm, that *nervous disorders*
> have now taken the place of fevers, and may be justly reckoned two thirds
> of the whole, with which civilized society is afflicted."

A bold claim, that, but one which Trotter sought to substantiate by extending the typical 18th-century assumption that nervous complaints are diseases of the leisured classes, diseases of luxury, to encompass virtually all of the urban population of Britain. A simple, energetic country life engenders health and vigour; anything which deviates from it is debilitating: want to fresh air, highly refined foods, tea, excessive alcohol consumption, fashionable dress, competitiveness, lack of sleep, novel reading, adultery, excessive passion, abuse of medicine, excessive study – these and a thousand other pitfalls await the unwary business man, labourer, or woman of leisure. Trotter could see no real and lasting solution save that which Charles Dickens was later to propose for all the social ills of his own day: the individual change of heart. Civilisation bred its own discontents and provided no easy solutions. To obtain health, men and women must return to the simple life which Tacitus had described for the ancient Germans: the life of fresh air, vigorous outdoor pursuits, simple food, uncomplicated relations between the sexes. What Trotter (1803, pp. 144–145) mourned was the passing of an England which he located in a romantic, organic past:

> "The rise and fall of a large commercial town, may be taken as an example
> of a nation. From a few fisherman's huts, on some river, or arm of the
> sea, it gradually extends and improves, till the exchange for business,
> and the theatre for amusement, become its ornaments. A narrow port
> is by degrees, widened into a capacious harbour: and the warehouse,

manufactory and shop, increase in proportion, till wealth and elegance dazzle in every lane and alley. The coffee-house, the inn, and the tavern, grow necessary appendages to business and pleasure: the morning begins with a bargain, and the evening closes with a banquet. Then the rout commences, to teach the young the arts of gaming: and the midnight masquerade initiates them into the wiles of intrigue. The riot disturbs sleep; the drunkard is seen staggering home, in danger of robbery and death; and the woman of the town, deserted by her destroyer, is seeking reprisals, and looking for prey in the streets. Now the hospital and bedlam appear in the suburbs; the first to receive the poor, sick and lame; and the other to confine the more wretched in mind. The physician and apothecary are seen gliding in their chariots, with retinues sometimes not much like men who are conversant with human affliction, and enriched by the luxuries and vices of their fellow mortals. Morals and health are alike committed in this vortex of wealth and dissipation.''

Trotter's nervous patient might suffer because of almost any organ of the body, because the nerves go everywhere. Thus, gout, liver disease, dyspepsia, and kidney stone were diseases of the nervous temperament as much as hysteria, hypochondria, and frank disorders of the mind (see also Sekora, 1977; Inglis, 1981).

During the half-century following Trotter's work, however, the new concern for spinal physiology directed medical attention towards the spinal cord and reflexes, provided a much more scientific-sounding vocabulary to describe nervous symptoms, and brought other disorders, particularly epilepsy, within the nervous pale (see Temkin, 1971; an intriguing, but unconvincing, account is given by Thornton, 1976). Of especial importance for the British scene were Marshall Hall and Thomas Laycock.

Hall was a controversial figure in his own lifetime and has continued to attract a divided historical commentary. That he was a thoroughly disagreeable man few would deny. He was vain, ambitious, opinionated, self-serving, arrogant, and gratingly pious. He was also exceptionally intelligent and hard working, an inveterate experimentalist at a time when vivisectional experimentation in Britain was rather frowned upon. He ran afoul of the Royal Society, whose physiological committee turned down his papers as essentially derivative from Whytt, Prochaska, and earlier pioneers of reflex physiology (Hall, 1861; Manuel, 1980). He never held a proper hospital appointment in a period when such consultancies were virtually essential for a place within the elite of medical London (Peterson, 1978). Denied a hospital-based practice, he set himself up in a practice which cultivated nervous disorders, trying to develop a specialty of neurology a generation before the British were ready to accept medical specialisms (Reynolds, 1896). He lived and died an aggrieved man; he wanted desperately, like Charles Bell before him, to be the William Harvey of the nervous system.

Yet, like Bell's, Hall's achievements were considerable, for, after him, it was impossible to think about neurological disorders without considering the reflex concept, even though Hall was not so successful at applying clinically his reflexology as he was at working out its experimental basis. Previous divisions of the nervous system had been into two: cerebrospinal and the ganglionic or sympathetic, or, as it was sometimes conceived, the voluntary and the automatic. Hall proposed to divide the cerebrospinal system further, into separate cerebral and spinal systems, or as he came to call the latter, the diastaltic nervous system. Diastaltic was congeneric with peristaltic, the chief characteristic of the sympathetic system; and this diastaltic system was the source of much physiological activity and the seat of many of the diseases called nervous: epilepsy, hysteria, tetanus, and other disorders characterised above all by their spasmatic qualities (Hall, 1850; see also Carter, 1855).

Hall's division of the central nervous system into two was not without its difficulties, for in emphasising the importance of his diastaltic system he made ambiguous the nature of the links between the higher, voluntary system, and the lower, reflex one. He had difficulty integrating moral and psychological factors, associated by him with the voluntary system, into the overall clinical picture of those spasmatic diseases of the diastaltic system which were his special province. But the reflex model was promptly applied to the higher centres by William Carpenter, Thomas Laycock, and others, and served as the basis of John Hughlings Jackson's mature work (see Young, 1970; Smith, 1973; Dewhurst, 1982b). Jackson and the work of Fritsch and Hitzig and, above all, David Ferrier on cerebral localisation, provided the basic neurological paradigms from which, from the 1880s, developed a structurally orientated neurology that gradually left the care of the nervous patient to the obstetricians and gynaecologists, the general physicians, and the office-based psychiatrists. Before looking briefly at this heroic, formative period in British neurology, let us glance at a work which pulls together many of the older strands, Charles Handfield-Jones's *Studies on Functional Nervous Disorders*, published in an enlarged second edition in 1870.

Handfield-Jones was a physician to St Mary's Hospital who had earned his fellowship in the Royal Society early in his career through his pathological and microscopical researches, particularly on the liver. In his later work, he sought to systematise current thinking on functional nervous disorders from the standpoint of general medicine. Three characteristics of his 800-page treatise on functional nervous disorders are worth noting. First, he refused to admit that the functional diagnosis was simply one of exclusion: a second-class disease to be invoked only when organic disease was eliminated. Rather, they were real diseases, possibly caused by molecular changes as yet undetected, but more significantly diseases in which the nervous system's vital powers were affected. Second, however, functional diseases were individual, occasionally, as in the case of hysteria, caused by a mixture of moral and physical factors, but always affecting individual patients in idiosyncratic ways. Handfield-Jones doubted if clinical medicine could ever achieve the simple cause-and-effect status of the physical sciences. Rather, the same morbid phenomena could be dependent on a variety of causes, the same causes producing a variety of effects in different individuals. For all diseases, especially functional ones, diagnosis and treatment must be individualised: "I hold that a diagnosis which goes no further than distinguishing a disease as gout, . . . erysipelas, chorea, etc., and does not attempt to appreciate the peculiar circumstances of the individual sick man, falls very short of what is needed for a rational therapy" (Handfield-Jones, 1870). Finally, it is worth noting the wide spectrum of conditions that Handfield-Jones included within the functional category: hysteria, headache, chorea, tetanus, and epilepsy had established places within the nervous camp, but malaria, Graves' disease, asthma, angina pectoris, and whooping cough are more surprising inclusions. Their presence in his book testifies to the continuing importance of periodicity and spasm in the definition of the functional disorder. That Handfield-Jones used the phrase 'cardiac neurosis' to refer to cases of angina (which he recognised frequently terminated in sudden death) reminds us that, in 1870, neurosis was still primarily a neurological, rather than a psychiatric, category.

Despite the impressive increase in neurophysiological and neuropathological knowledge between John Cooke in 1823 and Handfield-Jones in 1870, Handfield-Jones belongs more to that earlier world than he does to the neurological milieu which came just after. The years between 1870 and 1890 saw the emergence of a critical and mature neurological profession in Britain. It was located largely in the London hospitals (general hospitals like University College Hospital, King's College Hospital, and the London Hospital, but also in the specialised neurological hospitals – the National Hospital at Queen Square and the Hospital for Epilepsy and Paralysis, now the Maida Vale Hospital, both founded in the 1860s) (Holmes, 1954; Feiling, 1958). This new hospital orientation created the institutional basis for the systematic investigation of the neurological lesion.

If the flowering was in London, the roots are usually placed in the West Riding of Yorkshire, in the fruitful interchange between neurologists, psychiatrists, scientifically orientated general physicians, and pathologists in the newly created pathology laboratory of the West Riding Lunatic Asylum, presided over by the genial and long-lived psychiatrist, James Crichton-Browne. Crichton-Browne died when he was 97, and had strong views against teetotalism, maintaining that no writer had achieved much without alcohol. Although there is no systematic study of Crichton-Browne, his volumes of semi-autobiographical essays, published in his old age, are useful (Crichton-Browne, 1927, 1930).

As medical director of the asylum, he encouraged neuropathological and physiological experimentation in the asylum's laboratories; he held periodic scientific *conversazioni*, with music by the asylum band, which brought together a number of young, like-minded doctors from Leeds and further afield, including London. The group included Thomas Clifford Allbutt, who helped introduce the ophthalmoscope into British medicine (and ended his long career as Regius Professor of Medicine at Cambridge), W. B. Carpenter the physiologist and Thomas Lauder Brunton the pharmacologist, and John Hughlings Jackson and David Ferrier, both at the beginnings of their careers (Viets, 1938). The fruits of the new ethos were recorded in the *Reports of the West Riding Asylum*, edited by Crichton-Browne in six volumes between 1871 and 1876. The 79 papers published in the *Reports* detail a variety of approaches to both psychiatric and neurological disease: the use of modern diagnostic equipment such as the ophthalmoscope, sphygmograph, and laryngoscope; histological analyses of neuropsychiatric diseases; the investigation of pharmacological preparations such as hyoscyamine, amyl nitrite, and chloral hydrate; and the application of experimental physiology to the understanding of diseases of the human brain and spinal cord (Gatehouse, 1981). Two diseases predominated: epilepsy and general paralysis, both commonly seen in patients in Victorian asylums and both amenable to the neuropsychiatric approach characteristic of many of the contributors to the *Reports*. Although short-lived, the *Reports* were the natural predecessor to *Brain*, founded in 1878 by Crichton-Browne, Jackson, Ferrier, and J. C. Bucknill, long-time editor of the *Journal of Mental Science*. *Brain* was thus founded and initially edited by two psychiatrists and two neurologists (Henson, 1978). In 1886, *Brain* passed over to the control of the Neurological Society of London, founded that year under the presidency of Hughlings Jackson. The Neurological Society and its journal continued to a certain extent to represent the continued interest of psychiatrists and neurologists, but the successive meetings of the Society, and the successive volumes of *Brain*, reflect a growing alliance between neurologists and experimental physiologists such as Charles Sherrington, Edward Sharpey Schaefer, John Scott Burdon-Sanderson, Ernest Starling, and Michael Foster, all of whom were active members of what might at first blush be thought of as a purely clinical society.

Two events symbolised this increasing emphasis on diagnostic precision based whenever possible on localised, structural identification, which characterises this period of British neurology. The first was the operation, at the Hospital for Epilepsy and Paralysis, by Rickman Godlee, on a Scottish labourer named Henderson, for a brain tumour. His symptoms had been a succession of motor fits, which would now be called Jacksonian epilepsy, and the diagnosis of his tumour and its localisation had been confirmed by Jackson and Ferrier. It was performed in 1884, at which point Ferrier was under attack from antivivisectionists because of his experimental work (involving monkeys) on cerebral localisation. The operation provoked Crichton-Browne, as he revealed 50 years later, to defend Ferrier in *The Times*, under the *nom de plume* F.R.S. Two leading articles and 64 letters were published in *The Times*, debating the pros and cons of medical research which involved the sacrifice of animals. *The Times* was firm in its support of the doctors (French, 1975; see also Pearce, 1982).

The second event, two years later, was the publication of the first edition of William Gowers' *Manual of Diseases of the Nervous System*. Gowers systematised the newer knowledge of neurological localisation, neurophysiology, and pathology. His section on functional disorders, while extensive, reduced considerably from Handfield-Jones the range of diagnostic categories. Although hysteria and one of its varieties, anorexia, were fully described, he believed that the most important feature of the Weir-Mitchell treatment was the "opportunity for influencing the mind and to this the unquestionable success of the treatment is largely due" (Gowers, 1886–88, p. 938). As he pointed out, the main British exponent of the Weir-Mitchell rest cure was W. L. Playfair, an obstetrician, not a neurologist. Gowers relegated Beard's concept of neurasthenia to the neurological dustbin: it was, he insisted, a descriptive term but not a proper diagnostic category. "It is often better not to gratify the craving for nomenclature that is manifested by many patients, but rather to explain to them that to give their ailments a definite name would involve more error than truth" (p. 960).

The nervous patient of course had not disappeared by 1890 and neurologists did not entirely abandon him to the care of psychiatrists and others. In fact, recent works about two Victorian patients record the extent to which nervousness and the 'nerves' continued to play a significant role in both patient and medical perceptions of illness and major life events. The recent biography of Alice James (1848–92), the sister of William and Henry James, shows how she lived her claustrophobic life in the shadow of the two brothers, who shared much of her valetudinarianism and much of the same vocabulary concerning nervous energy and neurasthenia (Edel, 1964; Strouse, 1980; Yeazell, 1981). Alice's life, always plagued by ill-health, became, in its last decade, almost a quest for what she described as "divine cessation". She had been seen by many doctors in the United States and Britain, who had given her various functional diagnoses: hysteria, spinal neurosis, suppressed gout, neurasthenia, among others. Then, in May 1891, Sir Andrew Clark diagnosed a breast tumour. She felt "enormous relief" at his "uncompromising verdict". As she confided to her Diary:

> "To him who waits, all things come! My aspirations may have been eccentric, but I cannot complain now, that they have not been brilliantly fulfilled. Ever since I have been ill, I have longed and longed for some *palpable disease*, no matter how conventionally dreadful a label it might have, but I was always driven back to stagger alone under the monstrous mass of subjective sensations, which that sympathetic being 'the medical man' had no higher inspiration than to assure me I was personally responsible for, washing his hands of me with a graceful complacency under my very nose." (see Edel, 1964, pp. 206–207, my emphasis)

In a "beautiful and fraternal letter", William responded to the news that Alice had been given a 'real' diagnosis:

> "So far from being shocked I am, although made more compassionate, yet

(strange to say) rather relieved than shaken by the more tangible and immediate menacing source of woe. Katherine [Alice's friend and nurse] describes you as being so too; and I don't wonder. *Vague nervousness has a character of ill about it that is all its own*, and in comparison with which any organic disease has a good side." (See Strouse, 1980, p. 303, my emphasis)

Even at cost of an ominous diagnosis, Alice embraced this reality of a palpable lesion.

The second 'patient' was Virginia Woolf, whose treatment by four doctors a decade or two after Alice James's death has recently been examined by Stephen Trombley (1981). The cases cannot be easily compared: for one thing, Virginia Woolf never developed that "palpable disease" which characterised the end of Alice James's medical history. For another, her breakdowns occurred after 'dynamic psychiatry' had begun to make a little impact on British medicine (see Stone, 1985). Of the four primary physicians who treated her, three are recognisable as psychiatrists: Maurice Craig (1866–1935), T. B. Hyslop (1864–1933), and George Savage (1842–1921). One, Henry Head (1861–1940), was a neurologist. That Head seems to have adopted the most sensible attitude to Virginia Woolf's difficulties may or may not have been a direct consequence of his neurological orientation, but he believed that many 'nervous' diagnoses were but "camouflaged ignorance". "Diagnosis of the psycho-neuroses is an individual investigation; they are not diseases, but morbid activities of a personality which demand to be understood," he wrote in 1920 (see Trombley, 1981, pp. 170–171). More than his psychiatric colleagues, Head treated Virginia Woolf as a disturbed person rather than a patient. He distinguished between mental and physical diseases, and spent most of his professional time with the latter.

By World War I, most leading neurologists in Britain had followed Gowers' lead and had left the treatment of functional disorders to their psychiatric colleagues. Neurologists' professional identities were much more closely bound up with the new precision in structural localisation which the work of Jackson, Ferrier, and Gowers offered them. The reflex hammer rather than the couch, the rest cure, or the talking cure had become their symbol. In fact, what had happened during the course of the 19th century was a quiet reversal: in 1800 the nervous doctor had treated functional diseases of the nervous system, whereas psychiatrists had confidence in the underlying organic nature of the diseases which concerned them. By the century's end, the roles were reversed: nerve doctors – neurologists – were concerned primarily with organic diseases, whereas the psychiatrists had accepted the reality of primary mental disease and were the principal doctors for nervous patients.

Acknowledgements

I have benefited from the useful comments of Edwin Clarke, Chris

Lawrence, Michael Neve, and Roy Porter. Research expenses were generously met by the Wellcome Trustees.

References

ACKERKNECHT, E. H. (1968) *A Short History of Psychiatry* (trans. S. Wolff). New York: Hafner.
BLUSTEIN, B. E. (1979). A New York medical man: William Alexander Hammond, M.D. (1829–1900), neurologist. Unpublished PhD thesis, University of Pennsylvania.
——(1981) "A hollow square of psychological science": American neurologists and psychiatrists in conflict. In *Madhouses, Mad-doctors and Madmen* (ed. A. Scull), pp. 241–270. Philadelphia: University of Pennsylvania Press; London: Athlone Press.
BURTON, (1632) *Anatomy of Melancholy*. Oxford: Cripps.
CARTER, R. B. (1855) *On the Influence of Education and Training in Preventing Diseases of the Nervous System*. London: John Churchill.
CLARK, M. J. (1981) The rejection of psychological approaches to mental disorder in late nineteenth-century British psychiatry. In *Madhouses, Mad-doctors and Madmen* (ed. A. Scull), pp. 271–312. Philadelphia: University of Pennsylvania Press; London: Athlone Press.
—— (1982) The data of alienism: evolutionary neurology, physiological psychiatry, and the reconstruction of British psychiatric theory, c. 1850–c. 1900. Unpublished DPhil thesis, Oxford University.
COOKE, J. (1820–23) *A Treatise on Nervous Diseases* (2 vols). London: Longman.
CRICHTON-BROWNE, J. (1927) *Stray Leaves from a Physician's Portfolio*. London: Hodder and Stoughton.
—— (1930) *What the Doctor Thought*. London: Benn.
DEJONG, R. (1982) *A History of American Neurology*. New York: Raven Press.
DEWHURST, K. (1982a) Thomas Willis and the foundations of British neurology. In *Historical Aspects of the Neurosciences: A Festschrift for Macdonald Critchley* (eds F. C. Rose & W. F. Bynum), pp. 327–346. New York: Raven Press.
——(1982b) *Hughlings Jackson on Psychiatry*. Oxford: Sandford Publications.
EDEL, L. (ed.) (1964) *The Diary of Alice James*. New York: Dodd, Mead.
FEILING, A. (1958) *A History of The Maida Vale Hospital for Nervous Diseases*. London: Butterworth.
FISCHER-HOMBERGER, E. (1970) *Hypochondrie*. Bern: Huber.
FRENCH, R. D. (1975) *Antivivisection and Medical Science in Victorian Society*. Princeton: Princeton University Press.
GATEHOUSE, C. A. (1981) The West Riding lunatic asylum: the history of a medical research laboratory, 1871–1876. Unpublished MSc thesis, University of Manchester.
GOWERS, W. R. (1886–88) *A Manual of Diseases of the Nervous System*. London: Churchill.
HALL, C. (1861) *Memories of Marshall Hall*. London: Bentley.
HALL, M. (1850) *Synopsis of the Diastaltic Nervous System*. London: Joseph Mallett.
HANDFIELD-JONES, C. (1870) *Studies on Functional Nervous Disorders* (2nd edn). London: John Churchill.
HENSON, R. A. (1978) The editors of *Brain*. *Practitioner*, **221**, 639–644
HOLMES, G. (1954) *The National Hospital Queen Square 1860–1948*. Edinburgh: Livingstone.
HOWELLS, J. G. (ed.) (1975) *World History of Psychiatry*. New York: Brunner/Mazel.
HUNTER, R. (1973) Psychiatry and neurology: psychosyndrome or brain disease. *Proceedings of the Royal Society of Medicine*, **116**, 359–364.
—— & MACALPINE, I. (1974) *Psychiatry for the Poor. 1851 Colney Hatch Asylum, Friern Hospital 1973: A Medical and Social History*. London: Dawsons.
INGLIS, B. (1981) *The Diseases of Civilization*, London: Hodder & Stoughton.
JOHNSON, S. (1983) *A Dictionary of the English Language* (facsimile reprint). London: Times Books.
KROHN, A. (1978) *Hysteria: the Elusive Neurosis*. New York: International Universities Press.
LAWRENCE, C. J. (1984) Medicine as culture: Edinburgh and the Scottish Enlightenment. Unpublished PhD thesis, University of London

López Piñero, J. M. (1983) *Historical Origins of the Concept of Neurosis* (trans. D. Berrios). Cambridge: Cambridge University Press.

—— & Morales Meseguer, J. M. (1970) *Neurosis y psicoterapia; un estudio historico.* Madrid: Espasa.

MacDonald, M. (1981) *Mystical Bedlam.* Cambridge: Cambridge University Press.

Manuel, D. E. (1980) Marshall Hall, F.R.S. (1790–1857): a conspectus of his life and work. *Notes and Records of the Royal Society of London*, **35**, 135–166.

Meynert, T. (1884) *Psychiatrie. Klinik der Erkrankungen des Vorherhirns.* Vienna: Braumuller.

Okada, Y. (1982) 110 years of psychiatric care in Japan. In *History of Psychiatry* (ed. T. Ogawa), pp. 108–128. Tokyo: Saikon Publishing.

Pearce, J. M. S. (1982) The first attempts at removal of brain tumours. In *Historical Aspects of the Neurosciences: A Festschrift for Macdonald Critchley* (ed. F. C. Rose & W. F. Bynum), pp. 234–243. New York: Raven Press.

Peterson, M. J. (1978) *The Medical Profession in Mid-Victorian London.* Berkeley, California: University of California Press.

Porter, R. (1983) "The Rage of Party": a Glorious Revolution in English psychiatry. *Medical History*, **27**, 35–50.

—— (1985) The hunger of imagination: approaching Samuel Johnson's melancholy. In *The Anatomy of Madness, Essays in the History of Psychiatry*, vol. 1 (eds W. F. Bynum, R. Porter & M. Shepherd), pp. 63–88. London: Tavistock.

Prichard, J. C. (1835) *A Treatise on Insanity and other Disorders affecting the Mind.* London: Sherwood, Bilbert and Piper.

Reynolds, J. R. (1896) Specialism in medicine. In *Essays and Addresses*, pp. 194–207. London: Macmillan.

Romberg, M. (1853) *A Manual of the Nervous Diseases of Man* (trans. E. H. Sieveking). London: Sydenham Society.

Rosenberg, C. (1962) The place of George M. Beard in nineteenth-century psychiatry. *Bulletin of History of Medicine*, **36**, 245–259.

Rousseau, G. S. (1980) Psychology. In *The Ferment of Knowledge* (ed. G. S. Rousseau & R. Porter), pp. 143–210. Cambridge: Cambridge University Press.

Sekora, J. (1977) *Luxury: The Concept in Western Thought, Eden to Smollett.* Baltimore: Johns Hopkins University Press.

Smith, R. (1973) The background of physiological psychology in natural philosophy. *History of Science*, **11**, 75–123.

Spillane, J. D. (1981) *The Doctrine of the Nerves: Chapters in the History of Neurology.* Oxford: Oxford University Press.

Stone, M. (1985) Shellshock and the psychologists. In *The Anatomy of Madness. Essays in the History of Psychiatry*, vol. 2 (eds W. F. Bynum, R. Porter & M. Shepherd), pp. 242–271. London: Tavistock.

Strouse, J. (1980) *Alice James. A Biography.* London: Jonathan Cape.

Temkin, O. (1971) *The Falling Sickness* (2nd edn). Baltimore: Johns Hopkins University Press.

Thomson, J. (ed.) (1827) *The Works of William Cullen, M.D.* Edinburgh: William Blackwood.

—— (1859) *Account of the Life, Lectures and Writings of William Cullen, M.D.* Edinburgh: William Blackwood.

Thornton, E. M. (1976) *Hypnotism, Hysteria and Epilepsy: an Historical Synthesis.* London: Heinemann.

Trimble, M. R. (1981) *Post-Traumatic Neurosis: From Railway Spine to the Whiplash.* Chichester: John Wiley.

Trombley, S. (1981) *'All That Summer She Was Mad': Virginia Woolf and Her Doctors.* London: Junction Books.

Trotter, T. (1807) *A View of the Nervous Temperament.* London: Longman.

Viets, H. R. (1938) West Riding, 1871–1876. *Bulletin of the History of Medicine*, **6**, 477–487.

Whytt, R. (1768) *Works.* Edinburgh: J. Balfour.

Yeazell, R. B. (1981) *The Death and Letters of Alice James.* Berkeley: University of California Press.

Young, R. M. (1970) *Mind, Brain and Adaptation in the Nineteenth Century. Cerebral Localization and Its Biological Context from Gall to Ferrier.* Oxford: Clarendon Press.

9 The diary of a madman, 17th-century style: Goodwin Wharton, MP and communer with the fairy world

ROY PORTER

If there is something rather peculiar, as has been argued (Bynum & Neve, 1985), about putting the characters of fiction 'on the couch', the same must surely apply to psychoanalysing the dead. One problem, of course, is that there is almost certain to be a lack of adequately authenticated, independent information to go on. All too easily, as for instance with Freud's account of Leonardo da Vinci, aspects of the life are retrospective from the diagnosis, and the diagnosis from these presumed details in one self-reinforcing, circular act of myth making. But a more perplexing conceptual issue arises as well, the question of historical and cultural relativism. The norms of rational thought and the boundaries of insane behaviour have shifted enormously down the centuries. So do we use yesterday's criteria or today's if we are to go about arguing that historical personages were insane, were suffering from this neurotic condition or had that psychosis? It is one thing to say that John Perceval was mad, if all we mean by that is that his contemporaries thought him so (and that he, for whatever reason, came to accept the label). But it is a far different matter to judge the self-mortifying saints of the Christian calendar disturbed merely because their values and priorities appear bizarre or morbid to our sensibilities. The reader of the pages of the *Psychohistory Review* or the *Journal of Psychohistory* may be pardoned if he takes away the Swiftian conclusion that the history of mankind has been a history of the mad. When Freud examined the case of Christoph Haizmann, the 17th-century German painter who sold himself to the Devil, he argued it was the "case-history of a neurotic" (Freud, 1923). The Devil was a father substitute, inferred Freud, Haizmann himself a homosexual. In their subsequent account of Haizmann, Macalpine & Hunter (1956) showed how unwarranted and extravagant much of Freud's reading was, precisely because he insisted on treating the common culture of Christendom (e.g. belief in diabolical possession) as personal neurotic symptoms. Yet they titled their own account *Schizophrenia 1677*.

The solution to these dilemmas is not to abandon attempts to probe the individual and collective psychopathologies of the past. Neither does it lie in any magic formula which instantly resolves the discrepancies between the relativism of history and scientific method. Critical awareness of the claims of both approaches at least promises to show a path through the thickets, and further collaboration between psychiatrists and historians, as in the case of Hill and Shepherd's exemplary 'historico-psychiatric study' of the 17th-century Puritan preacher and prophet, Arise Evans, would surely prove fruitful (Hill & Shepherd, 1976).

In this paper, I examine another 17th-century figure, Goodwin Wharton, a man perhaps as familiar as a public figure as Arise Evans, yet one with an extraordinary private and mental life, unknown to his contemporaries. He is clearly someone whom contemporaries (had they known), no less than today's psychiatrists, might have termed mentally aberrant. As a historian, however, I offer no clinical analysis (although neither do I seek to preclude it). Rather I shall attempt an account of his mental state and shall offer some final suggestions as to how Wharton's life might be interpreted within a properly historical history of psychiatry.

In the eyes of the late 17th-century public, Goodwin Wharton seemed an ordinary enough middle-weight politician, enjoying a measure of position, power and prestige commensurate with being the younger son of a noble, land-owning family. Certainly he never commanded the moral stature of his father, Philip, Lord Wharton, often styled 'the good', that austere, unwavering paragon of dissenting and whiggish righteousness (Dale, 1906; Jones, 1967). Neither could he match his elder brother Tom as a man of the world and leader of men. Engrossed equally with his horses, whores and politics, 'honest Tom' rose to become a key figure in the whig Junta which ruled England in the 1690s, and not least penned the words of the anti-Jacobite hit-song, Lilliburlero, which was said to have whistled King James II out of three kingdoms. Nor even did Goodwin cut a dash like his two younger brothers, William, wit and gallant, who was slain in a duel, or Henry, soldier-politician, who died young campaigning in Ireland.

Yet Goodwin was no nonentity (Clark, 1984). Sitting as an MP from 1690 to his death in 1704, he was a vocal supporter of William III's belligerent anti-French, anti-Catholic foreign policy, an energetic champion of whig principles, and a ferret of Jacobite plotters. Appointed first a lieutenant colonel and then a Lord of the Admiralty, he saw active service in the Channel before a stroke suffered in 1698 put a premature end to his military career and surely hastened his death. By then he was a substantial squire. Inheriting estates in Buckinghamshire on his father's death, he had risen to become a JP and Knight of the Shire. Though never marrying, he kept a society mistress, Lady Elizabeth Gerard, in his later years, and an illegitimate son, Hezekiah Knowles, came to light in his will (an army commission was purchased for him). All in all, his public profile looked conventional enough.

Those who knew Goodwin at closer quarters may have found him a man of somewhat stranger mettle. From his 20s he fancied himself as a projector and entrepreneur. He invented a new patent fire-engine, pursued alchemical experiments, aiming to find what he called "the powder of projection", and sank a fortune, some his, some his father's, some other people's, in the wreck-salvaging business, diving for doubloons trapped in sunken Armada galleons. And his family clearly found him hard to cope with. Secretive, suspicious and brooding, he was for long stretches alienated from his father, step-mother and elder brother, family tensions being exacerbated by his mounting debts and his failure to hook an heiress to marry.

Yet who even suspected that behind this regular enough exterior lay a truly extraordinary inner self? – a self shared only with one other human being, although a wide range of spirits, demons and angels grew to know it intimately. We know, however, for we are fortunate to possess a window onto his soul, since from 1686 onwards he penned a monumental autobiography, which still sits, all half million words of it, in two folio volumes in the British Library (Wharton, undated). Written in a microscopic hand, its margins festooned with alchemical, astrological and occult symbols, Wharton's autobiography stands alongside John Perceval's *Narrative of the Treatment Experienced by a Gentleman During a State of Mental Derangement* (1838–40) or Daniel Schreber's *Denkwürdigkeiten eines Nervenkranken* (1903) as a testament of a mind enmeshed in the thickets of delusion. Unlike Perceval and Schreber, however, who wrote to come to grips with their illness or to vindicate their sanity, Wharton never even entertained the thought that he might be mad. Rather, he wrote his memoirs for the edification of his son Peregrine, painting his own life as "full of such unusual and unhappy circumstances", and suggesting how his son should learn from it (Wharton, i: 1). Yet in all likelihood no such person as Peregrine ever existed.

In Wharton's self-portrait, the conventional and the abnormal jolt against each other right from the beginning. He sets out by informing the reader, his phantom son, that he will record little of his childhood, since it was so ordinary. Yet from the opening page, he is explaining how he became an introspective youth, "secretly inclined", "addicted to reading and writing", given over to "musings and prayings", and aspiring towards personal communion with the angels (Wharton, i: 1). Even so, women always found him irresistible (he explains to Peregrine), panting suitors queued up; one even died for love of him; yet he rejected them all, saving himself for better things: beware the temptations of siren seductresses, he warns his son.

And not least, cataloguing the moils and toils that beset him, his family wronged him; he suffered endless "injuries" and was treated "like a slave", coming under their "remedilesse lash" (Wharton, i: 2). His own piety and purity notwithstanding, his relatives shamelessly cheated, exploited and abused him. His father, a man, according to Kent Clark, Goodwin's recent biographer, "easier to honour than to obey, easier to obey than to love, and easier to love than to please", bullied him into surrendering to his favourite elder brother the estate, Wooburn, bequeathed him by his mother (Clark, 1984: 3). His step-mother then (he alleged) tried to lure him into bed, and when be rebuffed her, she wreaked revenge by turning his father against him. His sister-in-law, Tom's wife, Anne, then seduced him and afterwards rejected him in wanton cruelty. Later still, after her death, Tom remarried and finally produced an heir, thus robbing Goodwin of his expectations of inheriting the family property. "Neither loved or respected at home", he grew up "under a heavy load of groans" (Wharton, i: 8).

Early manhood saw things get no better. So disastrous were the financial losses on his diving and alchemical ventures, that in effect he had to go into hiding from his creditors, and soon he had to lie low politically as well. Briefly sitting in the Commons at the height of the Exclusionist Crisis in 1680, Wharton delivered an extraordinary harangue against Charles II's brother, James, then heir to the throne, and spent the next years in dread of reprisal. Through these dark times, all he had to fall back upon was an unshakable assurance of his own virtue and of God's righteousness. The early pages of the autobiography bear eloquent witness to Wharton's pervasive conviction of "divine deliverance" and "particular providence" (Wharton i: 8). In his teens he had been miraculously saved from drowning at sea, and he shortly began seeing God in dreams and bearing a divine voice which, countering "afflictions outward" gave him "spiritual directions", "inwardly" (Wharton 1: 3). Soon he found himself entrusted with supernatural powers. A friend fell sick and was at death's door; Wharton prayed, the friend recovered. A blaggard maliciously challenged him to a duel. Wharton prayed; his foe fell mortally sick. No wonder from an early age he grew to nurture the conviction of greatness thrust upon him; as he put it, God would make him "greater in his service than either Moses or Aaron" (Wharton, i: 10).

But how? This gradually became clearer once in 1683, seeking someone to put him in touch with the angels, Wharton was directed to a certain Mary Parish, a London healer, a cunning woman and medium – some would call her a witch. The first service Mary Parish actually performed for him, however, was to make him a play piece, a gambling charm, to guarantee that he would always win at the tables. It did not work, in fact, but in the course of making it, testing it, and probing its failure, Mary Parish began spinning out her life-story to him, and, rather like Sheherazade, she was to weave a narrative of fact, fiction, romance, delusion or what you will, which captivated Wharton for the next 20 years. A Catholic in her early 50s, she had been married three times, and vilely abused by each of her husbands; she had had scores of children – 14 had died in the Plague of 1665 alone; she had been in and out of debtors' prisons. Yet she was a profound adept in alchemy, expert in tracking buried treasure, and, above all, she was in tune with spirits, below and above. Through her, Wharton saw how he could realise his frustrated drive for wealth, power and holiness (Wharton, i: 18f.).

Mary Parish was familiar with the fairies. In better days, she had personally descended into their lowland kingdom (which was monarchical in government and papist in religion) and became party to the secrets of the 'Lowlanders', creatures about half human size, combining some human attributes (they were mortal, although enjoying extreme longevity) and some supernatural (they had the power to fly, pass through walls, and make themselves invisible by popping a magic pea into their mouth). Although now, following a tragic contretemps, excluded from their realms, Mary Parish still kept track of their dealings, through the services of spiritual go-betweens, such as George Whitmore, the ghost of an executed highwayman, Mr Ahab, the spirit of a Jewish alchemist, and a friendly fairy, Father Friar.

Wharton, who could neither hear nor see these intermediaries, ached to meet the fairies; all the more so because Mary Parish assured him that through the Lowlanders' good offices, they would locate and liberate untold stores of buried treasure. Moreover, Mary soon hinted, Penelope, the Queen of the Fairies, had taken quite a fancy to him.

So a meeting was arranged. Mary was informed by the spirit George that the Queen would pay Wharton a nocturnal call in his chamber; he must wait up in bed for her. To his chagrin, however, the first couple of rendez-vous proved abortive: on one occasion, the Queen fell sick, on another the King did. At last she did get through, only to find that this time Wharton had fallen asleep, and, with regal courtesy, she declined to wake him and stole away unnoticed (Wharton, i: 78–98).

So the plans changed. Mary Parish and Wharton, shadowed by George as scout, would visit the fairy kingdom. The main entrance to this was on Hounslow Heath, at a spot alas hidden today under one of Heathrow's runways. It was accessible to humans only for a few minutes at new moon. They journeyed down at new moon in May 1683, only to be told the meeting was off; the Queen was sick. Down they came again in June, but now the King was ill again. Once more they rode down in July, but now the encounter had to be abandoned because the King, an old debauchee named Byron, had just expired. Month after month they travelled down; month after month the best laid plans were frustrated by last-minute hitches – the weather, unforeseen state visits, Mary's illnesses, and not least, the Queen's menstrual periods, for the Lowlanders observed strict Mosaic purity laws, requiring ritual purification during menstruation to prevent women defiling their menfolk.

Yet it is an ill wind that blows nobody good, and in the course of these agonising trips, Mary Parish and Wharton, aided by trusty spirits (still invisible to Wharton) located priceless treasure hoards at adjacent sites, beneath a clump of trees on Hounslow Heath, in a haunted house nearby (which they subsequently rented), and at Northend in Buckinghamshire, near where Mary had grown up. These riches they set about recovering through spells and rituals designed to make the earth disgorge its secrets. Once again, however, easier said, easier planned, than done. Sharp frosts,

curious wayfarers, a rampaging cow – all these successively wrecked operations at the crucial moment; not least it transpired that evil spirits were
guarding the hoards, which in turn would require exacting and costly
exorcism. Meanwhile, other projects, especially alchemical experiments
designed to transform mercury into gold, were put in motion, supported by
the capital of that inveterate opportunist plotter Major John Wildman
(Ashley, 1947).

In the course of all this, the footing of the relationship changed, turning
from business to friendship, and then to deep emotional partnership; finally
it became sexual. Although now in her 50s, Mary Parish conceived immediately at their first love-making, the first of 106 conceptions she enjoyed
by Wharton right up to the time of her death, at the age of 72. A deep and
enduring bond had been struck. In each others' eyes, and also in God's (so
the spirits told Mary) they were truly man and wife, although they never
went through a legal marriage ceremony, which would have constituted an
abominable misalliance in the eyes of the Whartons.

Their union was only occasionally threatened by the fact that, after her
husband's death, Queen Penelope herself vowed to marry Wharton, make
him her King, and have him sire an heir; she even used Mary as her
matchmaker. This sign of fairy favour cannot have surprised Wharton, for
he knew that all women fell at his feet. But there was a sound scientific
reason too for the Queen's choice. The Lowlanders were cold creatures.
Although long lived, they were sluggish breeders. Penelope was childless,
her kingdom heirless. Naturally she would grab the opportunity to mate
with a lusty Uplander, for they were far more potent (Wharton, i: 99f.).

Indeed, so hot was Penelope's passion that she could not wait for their
nuptuals. She fell into the habit of slipping invisibly into Wharton's
chamber as he lay asleep, riding him through the night, and hastening away
before cock-crow. Wharton had no direct awareness of this succubus experience, this rape, yet he now found himself unaccountably aching and
exhausted when he awoke in the morning. It took the spirit George and
Mary Parish to reveal to him the cause of his symptoms; indeed so great had
been Penelope's predatory ecstacy, that she drew in the very marrow from
his bones and almost "sucked my life and nature from me" (Wharton, i:
95).

Penelope was probably wise to take her chances when she could, because
each time she travelled up in state to London finally to make the acquaintance of her husband-to-be on a lawful occasion, yet more obstacles super-
vened. Not least, furious machinations arose from rival suitors for her hand,
such as the fairy Duke of Hungary, and from her double-dealing younger
sister, Ursula (Ursula was only 50, whereas the Queen was 350), who had
developed an itch for Wharton herself. On one occasion, Queen Penelope
lodged underground at Moorfields (just a stone's throw from Bethlem!) to
be near the seat of the fairy Pope, who would marry the royal pair, only to
find that all the tunnel exits had been mined by her enemy, the Duke of

Hungary. The ensuing damage took months to repair, and spelt still more interminable delays. At another time, the royal carriage was involved in a street accident with a careless carter at Knightsbridge; numbed with shock, she slipped into a tavern for a soothing drink; became fuddled, took a nap, awoke menstruating, and headed back to Hounslow. Wharton followed all this aghast, as the spirit George told it to Mary and Mary relayed it to him. Beside himself with frustration, Wharton urged pursuit; he would overtake and abduct her. But as George reminded him, such desperate measures would be useless; by now Penelope had popped her magic pea in her mouth, and rendered herself invisible.

Such "troubles and delays" stretched Wharton to breaking point; so near and yet so far. Months of heroic effort and expenditure had yielded not a penny of treasure nor even his promised wife. "Being thus disappointed in every thing", small wonder he exploded occasionally in fits of rage, cursing the feckless fairies for their infidelities – a rage, as Mary sternly rebuked him, which must prove totally counter-productive, for it drove the spirits away, a reminder which brought Wharton contritely to heel (Wharton, i: 102).

The nub of Wharton's problem was that, despite endless fairy promises, no spirit had yet either appeared or spoken directly to him. George for instance conducted his dealings with Mary alone, in a separate room; at best Wharton caught fragmentary and garbled snatches of their conversations. When distant from Mary, as when visiting his father, cap in hand to wheedle further loans, Wharton felt totally cut off from the spirit powers which should be his lifeline.

It was fortunate then, and in the nick of time, that Mary Parish started being visited not just by exasperating fairies but by the angels, unambiguous signs of divine favour. The fairies were alluring, but who could trust a race who in immorality and skulduggery were a fit match for the Uplands court of the Merrie Monarch himself? Angels by contrast were God's servants, regulars in the divine battle against Anti-Christ depicted by Wharton's Protestant indoctrination. From his childhood Wharton had been reaching out to meet the angels (Wharton, i: 227f.).

To the end of his days, Wharton never directly encountered the Lowlanders, but the advent of the angels did indeed herald better things. Soon angelic marks of heavenly blessing began to appear. Of course, Wharton did not at first experience these personally; he still relied on Mary's witness:

> "She, being awake in the night (but I was asleep), [his autobiography records] sees a great light round my head, and a sort of white fire as it were on the bed; and then heard these words spoke loud and intelligibly:
>   'Be patient Wharton, and a croune
>   Thou shalt weare with great renoune'." (Wharton, i: 204)

Before long, promises were flowing thick and fast from the angels, Gabriel, Uriel, and Ahab, and sure enough Goodwin himself began to have first-hand experiences, at first in dreams, and then awake, hearing sonorous noises, seeing bright and flashing lights, and finally receiving personal messages. Typically these came to him as he lay in bed, half asleep; often they were preceded by the ringing of a bell somewhere outside his room, and a voice would come from beyond his door. Sadly the syllables themselves were frequently hard to distinguish (all he could pick up of one message was "I have no more to say now"), and Wharton typically had to consult Mary Parish who would offer him, via her spirit interlocutor, a full transcript and elucidation.

Unlike many of his contemporaries when they heard disembodied voices, Wharton did not harbour sharp suspicions that they were surely the suggestion of the Devil, although he certainly did not doubt the power of His Satanic Majesty to thwart his treasure-hunting and matrimonial plans (Walker, 1981). Neither did it occur to him that the lights and voices might be part of elaborate 'theatricals' staged for his benefit by Mary Parish. That is why, on the occasions that such suspicions crossed his mind, they proved so devastating. One day, kneeling at prayer in the candle-light and hearing himself addressed by Gabriel from somewhere over his shoulder, he glanced up and glimpsed Mary's lips moving to the words (Wharton, i: 164). Shattered, he accused her of fabricating the divine message. Her response was outrage: Wharton's distrust was offensive to the angel. Riddled with guilt, he begged forgiveness. There was now, he wrote, "no remedie but prayer" (Wharton, i: 169).

Episodes such as this must have made Wharton trebly grateful that in time he ceased to be dependent upon such outer voices speaking from beyond his door. Eventually, he began to be able to pick up an inner voice as well. For a spell, he regularly enjoyed an intense experience of divine indwelling. Angels would instruct him to lie expectant on his bed at a stipulated hour, primed to receive divine communications. These would generally come in the form of doggerel rhymes, verse being the elevated prophetic tongue. And, as he comforted himself, there was no risk of mistaking mere imagination or satanic suggestion for the true divine inner voice, for the heavenly revelations were "all infallible" (Wharton, i: 157).

Now it was – in the dark days of James II's tyranny, about the time of Monmouth's rebellion, in which Wharton's partner, Major Wildman, was implicated, and when his brothers fell under deep suspicion, his father found it prudent to travel abroad for his health, and Goodwin himself was checked out by government spies – that his destiny as the Lord's anointed came gradually to be unfolded. Already he had been awarded by Queen Penelope the crown of King of the Lowlanders. Now God revealed his human calling: he would be made priest, then prophet, then saviour. "You, my son, should be King of Kings, and Solar King of the world"; "I should see the Lord in Glory," glossed Wharton, "I should save much people" (Wharton, i: 165).

From time to time tokens of his translation started to appear around the little altar Mary Parish had fitted out in her room: a sceptre, a scroll, an oak branch as a symbol of his strength, a heart-shaped relic the size of a walnut which bled real blood. Angelic voices told him he had been renamed Hezekia (Mary became Lucretia), that he would be "such a king, as was never before nor since Christ", and that his glory would be to rebuild the walls of Jerusalem. And the godly messages kept up their doggerel promises of glory just around the corner:

> "Hezekia thou art my true and well beloved son
> On wednesday next this business shall be done
> And so to thee it shall be said
> That thou no more shall be dismaid
> Without thy woman thou shalt surely know
> The things above, and things below." (Wharton, i: 214)

Yet these same voices also warned him of necessary delays while the rituals of his purification were completed. God's pledge to him had been the delivery of a "first convenant"; at the promulgation of the second, God's business would reach perfection.

Divine trials were no problem to Wharton. After all, he had had much fairy prevarication to bear, and he knew the tribulations that Abraham, Moses and Job had undergone for the Lord. When the angels started mentioning martyrdom, that was a cross he was only too pleased to bear, now that he had been proclaimed God's "only son" (Wharton, i: 197).

Thus fortified, new horizons of prosperity opened out before him. The prospects of growing rich beyond the dreams of avarice brightened as Mary Parish managed to run across the spirit of Cardinal Wolsey, who had his fingers on fabulous buried treasure stashed away in the cellars of various London houses (mainly in pubs, which unfortunately resulted in her frequently returning home much the worse for brandy). In principle, the Cardinal was happy to release the hoards, although in practice he proved fractious and petulent; the predictable delays ensued, and when some of the wealth was at last transferred to the Wharton household, it arrived in trunks securely padlocked under strict instructions not to be opened till spiritual command (Wharton, i: 278f.).

Moreover, Wharton's own future now seemed about to blossom forth, in directions personal, sexual and imperial. To a prophet king, attending partriarchally to the need to populate his kingdom with blessed stock, lying only with Mary Parish could hardly suffice. He may have been perturbed by his lack of visible offspring by her. It was all very well that she conceived regularly, often having multiple conceptions (at one time she was carrying 38 of his children), but she commonly lost them, or they died just after birth, and in any case he was never allowed to see them, not even Peregrine, the dedicatee of the autobiography. He may also have been worried for his health. For Mary did not come to lie with him every night, and he found that a few days' enforced abstinence resulted in the discomfort of "an unimaginable quantity of seed". To solve these problems, he launched himself upon brief encounters: he bedded Mary's friend, Mrs Wilder (or rather she bedded him, since she leapt upon him even before he had finished propositioning her) and then on a trip to Bath his landlady too (and she too, like the original Wife of Bath, was beside herself with desire for him) (Wharton, i: 198). But both episodes left him poxed, led to anguished scenes with the outraged Mary, and resulted in an alienation from her which cut Wharton to the quick, and from which reconciliation was slow (Wharton, ii: 31f.).

Racked by sexual torments, he prayed for heavenly guidance. The divine answer came back loud and clear with instructions even conveniently numerically tabulated:

"1. Swear not at all"
"2. Fuck (every weeke) where you used to do,"
 here Wharton interjects, "at this broad word (as we call it) my thought stuck, as if I had not rightly understood it; upon which, it was repeated and then was added" –
"3. That is, give to her her due"
 and then (as Wharton puts it) "thinking suddenly on the unruly rising of the flesh, it was added"
"4. Throw water on yourself, so shall the Lord prosper you."

Pondering the heavenly precepts, or rather the divine vernacular, Wharton explained that on reflection God's use of the broad expression seemed proper: "the God of nature, I hope, may be allowed to speake plainly of all things whatever . . . I hope I need not plead for God further; who dare accuse or censure him?" (Wharton, i: 292).

Goodwin's problem remained to decide where exactly his service was due. Clearly with Mary, and surely also with Queen Penelope, his other lawful, Lowland wife, if ever he met her. But also, surely, with those other great ladies spiritual voices told him it was his mission to lie with as king of kings. First there was James II's spouse, Mary of Modena, who, providentially, was childless like Penelope. Obviously God intended Wharton to give her an heir, at which point, he presumed, James II would abdicate out of gratitude, Wharton would replace him, and he would reconvert the court to Protestantism. When Mary ignored his advances, like Malvolio he took it as a come-on, as a sign of just how smitten she was (Wharton, ii: 65f.).

Of course, James speedily fell (God's punishment for his neglect of Wharton's deserts), to be succeeded by William of Orange. Wharton soon discovered that his wife, Queen Mary, was also providentially infatuated with him; he paid her court, even vouchsafing her copies of his prophetic writings. When she fell desperately ill with smallpox, he seized his chance. Commandeering spiritual aid, he would cure her, and melting with gratitude she would admit him. Unaccountably, however, she died. But when William himself perished soon after (a further divine blow, to smite him for his failure to advance Wharton), Goodwin knew his day at last had come: for while yet a princess, Anne, now Queen Anne, had long been eying him up. Once more, death intervened, although this time it was Wharton's (Wharton, ii: 105f.).

Yet as the saga of Wharton's amours unfolded, his life had been undergoing great changes. The Protestant wind that in 1688 won William of Orange the English crown also blew Wharton out of hiding, onto the public stage. Up to his 37th year, he had lived under a cloud, in debt and obscurity, focusing his energies on the intensest of inner lives, on Paradise within. Now, as part of the Wharton dynasty, he was expected to play his part in public affairs. His family secured him a Commons seat in 1690, and from then on his life became one of Parliamentary sittings, manoeuvrings, committee work, vetting finances, and organising military supplies – all these engrossing more of his attention over his remaining 15 years.

Wharton's autobiography gives no sign whatever that he regarded his spiritual life as hermetically sealed from his public duties. Far from it: they were utterly intertwined. After all, his divine mission was to become an earthly power, and initially at least, he automatically expected fairy help and divine prompting when about to embark upon his Commons speeches (in fact, no voices came, and their silence schooled him to fall back upon his own rhetorical resources, at which he proved not unsuccessful). Very gradually, however, Wharton seems to have looked less to communications from the Lowlanders and spirits. Perhaps he grew disenchanted. Delays were one thing, blunders another. Thus during the siege of Mons in 1691, Wharton, like many others, laid a bet on the outcome. It was odds on that Mons would fall to the French. But the angels told him it would hold out. Wharton staked his £100. Not only, however, did Mons fall, but Wharton discovered it had already capitulated when the angels slipped him their tip. Whatever had happened? He quizzed George and Mary but answer came there none. By this time, however, Wharton had grown stoical about these matters.

Indeed, during his last decade, the intensity of his involvement with the spirit world probably diminished (Wharton, ii: 162f.). He must have felt less of a fugitive. He got a taste at least of power; on the death of his father in 1696 he had stopped being hounded by creditors; and from 1695 he got himself a society mistress, Lady Elizabeth Gerard, rich, handsome, respectable. The springs of anxiety which had caused his cup of troubles to overflow dried up. His father's death removed a source of constant censure; the deaths of Henry and William took away rival siblings, the death of his step-mother removed a temptress and a predator. Mary Parish remained, steady as a rock. She, at least, kept communing with the fairies to the end of her days, kept up the fruitless treasure hunt. When she died, Wharton gave her a fine burial at St Giles-in-the-Fields, and mourned "the best of women". But, contrary to all her promises, she did not appear to him translated into a spirit, and so Wharton's spiritual life dried up. The span from her death to his own occupies only one page out of 500 in the autobiography.

What is the historian of psychiatry to make of all this – of all the thousands of hours Wharton and Mary spent haggling with the Lowlanders or straining for angelic voices? What is the meaning of the Byzantine politickings in the smoke-filled Lowlander corridors of power which occupy over 100 000 words in Wharton's text and who knows how many more pages of notes he later destroyed? How are we to interpret the bizarre Lear-like scenes on Hounslow Heath, with a nobleman's son and his hag-like medium addressing clumps of trees, strewing them with parchments and sprigs of witch-hazel, and commanding the ground to open? How do we understand the autobiographer whose voices assured him that he was irresistible to women and called to be the saviour of men?

One approach is to refuse to enter into the business of interpretation altogether. This is the line adopted by Clark, whose admirably researched biography of Wharton reads simply as a paraphrase of his diary. Clark chooses to avoid any discussion of what was objectively real, and what fantasy, in the lives of Wharton and Mary Parish; hence the question of Wharton's mental state is never even broached (Clark, 1984).

Another approach, of course, would be to hazard a diagnosis. It is easy to see how the evidence of Wharton's diary would give plenty of clues for the intrepid psychoanalyst of Freudian, Jungian, or any other persuasion. The great danger in this tack, however, is that it risks failing to distinguish between those aspects of Wharton's mind and life which may genuinely have been part and parcel of a personal psychopathology, and those which are essentially expressions of the *Zeitgeist*. For, as a cultural historian of early modern times might insist, so many of his so-called crazy symptoms, his absorption in alchemy, in demons, in spiritual agency, when set within the religious, scientific and personal belief systems of the Renaissance and the Reformation, appear utterly normal, rational, even orthodox (Thomas, 1971). There was nothing odd for instance for a 17th-century Christian to expect direct personal revelation; what would have been abnormal, indeed spiritually terrifying, was if God never communicated His Will. Similarly, Mary Parish's preoccupation with fairies and treasure might *prima facie* seem part of her psychopathology. But that would be highly anachronistic. After all, she had absorbed those beliefs from her grandfather and uncle and their own cultural milieu (Spufford, 1981). Searching for treasure made sense in the pre-bank era when people, squirrel-like, commonly buried their valuables for safety.

There is merit in all these approaches, although applied exclusively or dogmatically they end up cutting the Gordian knot. Instead, however, of following any of them through now, I wish to approach the problem of interpreting Wharton by another avenue. Building upon some suggestions made in Peter Barham's *Schizophrenia and Human Value* (1984), I propose to draw attention to narrative, story telling, as one clue to the turmoils of Wharton's psyche, to how he battled to turn the dislocations and contradictions of his experience into coherent meaning. After all, the document by which we know Wharton is his story, told to his (phantom?) son, both as vindication of himself and as his implicit commentary on what fathers, sons, and their communications should be. Wharton's story in turn also incorporates God's story for Wharton, told by the angels, and, above all, Mary Parish's stories, of her own life and of Wharton in spirit land, that spell of words she wove round him for 20 years.

Wharton's text thus witnesses a fertile coupling of stories which, once united, then spawned a superabundant progeny of still further conceptions. Both Wharton and Mary Parish came to their relationship already armed with copious stories to tell: Wharton a story of how he was persecuted by men, and women, but called upon by God; Mary Parish as a Columbus back from the new-found fairy land, uniquely apprised of occult secrets. Yet despite their separate stories of boundless power, both were derelict and bankrupt when they met. Their stories did not add up. They needed each other's myths. For Wharton, Mary's drama of spiritual secrets promised him the means whereby his sense of manifest destiny could be realised. For Mary Parish, Wharton was the protégé she could midwife, a hero to play the lead role in all her future enactments. For Mary to cast Wharton in the star part might, at one level, be fraught with perilous ambiguity for herself, since his paths to glory would lead but to her grave. Did she not foretell she was to sacrifice herself in finding him his queen? Angels told her she would die once he attained his majesty. Yet, crucially, these were roles in a script of which she clearly remained the leading author. Indeed, even once Wharton started hearing voices in his own right, their messages remained remarkably faithful to the Gospel according to Mary, being (one might say) ghost-written by her.

Put another way, we might say that Wharton's and Mary Parish's stories became whirled together in the psychodynamics of a *folie à deux* vortex; yet this world of their own was one in which she exercised sway. Doubtless she possessed charisma, and whether or not she was consciously manipulative, she certainly succeeded in stage-managing Wharton. For it was her story of their pilgrim's progress through a spiritual maze that set the stage on which his story, in which he starred as saviour-cum-ladykiller, could be enacted. We need not suggest that her imaginative world was a crude fiction, cynically concocted to captivate Wharton: after all, she had communed with the fairies ever since infancy. But she was superbly adroit at managing Goodwin's expectations, providing just the right measures of encouragement and disappointment, and intuitively grasping what every seductress or teller of tall stories knows, that spinning it out is of the essence; in delay lay her salvation. And, how much by design it is impossible to say, the backdrop she conjured up, with fairy conspiracies at court, its vampish harpies, its bright promises, its dashed hopes, conjured an environment of the imagination which helped Wharton orient his way through the world around him. Housed within Mary Parish's story world, Wharton's crazy obsessions assumed their rightful logic and rationality. His Parish was all the world.

Of course, Wharton had to be willing to knuckle under in his role, living out a scenario in which the hero's halo continually dissolved into a crown of thorns; but that was easy. Suckled in the Protestant culture of *Paradise Lost*, he instinctively believed that the pilgrim's progress was beset with briars.

In any case, Wharton clearly was a little boy lost waiting to be taken in hand, helpless, dependent, most comfortably living in the eyes of others, except that he could never be good enough for his father, never swaggering enough for his brothers. At last in Mary Parish's fairyland epic, he found himself playing a role which boasted his identity, and externalised conflict firmly onto forces outside.

Wharton must have found something very safe in Mary: twice his age, gross, plain, battered by life, boozy, in need of his money. Did he here find his long lost mother? His own had died when he was five; as in all fairy stories, his step-mother had wanted to gobble him up, and he had been symbolically punished by being sent away from her at puberty. At last in Mary Parish he had someone who would really mother him with fairy stories. A trite suggestion, perhaps; yet surely in her he found a woman who was not sexually threatening, unlike all the other society ladies who fascinated him with their illicit, even incestuous desires, and then (literally or metaphorically) unmanned him. When for instance he records that he went to bed with his sister-in-law, Anne, he suffered premature ejaculation, which he subsequently saw as a divine let-off. By contrast, safe with Mary, he could exult in a sexual power which he craved. There is a brutality about his description of his first bedding of her. "It is hard for a woman to resist where she loves," he writes, going on to describe how she first fell "in my power," and then came "yet farther within my power," and finally "absolutely in my power" (Wharton, i: 87).

In the light of all this it is tempting to read Wharton as a Puritan hypocrit or as a kind of dummy run for Lemuel Gulliver, worthy target of all the contempt Swift reserves for his hero. Like Gulliver, Wharton is a gull, credulous, self-deceiving – how can he have believed in Mary Parish's 106 conceptions, or have penned an autobiography for a son he had never seen? Also like Gulliver, he can be cruel and self-absorbed. Yet such a verdict would be too harsh. Wharton and Mary were more like two castaways who, by clinging to each other, almost drowned, but probably ended up by keeping each other afloat.

This *folie à deux* was perhaps their kind of psychotherapeutic bonding, built on mutual need (after all, feminist historians have invited us to view the witch or cunning woman as a sort of proto-psychotherapist, destined to be snuffed out by the rise of the professional male psychiatric doctor). The pairing clearly helped Mary Parish to survive. After her catastrophes with three previous husbands, her life with Wharton must have been secure. But what did she do for Wharton? Should we congratulate her for entering sympathetically into his delusions – something few doctors would have done? Or do we conclude that her fairy Never-Never Land only delayed his emergence from infantile fantasy, proving yet another case of analysis interminable, terminated in fact only by death?

Yet to speak in these terms about the couple, presenting them as a psychotherapeutic duo, leaves too much out. Above all, it neglects their love. On a trip to Bath to seek sexual adventure, Wharton heard a voice telling him that Mary was dead. Clearly part of him wanted his liberty. But soon his grief became almost insupportable; he was lost. In fact Mary was not dead, and reconciliation proved slow and painful; but when it was achieved Mary reported that she never saw so much joy among the angels.

So was Goodwin Wharton then mad? If his case had come before a 19th-century psychiatrist, the answer would have been plain; diagnosed religiously insane or monomaniacal, he may well have ended up in Tice-hurst swapping stories with John Perceval. Even in his own times, his contemporary doctor and psychological philosopher, John Locke, would also probably have pronounced him mad, suffering from (mis)association of ideas, although, not being a public danger, he would not have had him locked up.

Deciding whether Wharton was mad, however, should be a lesser priority for the history of psychiatry. More urgent, more intriguing, is the task of exploring where the boundaries between sanity and insanity were perceived in any particular age, how they shifted over time, so that one age's cognitive coherence might prove another's cognitive disturbance. We must explore how psychiatrists have treated the mad, or, to put it more tendentiously, how psychiatry and society have colluded in what has been called the manufacture of madness (Szasz, 1972). But that enterprise will proceed in a vacuum, unless we can also get inside the minds of the mad themselves. This is no easy task, for comparatively few of the insane have left us their testaments, although, as Peterson has shown, far more such accounts survive than we commonly assume (Peterson, 1982). Even the most famous, such as Perceval's *Narrative*, have never been interpreted carefully using the full richness of hermeneutic techniques. Marvellous sources, such as Goodwin Wharton's autobiography, the surface of which I have barely skimmed, lie almost untapped, and yet offer piercing insights into facets of the history of mental disturbance utterly neglected: in Wharton's case, the cultural dynamics of *folie à deux*. Nowadays, in many fields, doing history from below is in favour and is casting the familiar in a new light. Exploring the development of psychiatry from the viewpoint of the disturbed, would, I suggest, enormously enlarge our understanding of the history of mental illness (Porter 1985*a*, *b*).

References

ASHLEY, M. (1947) *John Wildman, Plotter and Postmaster*. London: Jonathan Cape.

BARHAM, P. (1984) *Schizophrenia and Human Value*. Oxford: Basil Blackwell.

BYNUM, W. F. & NEVE, M. R. (1985) Hamlet on the couch. In *The Anatomy of Madness. Essays in the History of Psychiatry*, vol. 1, *People and Ideas* (eds W. F. Bynum, R. Porter & M. Shepherd), pp. 289–304. London: Tavistock Publications.

CLARK, J. K. (1984) *Goodwin Wharton*. London: Oxford University Press.

DALE, B. (1906) *The Good Lord Wharton. His Family, Life and Bible Charity*. London: The Congregational Union of England and Wales.

FREUD, S. (1923) A neurosis of demoniacal possession in the seventeenth century. In *Collected Papers*, vol. 4, pp. 436–472. London: Hogarth Press.

HILL, C. & SHEPHERD, M. (1976) The case of Arise Evans: a historicopsychiatric study. *Psychological Medicine*, **6**, 351–358.

JONES, G. F. T. (1967) *Saw-Pit Wharton. The Political Career from 1640 to 1691 of Philip, Fourth Lord Wharton*. Sydney: Sydney University Press.

MACALPINE, I. & HUNTER, R. (1956) *Schizophrenia 1677. A Psychiatric Study of an Illustrated Autobiographical Record of Demoniacal Possession*. London: William Dawson and Sons.

PETERSON, D. (1982) *A Mad People's History of Madness*. Pittsburgh: Pittsburgh University Press.

PORTER, R. (1985a) Introduction. In *Patients and Practitioners. Lay Perceptions of Medicine in Pre-Industrial Society* (ed. R. Porter), pp. 1–22. Cambridge: Cambridge University Press.

—— (1985b) 'The hunger of imagination'; approaching Samuel Johnson's melancholy. In *The Anatomy of Madness. Essays in the History of Psychiatry*, vol. 1. *People and Ideas* (eds W. F. Bynum, R. Porter & M. Shepherd), pp. 63–88. London: Tavistock Publications.

SPUFFORD, M. (1981) *Small Books and Pleasant Histories. Popular Fiction and Its Readership in Seventeenth Century England*. Cambridge: Cambridge University Press.

SZASZ, T. (1972) *The Manufacture of Madness*. London: Paladin.

THOMAS, K. (1971) *Religion and the Decline of Magic*. London: Weidenfeld and Nicolson.

WALKER, D. P. (1981) *Unclean Spirits. Possession and Exorcism in France and England in the Late Sixteenth and Early Seventeenth Centuries*. London: Scolar Press.

WHARTON, G. *The Autobiography of Goodwin Wharton*, 2 vols. London: British Library, Add. MSS 20,006-7.

10 Desperate remedies: a Gothic tale of madness and modern medicine

ANDREW SCULL

"Give me Leave to say, that no Man can have a tenderer, or more compassionate Concern for the Misery of Mankind than my self; yet it is Cruelty in the highest Degree, not to be bold in the Administration of Medicines, when the Nature of the Disease absolutely demands the Assistance of a powerful Remedy, and more especially in Cases where there can be no Relief without it. It is owing to these safe Men, that do but little Good, and a great deal of real Mischief, that chronick Diseases are so rife now-a-days, and so generally incurable; not that they are so in themselves, but only render'd so by those, that are afraid to proceed in a Way only capable of curing them." (Robinson, 1729)

My title promises a Gothic tale, one that links together madness and modern medicine. And my story does so, I think, in ways that suggest that the intrusions of the medical *savoir* into the realm of mental disorder have not always constituted the unambiguous blessings we sometimes like to pretend they have. The major protagonists in my saga (anti-heroes is perhaps a better term, for this is a history from which few emerge with much credit) include the former presidents of such august institutions as the Royal Medico-Psychological Association and the Royal College of Surgeons; perhaps the most eminent and influential American psychiatrist of the first half of the 20th century; and a leading New York psychoanalyst; as well as a host of lesser figures now largely consigned to oblivion.

Our story opens at the turn of the present century, a period when psychiatry was, in my judgement, in rather dire and desperate straits. Presiding over a ramshackle and decaying empire of ever-more over-crowded and run-down institutions, and swamped by legions of the poor, the aged, and the chronically disabled, institutional psychiatrists could do little more for their charges save to provide a dubious haven from a heartless world. "Our therapeutics," C. G. Hill openly conceded in his 1907 Presidential Address to the American Medico-Psychological Association, "is simply a pile of rubbish" (Hill, 1907, p. 6). Some two years later, in his own Presidential Address, this time to the Neurological Association, Silas

Weir Mitchell echoed this assessment: "Amidst enormous gains in our art, we have sadly to confess the absolute standstill of the therapy of insanity and the relative failure, as concerns diagnosis, in mental maladies of even that most capable diagnostician, the post-mortem surgeon" (Mitchell, 1909, p. 1; see also Abbott, 1902).

Therapeutic impotence and aetiological ignorance were scarcely novel problems for organised psychiatry, but the difficulties they created for the profession, both self-doubts and questioning, and damage to its public image, were unquestionably exacerbated quite profoundly by the changing status and prospects of medicine at large in the late 19th and early 20th centuries. Thanks in part to reforms in medical training, which served to constrict the supply of physicians, improve the quality of training provided, and to furnish firmer social warrants of medicine's scientific credentials (Larson, 1977; Starr, 1984), and in part to the bacteriological revolution (with its associated breakthroughs in the understanding and treatment of infectious diseases), general medicine's prestige and social standing grew markedly, and it rapidly acquired an enviable position in the social division of labour. The contrast with the recalcitrance of mental disorders and the almost purely custodial functions fulfilled by those engaged in their 'treatment' could only be a painful one for those committed to this more specialised branch of the medical trade.

American psychiatry, in particular, had attempted to emulate some of the reforms being undertaken in the profession at large: reorganising its professional association in the mid-1890s to include assistant asylum physicians as well as their superintendents; half-heartedly welcoming neurologists and pathologists into laboratories in mental hospital basements; and searching for new and usable scientific theories with which to explain and treat mental disorders. A segment of the profession, casting about for alternative bases of understanding and treatment, was tempted to abandon traditional medico-somatic approaches, which had, after all, brought neither insight nor results. Faced most threateningly by the extraordinarily rapid proliferation of religiously based mental-healing cults (of which the most notable were Christian Science and the Emmanuel Movement), and the associated "exodus of patients from the doctor's waiting room to the minister's study" (Sicherman, 1967, pp. 269–270), many concluded that medicine must perforce abandon its traditional "antagonism to methods of treatment which appeal to other than physical means . . ." (Taylor, 1908, p. 420).

But for every psychiatrist who was tempted to experiment with psychotherapy, there were several others who remained unalterably opposed to any but somatic approaches, and who continued to stigmatise those who strayed from the path of scientific virtue as teetering on the brink of charlatanry. For most members of the profession, as was true of medicine at large, "The moral and professional authority of the physician, and his unswerving commitment to the practice of orthodox somatic medicine were seen as bound together in a chain of common connection and mutual dependence; and anything which tended to weaken or undermine either of the interdependent elements would, it was firmly believed, eventually tend to weaken or undermine the other as well" (Clark, 1981, p. 299). At best, one might embrace the loosely defined 'psychobiological' approach offered by the Swiss-turned-American Adolf Meyer, where, safe within a fog of verbal obfuscation, one could draw eclectically upon a variety of psycho-therapeutic techniques while remaining fundamentally committed to the primacy of the body and the *biological* component of the disorder.

Born on 13 September 1866 near Zurich, Meyer had arrived in the United States in 1892. Ambitious, compulsively organised, and with the advantage of a rigorous European training, he secured a position as pathologist at the Illinois State Hospital in Kankakee the following year, undoubtedly aided by the new emphasis on laboratory researches into the causation of mental disorders. In 1895, Meyer moved to a similar position at the Worcester State Hospital in Massachusetts, now acquiring a small coterie of assistants. Seven years later, he moved again, this time to occupy the newly created post of Director of the Pathological Institute at Wards Island, serving as the research centre for all of New York's state hospitals. Finally, in 1908, he secured a still more influential position, as Professor of Psychiatry at Johns Hopkins University, and Director of the Phipps Clinic, an institutional niche from which he dominated American psychiatry until his retirement, more than 30 years later.[1]

One of Meyer's first assistants at Worcester had been Henry A. Cotton, ten years his junior and trained at Hopkins and the University of Maryland. Cotton remained at Worcester when Meyer moved to New York, subsequently taking a better-paying position at Danvers, another state hospital in Massachusetts, and keeping in frequent contact with his mentor.[2] A leave of absence for study in Europe brought a request for guidance from Meyer, and the latter responded with a letter of introduction to Kraepelin (Meyer Archive I/767/1–13). For the next two years, Cotton was to study under the latter, and in Alzheimer's clinic in Munich, further cementing his commitment to somaticism as the key to understanding mental disorder. With this impressive professional pedigree and strong backing from Meyer, he was

1. His influence on British psychiatry was, of course, far from negligible, as is partially indicated by his delivering the 14th Maudsley Memorial Lecture in 1933. Of particular significance in this regard were the number and prominence of the British psychiatrists who trained under him at Johns Hopkins, of whom the most notable of all was perhaps the late Aubrey Lewis. In his letter of 22 April 1949 inviting Meyer to become an honorary Foreign Corresponding Member of the Royal Medico-Psychological Association, R. C. Gordon employed only a modicum of flattery when he informed Meyer that he was "one whom in this country we all regard as the foremost psychiatrist of the century" (Meyer Papers, II/137/12).
2. Cotton's letters include: assurances to Meyer that he continued the work on the pathology of general paralysis of the insane, begun under the latter at Worcester; requests to be allowed to spend his vacation at Wards Island in further study under Meyer; minor domestic details; and a request on 6 October 1909 to be allowed to name his second son after Meyer (something Meyer graciously allowed) (Meyer Papers I/767/4).

able, in 1907, to secure the position of superintendent of the Trenton State Hospital in New Jersey, at the relatively young age of 31.

Cotton was only the third superintendent Trenton had had since its foundation in 1848 at the instigation of Dorothea Dix,[3] and he assumed his position there under less than auspicious circumstances. His predecessor, John Wesley Ward, a member of the hospital staff since 1867, had been dismissed in the aftermath of a typhoid epidemic and a scandal concerning the death of a patient at the hands of one of the attendants. Sunk into a routine typical of state hospitals of its era, Trenton provided Cotton with a challenge he sought energetically to meet. "Such a deplorable condition of affairs," he wrote to Meyer within weeks of taking the job, "one would not believe could exist in an insane hospital today . . . . Patients had been restrained for years, and no-one knew why" (Cotton to Meyer, 21 November 1907, Meyer Papers I/767/14). Within two months, he had eliminated all mechanical restraint, freeing 96 patients from their shackles, and tossing aside more than 700 restraining devices (Cotton, 1921, p. 5).

Alongside the adoption of a policy of non-restraint, Cotton introduced a series of administrative reforms: the wards were reorganised; a training programme was established for the nurses; fire alarms were installed; occupational therapy introduced; strong rooms torn down; individual patient records kept more systematically; and the first two social workers appointed, in keeping with Adolf Meyer's emphasis on the importance of after-care (Meyer's wife was often referred to as America's first social worker). Such administrative modernisation was clearly subordinate, however, to Cotton's primary concern, which was to introduce the principles of modern medicine into the treatment of his patients. In the words of Harold Magee, his assistant in the late 1920s (and himself the superintendent of Trenton State Hospital from 1949 onwards), Cotton "was no bughouse doctor, not one of those fellows who knew the routine and that's all. He was a *real* doctor. He wanted you to *study* the patient's condition" (quoted in Leiby, 1967, p. 121).

As part of his programme of bringing the asylum into the medical mainstream, he encouraged his assistants to publish and to attend conferences, engaged a series of local physicians as consultants, built an infirmary and an isolation ward for tuberculosis sufferers, established a clinical laboratory, and set up a modern operating room. Convinced, as he later put it, that "even if we did not have the evidence of cortical lesions in the 'functional' psychoses, we would have to assume their existence, if we accept modern biological teachings" (Cotton, 1923, p. 436), he pursued any and all means of physical treatment for the underlying brain disease: hydrotherapy, salvarsan for syphilitics injected intraspinally and intracranially, the use of glandular extracts, all without result. By 1916, almost a decade

3. Trenton State Hospital was, in Dix's words, her "favorite child", and she lived out her declining years in a small room in the hospital's central administrative building. The room, and a number of her possessions, are still preserved there to this day.

after he had assumed control of the hospital, Cotton had to confess that his therapeutic gains from all this activity were non-existent, his cure rate as dismally low as ever, and the prospects for realising his ambition to make a major breakthrough in psychiatric therapeutics apparently hopeless (Trenton State Hospital *Annual Report*, 1916; Cotton, 1923, pp. 436–437).

Casting about for fresh sources of inspiration, Cotton now happened upon a doctrine that was to transform his practice and his hospital, and to bring him a measure of the fame he had long coveted. Despite the initial scepticism with which the work of Pasteur and Lister had been greeted in the profession at large, the bacteriological theory of disease had eventually triumphed, bringing with it gains in both aetiological understanding and therapeutic efficacy. Within five years, the typhoid bacillus, malaria planodum, tubercle bacillus, cholera vibrio, and diphtheria bacillus were all identified in the laboratory, and with the development of antiserums for diphtheria and tetanus, the medical outlook seemed transformed. A number of well known and institutionally powerful physicians had recently begun to extend the idea of bacterial infection to account for the existence of a variety of puzzling, poorly understood, and intractable disorders. Franklin Billings, for example, Dean of the Rush Medical School in Chicago, and past president of both the American Medical Association and the American Association of Physicians, used the occasion of his 1915 Lane Lectures at Stanford to suggest that such chronic diseases as arthritis, rheumatic fever, nephritis, and degenerative disease of the arteries "might be caused by bacteria disseminated through the lymph or blood-streams from a hidden primary focus of infection" (Billings, 1916; cf. Hirsch, 1966, p. 86). William Thayer and Llewellys Barker (1920) of Johns Hopkins, and Edward Rosenow (1919) and Charles Mayo of Minnesota had also thrown the weight of their authority behind focal infection as an explanation of chronic illness, as had men like William Hunter, Chalmers Watson (1923), and William Willcox in Britain (Hunter, 1927). Beginning in 1916, Cotton became steadily more convinced that these ideas provided the key to the intractability of mental disorders, and that further investigation would demonstrate "that focal infections and toxins may appear in the etiology of certain groups [of psychoses] previously held to be purely psychogenic in origin" (Trenton State Hospital *Annual Report*, 1916).

As Cotton was to acknowledge, others had made this particular intellectual leap before him. As early as 1900, the British surgeon, William Hunter, seeking to apply the principles of 'Listerism' to general medicine, had suggested a role for focal infection in the causation of "dementia praecox, manic depressive insanity, paranoid conditions, psychoneurosis, and toxic insanities" (Hunter, 1900, 1927). Among psychiatrists, both Henry Upson (1907, 1909, 1910) of the Cleveland State Hospital and Lewis Bruce (1906) of Scotland had subsequently implicated infected teeth in the causation of insanity. Cokenower (1904) blamed "fermentation and putrefaction within the intestinal canal . . . produc[ing] autoinfection . . . pathologic changes in the blood, which, in turn, causes malnutrition of the nerve centers." But these remained, in Cotton's words, isolated voices "in the wilderness" (Cotton, 1923, p. 435, 1921, p. 41), prophets without honour or notice in their own time: in part because they lacked his flair for publicity and self-promotion; and in part because their claims were more hedged about with qualifications. Bruce (1906, pp. 8–10), for example, while urging that "there are good grounds for believing that oral sepsis is in some patients the starting point for a condition of toxaemia which may end in insanity in those predisposed to mental disorders . . . ," continued, in orthodox fashion, to place primary emphasis on hereditary factors, in the absence of which infection and exhaustion were without discernible effects on mental stability.

If others had tentatively hinted at a role for autoinfection in a certain proportion of cases, Cotton exuded certainty about the *general* significance of focal infection, and trumpeted his claims of therapeutic success from the practical application of his theories. In his earliest applications of focal infection theory, in 1916, he had extracted all apparently infected teeth from a group of some 50 patients, without discernible results. Convinced he was on the right track, however, he set up a dental surgery department at the hospital, and in 1917, extended his field of operative intervention to include the tonsils as well. The results, he claimed, were immediately gratifying, producing a dramatic surge in hospital discharges. Thus encouraged, "we started to literally 'clean up' our patients of all foci of chronic sepsis" (Cotton, 1923, p. 438). At the same time, he launched a many-sided campaign to publicise his achievements, justifying his self-promotion by arguing that "in no other field of medicine can such results be obtained by educating the laity to the dangers of chronic foci of infection" (Trenton State Hospital *Annual Report*, 1920, p. 29).

Preliminary findings were presented in conference papers read before the New Jersey and New York medical societies, the Neurological Association, and at the American Medical Association meetings in 1919 and 1920. On the latter occasion, in New Orleans in April 1920, Cotton also prepared an exhibit including lantern slides and "moving pictures of the work of the hospital" which "attracted considerable attention" (Trenton State Hospital *Annual Report*, 1920, p. 29). At the hospital itself, he entertained a stream of visitors from both the United States and abroad,[4] and he published prolifically in both medical and dental journals. He was equally aggressive in seeking a lay audience, most successfully, perhaps, in his 1921 Vanuxem Lectures at Princeton University on the defective delinquent and the insane (published later that same year by the Princeton and Oxford

4. In 1919–20, these included George H. Kirby, Meyer's successor at the New York State Psychiatric Institute, physicians from Norristown State Hospital in Pennsylvania, the Pennsylvania Hospital for the Insane, Kankakee, Illinois and Georgia State Hospitals, as well as the dentist from the mental hospital in Sydney, Australia (Trenton State Hospital *Annual Report*, 1920, p. 29).

University Presses with a preface by his mentor, Adolf Meyer (Cotton, 1921)); and in a long *Review of Reviews* piece written by his superior, Burdette Lewis, the State Commissioner of Institutions and Agencies, lauding his breakthrough in the treatment of mental disorder (Lewis, 1922; see also Shaw, 1922). On a number of occasions, his aggressive pursuit of publicity brought negative reactions from his psychiatric colleagues. In 1919, one of his earliest reports of his 'defocalisation' work was scheduled to appear in Hoch's new journal, *The Psychiatric Quarterly*, but was rejected by the editorial board when its substance appeared first in the lay press (Cotton to Meyer, 18 January 1919, Meyer to Cotton, 21 January 1919, Meyer Papers, 1/767/16). Meyer subsequently criticised his role in the publication of the *Review of Reviews* piece, for bringing wholly professional concerns before a lay audience (see Meyer to Cotton, 20 June 1922, Meyer Papers, I/767/18).

Cotton framed his work in the context of "the alarming increase in insanity" recently documented by the National Committee on Mental Hygiene (Cotton & Draper, 1920, p. 1), noting that "there are over 417,000 insane confined in institutions in this country and . . . in a large majority of such hospitals no attempt whatsoever is made to treat such patients" (Trenton State Hospital *Annual Report*, 1920, p. 18). From many points of view, a "great opportunity for synthesizing psychiatry with scientific medicine" had been lost during World War I, but the new work on focal infections, requiring laboratory analyses, antitoxins, X-rays, and operative interference, all the most up-to-date trappings of modern medicine, provided a new opportunity to effect the synthesis. If his own results could be replicated, such a *rapprochement* could at once be expected to have a spectacular effect on cure rates, and hence on hospital populations and state mental health expenditures. Within 12 months of adopting aggressive techniques to counter infection, he claimed his recovery rate had grown by some 23% (Trenton State Hospital *Annual Report*, 1919, p. 8), and with greater experience and more extensive intervention, it soon reached as high as 85% of those treated (Cotton, 1923, p. 438), producing savings for the state of almost $250 000 over three years (Trenton State Hospital *Annual Report*, 1921, p. 16, but for divergent claims about cure rates and estimates of the resultant savings, see Cotton 1922*a*, p. 188; Cotton, 1921, p. 80; Trenton State Hospital *Annual Report*, 1920, p. 14). Follow-up visits had demonstrated "that those we consider recovered are earning their living, taking care of families, and are normal in every respect" (Trenton State Hospital *Annual Report*, 1921, p. 16).

Although occasionally still genuflecting in the direction of Meyer's emphasis on the multiple determinants of behaviour (environment, hereditary make-up, and individual psychology, as well as organic factors), Cotton increasingly stressed a monocausal biological account of mental disorder, rejecting the very concept of 'functional' disorders as "untenable" (Cotton, 1921, p. 77). Psychoses, as the discovery of the syphilitic origins of general paresis had begun to make clear, were *symptoms*, not diseases. Only now, by exploiting "all the methods of modern diagnosis" (Cotton, 1922*a*, p. 163), had it been possible to bring the true state of affairs to light: "The insane are physically sick . . . our researches prove the presence of an unusual amount of pathology among the insane, due to bacteriological invasion" (Cotton & Draper, 1920, pp. 2–3).

The lesions in question had hitherto gone undetected and unsuspected because they were not acute, fulminating disorders "in which the patient, by reason of pus, pain, temperature, and other symptoms, is only too well aware of the presence of infection" (Cotton, 1921, p. 74; see also Cotton, 1919, p. 287). Rather, the damage was done by chronic, latent, masked infections, which lurked unnoticed in the body, occasionally directly invading the tissues of the brain, but more commonly and insidiously poisoning the system through "the toxin, generated by the bacteria and transmitted to the brain via the bloodstream" (Cotton, 1921, p. 72). Fortunately, and so far as laymen were concerned, almost magically, "modern methods of clinical diagnosis – such as the X-ray, bacteriological and serological examinations – in conjunction with a careful history and a thorough physical examination, will, in the majority of cases, bring to light these hidden infections," and they could then "be removed by the knife or by vaccine" (Cotton & Draper, 1920, p. 7). Not that the task was easy, even for the skilled physician alert to the problem: "I can state," said Cotton, "that not only is the difficulty of locating foci of infection a tremendous one but the problem of eliminating them when found is almost stupendous. It takes patience and ability to stick to the work of elimination" (Cotton, 1919, pp. 286–287) – a choice of words that was, I might add, closer to the mark than perhaps his audience realised.

Necessarily, as Cotton acknowledged, "In taking this stand we have to some extent antagonized those who believe that psychogenic factors are the only ones to be considered in the causation of the psychosis" (Trenton State Hospital *Annual Report*, 1920, p. 17). But when all was said and done, psychoanalysis and related techniques rested upon the "gross error" of viewing the mind as "independent of the brain" (Cotton, 1921, p. 13). Psychologists had illegitimately trespassed on the physician's turf, and without even the excuse of being able "to show any marked results in recovery of the patients treated in institutions under their control" (Cotton, 1922*a*, p. 188). Henceforth, they should be "confined to a study of the symptoms and . . . not permitted to wander in the field of causation and treatment" (Cotton, 1921, p. 185). The somaticist could not resist one last dig: "More in truth than in jest may it be said that psychoanalysis will in time be superseded by gastric analysis" (Cotton, 1921, p. 185).

All of this, of course, was scarcely likely to win Cotton friends in the analytic community, but analysts were inevitably bound to be fiercely critical of his work, and in attacking their medical credentials, Cotton was appealing to sentiments widely shared by mainstream medical practitioners and, more especially, by most American psychiatrists (Grob, 1983). But Cotton was equally caustic and dismissive when he turned to hereditarian accounts of mental disorder, attacking them as a prejudice based upon inadequate evidence. "Modern biological research," he asserted confidently, "tends to show that the inheritance of mental disorders . . . is next to impossible" (Cotton, 1922*a*, p. 158; see also Cotton, 1921, pp. 21–23). Moreover, while "infection can be eliminated", heredity was all but unmodifiable, save by the clumsy and uncertain means of eugenics (Trenton State Hospital *Annual Report*, 1920, p. 17).

The contrast with focal infection theory could scarcely have been starker, for if an emphasis on heredity constituted a confession of therapeutic impotence, Cotton's approach provided an almost unrestrained field for active therapeutic intervention. In the very earliest years, teeth were Cotton's favourite target, soon joined by the tonsils. "Without exception, the functional psychotic patients all have infected teeth" (Cotton, 1922*a*, p. 163), and the only solution in such cases was extirpation. "If the tooth is at all suspicious, we are of the opinion that it should be extracted" (Cotton, 1921, p. 57; see also 1919, p. 279; 1922*b*, p. 10; Trenton State Hospital *Annual Report*, 1921, p. 21). "This does not mean that every patient should have all his or her teeth extracted" (Cotton, 1922*a*, p. 164), but even "apparently toothless" patients needed careful scrutiny with X-rays, lest they have some remaining impacted or unerupted molar lurking unseen to perpetuate their madness (Cotton, 1921, p. 95). "Perhaps we shall be accused of being too radical in our opinion . . . but, after many serious mistakes in not extracting such teeth, and with the good results obtained in the patients by reconsidering our decision and later extracting all such teeth, our position is impregnable." Modern dentistry was "a menace" to the community, producing "wonderful cosmetic work" that did "incalculable damage" by producing "serious systemic disease" (Cotton, 1921, p. 42). Properly regarded, in the light of modern medical knowledge, "Instead of creating the impression of advancing age and as ushering in a period of decline, artificial dentures are in reality the greatest possible safeguards against premature old age" (Cotton, 1921, p. 74). Acting vigorously on these opinions, Cotton's staff extracted more than 4000 teeth in 1919–20, and over 6000 the following year, taking time to enucleate the tonsils of at least 90% of the patients coming under their care.

As Cotton acknowledged at the outset, such interventions did not always meet with unanimous consent from patients and their families. But all protests must be ruthlessly pushed aside, as short-sighted preferences based upon imperfect knowledge: "If we wish to eradicate focal infections, we must bear in mind that it is only by being persistent, often against the wishes of the patient . . . [that we can] expect our efforts to be successful. Failure in these cases at once casts discredit upon the theory, when the reason lies in the fact that we have not been radical enough" (Cotton, 1919, p. 273).

Being "radical enough," it soon transpired, entailed a willingness to track down and eliminate infections that extended their reach far beyond teeth and tonsils. While oral surgery alone often sufficed to produce "marvelous results", it on other occasions produced "no results whatever" (Cotton, 1922a, p. 166). The explanation, for Cotton, was obvious: the infection must have spread elsewhere, either through the lymph glands or through the bloodstream or secondarily by swallowing bacteria in the saliva. Consequently, those committed to "surgical bacteriology" must also turn their attention to "stomach, duodenum, small intestine, gall bladder, appendix, and colon", as well as to the genito-urinary tract (Cotton, 1922a, pp. 166 167). Most suspicious of all was "the segment of the bowel . . . developed from the hind gut and lying on the right side", a troublesome piece of tissue that well deserved the title of " 'the wisdom tooth of the gut' " (Cotton & Draper, 1920, p. 14). The solution in this instance was to remove the terminal portion of the ileum, the caecum, and the first portion of the colon, an operation Cotton referred to as the "developmental reconstruction of the colon" (Cotton & Draper, 1920, p. 12). Such operations, fortunately, were needed in only about 20% of functional cases, the necessity being indicated by the presence of any or all of a variety of symptoms: a history of constipation or bilious attacks; any "pain or tenderness in the right or left lower quadrants"; or where "X-ray studies . . . demonstrate conclusively the presence of marked delay in the test meal" – an indication of "stasis and infection" (Cotton, 1922a, p. 180).

Given the obvious hazards associated with such a procedure, "This research work should not be undertaken by novices or even by general surgeons but, until standardized, should be left in the hands of the highly specialised gastro-intestinal surgeon" (Trenton State Hospital *Annual Report*, 1921, p. 23). (With Draper's death, Cotton was shortly to ignore his own advice on this point, and begin to operate himself.) However, Cotton hastened to assure his colleagues that "in competent hands this procedure may properly be looked upon as a conservative and preventive measure" (Trenton State Hospital *Annual Report*, 1921, p. 22). ("Conservative" obviously had a somewhat idiosyncratic meaning here, for elsewhere in the same document, Cotton revealed an operative mortality rate of "about twenty five per cent", with "many" of the deaths resulting from post-operative peritonitis[5] – something he attributed to the fact that "psychotic patients in whom the infection has been long-standing and of great and specific virulence, are not good surgical risks and yield a higher mortality rate"[6] (Cotton, 1921, p. 101).) While one would obviously have preferred

5. The following year, reporting on a series of 250 colon operations, he claimed 25% recoveries, 30% deaths, 15% improved, and 30% unimproved (Cotton 1922a, p. 186).
6. Compare Cotton *et al* (1920), who report a mortality rate of 28% in a series of 50 patients, with only ten patients "recovered sufficiently to leave the hospital". Comparing this with the same surgeon's mortality in his general practice of some 7.7%, Cotton cheerfully attributes the difference to the fact that the insane obviously suffer from "a much lower vitality" than the rest of us. Incidentally, this report records only three of the patients involved as "not benefitted" by the operation. Apparently the dead were to be counted among those who had "benefitted" from surgical intervention!

that the risks be lower (and recent improvements in operative technique promised dramatic improvements in this regard), "where there is no question as to the outcome of the psychoses, being terminal dementia, we feel justified in performing a colectomy, with the possibility of a recovery" (Cotton, 1922*a*, p. 186).

The emphasis here should clearly be on the word 'possibility', for even though Cotton expressly noted that the most likely candidates for bowel surgery were manic–depressives (Cotton, 1922*a*, p. 182), his claimed cure rates were only on the order of 20–25% (Cotton *et al*, 1920, p. 20; Cotton, 1922*a*, p. 186; Trenton State Hospital *Annual Report*, 1921, p. 25). Two explanations suggested themselves. First, perhaps the "surgical bacteri-ology" remained incomplete. This, of course, implied a need for further surgery, a conclusion Cotton did not shrink from. In some instances, where only the right side of the colon had been resected, "Examination, in the unsuccessful cases, proved that the left side was infected, so that it was wiser to remove it" (Cotton 1922*a*, p. 185), and henceforth, this became a routine practice. In other cases, infection must surely still lurk elsewhere. For-tunately, the stomach "is one of the least important organs in the body . . . . The principal function of the stomach is storage and motility, each easily dispensed with . . . . The stomach is for all the world like a cement mixer often used in the erection of large buildings and just about as necessary. The large bowel is, similarly, for storage and we can dispense with it just as freely as with the stomach" (Cotton, 1921, p. 66).

Retrospective examination of Cotton's records indicates that 78% of his colectomies were performed on female patients. Subsequently, he was to opt for a less drastic procedure to eliminate "intestinal adhesions" (Lane's operation), and in this later phase, the proportion of women being operated on rose to 84% (cf. Frankel, 1932). In female patients (for some strange reason, "In the female patients the colon is involved twice as often as in the male cases"), the "gynecological complication . . . is also very important. The cervix is infected in about 80 per cent of the cases. The good results obtained from enucleating the cervix have convinced us of the importance of this lesion" (Cotton, 1922*a*, 182–183). Less often, but still in 25–50% of cases, male patients required resection of the "seminal vesicles" and in some cases "these infected vesicles have been enucleated with gratifying results" (Trenton State Hospital *Annual Report*, 1920, p. 20; Cotton, 1922*a*, p. 185; Cotton, 1925, p. 12). Such regions as the gall-bladder and sinuses might also require attention. Consequently, "In many of the cases it has been necess-ary to do several operations, such as resection of the colon, enucleation of the cervix, cholecystectomy, hysterectomy, oophorectomy, and repair of the perineum" (Trenton State Hospital *Annual Report*, 1920, p. 24).

Such surgery did have its limits, to be sure, and where one physically could not remove further organs or parts thereof, recourse was had to inoculations with a special serum, prepared, appropriately enough in view of the sponsorship of this lecture, by Squibb's Laboratories via the inoculation of horses with a variety of strains of streptococci and colon bacilli (Trenton State Hospital *Annual Report*, 1920, pp. 21–22). One begins to understand why Cotton protested the spread of the unfortunate impression "that we claim infected teeth to be the sole cause of insanity" and his hospital being referred to sarcastically as "the mecca of exodontia" (Trenton State Hospital *Annual Report*, 1920, p. 18).

Of course, even with such extensive surgical treatment, some recalcitrant patients obstinately refused to recover. All this proved was that "the longer the duration [of the psychosis] the less effective detoxification is in restoring the patient's mental health. Such failures can be explained on the ground that the brain has become permanently damaged, and no amount of detoxification has any effect in restoring the mental condition" (Cotton 1923, p. 460). Since "nothing can be done for chronic patients" because "the brain tissue has probably become permanently affected", the work of "arresting the ever-increasing number of mental derelicts" must necessarily embrace efforts at prophylaxis rather than cure (Cotton, 1921, pp. 120, 122). "Cases of long-standing constipation," for example, "should be treated by preventive surgery long before the psychosis develops" (Trenton State Hospital *Annual Report*, 1921, p. 25). Children were an especially important target for early intervention, with at least 40% of juvenile delinquents showing "some very marked pathological lesions or physical disturbances which we think account for their delinquency" (Cotton, 1921, p. 173). Properly understood, that is, the problem of this group becomes one for the psychiatrist, physician and surgeon (Cotton, 1921, p. 11) – a conclusion Cotton had already begun to put into practice, extracting teeth and tonsils at the Jamesburg Juvenile Reformatory, as well as at the Trenton and Rahway Prisons, and securing state funding for an X-ray laboratory and a bacteriological laboratory at the former institution so as to extend the valuable outreach work (Trenton State Hospital *Annual Report*, 1921, pp. 36–47).

Even these interventions, he later decided, came too late in the process. Far better results could be anticipated were one to intervene still earlier, before the systemic poisoning had produced mental disorder. He therefore recommended the screening of all schoolchildren, who "may be harboring infection at that time which will later produce a psychosis" (Cotton, 1925, p. 18). Defective children were frequently abnormally bright, since "The first effects of cerebral toxemia is [*sic*] to stimulate the mental activity in the same way as a small amount of alcohol" (Cotton, 1925, p. 13 – he had not examined Leopold and Loeb, but "would unhesitatingly say they were suffering from chronic sepsis and toxemia"). He himself had operated with great success on the colons of a six- and an eight-year-old. Abnormal childhood sexuality was an equally strong clue to the presence of "chronic sepsis and toxemia, . . . [and] in a number of these cases the colon has been resected with improvement in the individual and cessation of the abnormal sex practices, such as masturbation" (Cotton, 1925, p. 17).

By 1922, Cotton's numerous articles and his Princeton lectures had given wide publicity to his work and theories. Other psychiatrists reported being besieged by families who had heard of the revolutionary new treatment, and urged its application to their mentally diseased relatives. Others had flocked to Mecca itself. Between 1916 and 1921, the proportion of private-paying admissions to Trenton State Hospital had grown from 11% to 45%. Suitably proud of his subordinate's revolutionary successes, the New Jersey State Commissioner of Institutions and Agencies, Burdette Lewis, now published a widely circulated *Review of Reviews* essay on Trenton, to which the editor of the journal, Albert Shaw, appended a survey of 'expert' opinion on the merits of Cotton's work (Lewis, 1922; Shaw, 1922). "New Jersey's experience," Lewis boasted, "has made the old fashioned asylums, camouflaged as hospitals, as extinct and out of date as are the prison grottoes of Old Venice, or the old Bethlehem Hospital for the Insane" (Lewis, 1922, p. 16). Through Cotton's genius, "this hospital has been freed of those terrors, partly real and partly imaginary, which curse and torment the mind of the insane patient" (Lewis, 1922, p. 8). Illustrating his text with photographs of the three operative services at Trenton "which are busy most of the time [combating] the menace of toxic poison," he informed his readers that "The application of all of the well-tested methods of modern medicine, surgery, and dentistry has penetrated the mystery which has enshrouded the subject of insanity for centuries . . . freedom for these patients appears near at hand" (Lewis, 1922, pp. 5, 14, 15).

In support of these apocalyptic statements, Shaw then paraded an impressive array of medical authority. Charles Page, Cotton's former superior at Danvers State Hospital in Massachusetts, praised his "triumph" in "this humane undertaking". Stewart Paton expressed the "wish that what Dr. Cotton is doing at Trenton could be done at every state hospital for the insane in this country," an opinion endorsed, on the basis of his first-hand acquaintance with the work, by his Princeton colleague, Edward Conklin. The distinguished Dr Mayo of Rochester, Minnesota, found Cotton's theories "in line with modern investigations as to the origins of disease," while Hubert Work, the President of the American Medical Association, present to open two new treatment units at Trenton, praised Cotton as a "pioneer" who had transformed a benighted asylum into "a general hospital, the first I ever saw." A number of Cotton's fellow asylum superintendents offered their endorsements, adding only that their own attempts to replicate his achievements were handicapped by the parsimony of their state legislatures, so that inadequate facilities constrained their ability to engage in abdominal surgery, or even to extract teeth in the necessary volume. (Quotations from Shaw, 1922.)

Others whom Shaw contacted were more cautious or even agnostic, a number of them deploring the "discussion of highly technical and controversial matters" before a lay audience. Even the sceptics, however, conceded that "There cannot be two opinions as to the advisability of removing sources of infection, whether located in the tonsils, the roots of the teeth, or elsewhere" (R. C. Hutchings, quoted in Shaw, 1922). The more cautious voices included Franklin Billings, who noted that while focal infection was a well established cause of systemic disease, "the application of these principles is frequently utilized with poor judgment and discretion by individual medical practitioners." Unable to evaluate Cotton's work "fully," he *hoped* it was of value in the treatment of the insane (Shaw, 1922, p. 41).

That Shaw had only selectively represented psychiatric opinion of Cotton's work is demonstrated by the far more hostile tone of a number of the commentators on the paper the latter gave to the American Psychiatric Association in the summer of 1922. The discussion session that followed saw calls for more thorough documentation, complaints of overenthusiasm, worries that colectomies were being treated as though they "were as simple and devoid of danger as the extraction of a tooth," and doubts about whether the cures could validly be attributed to surgery since, particularly in manic–depressive cases, the "attack is practically self-limited" (*American Journal of Psychiatry*, 1922, pp. 198–202). More threateningly still, Cotton's paper was followed on the programme by some preliminary research by Kopeloff & Cheney (1922) of the New York Psychiatric Institute (amplified the following year (Kopeloff, 1923)), which systematically compared patients randomly assigned to operative treatment and to a control group, concluding that the surgery was if anything counter-productive and that Cotton's methods for discovering infection were arbitrary, scientifically unreliable, and even worthless. Privately, some psychiatrists were even harsher. William Alanson White, for example, wrote that he could "not conceive how such results can be accepted by the scientifically trained mind" and denounced Cotton's work as "profoundly unfortunate for psychiatry" (W. A. White to A. T. Hobbs, 7 March 1924, W. A. White Papers).

None of this deterred Cotton in the least. Kopeloff was dismissed as someone who was not even medically qualified, "a very dangerous individual whose main idea is to refute the work here . . . " (Cotton to Meyer, 16 May 1922, Meyer Papers I/767/19). Kirby, his superior at the Institute (and Meyer's successor in that position) had naively swallowed his findings, although "the work was very inadequately done", and must obviously have left sites of infection untreated (Cotton to Meyer, 20 June 1922, Meyer Papers I/767/18). Still, it must have been a relief when, in 1923, he was invited to Britain to address the Medico-Psychological Association and found himself in front of an audience disposed to view his work with almost wholly uncritical admiration.

Following Cotton's by now standard presentation of his efforts, modified only to emphasise the English origins of focal infection theory (and including a passage in which he noted a mortality of over 36% in his abdominal surgery cases (103 of 281 cases)), a chorus of approval greeted what was dubbed "one of the greatest contributions connected with the subject of mental disease" (*Journal of Mental Science*, 1923, p. 553; see also Graves, 1923). Sir Frederick Mott, the pathologist to the London County Mental Hospitals, who two years earlier had delivered the second Maudsley Memorial Lecture, hastened to offer extravagant praise for Cotton's accomplishments. Chalmers Watson, Physician to the Edinburgh Royal Infirmary, found Cotton's work "wholly admirable" (*Journal of Mental Science*, 1923, p. 556); and not surprisingly, William Hunter, the surgeon to whom Cotton attributed the pioneering role in connecting mental illness and focal infection, pronounced the latter's conclusions "utterly sound" (*Journal of Mental Science*, 1923, p. 553). Not least, said George M. Robertson, President of the RMPA, Professor of Psychiatry at the University of Edinburgh, and Superintendent of the Royal Morningside Mental Hospital, his paper "should have served to draw members from the alluring and tempting pastures of psychogenesis back to the narrower, steeper, more rugged and arduous, yet straighter paths, of general medicine . . . ." For after all, "here . . . were results which no-one could deny" (*Journal of Mental Science*, 1923, p. 558, 553).

In the United States, however, as Cotton found once more on his return, all too large a fraction of his colleagues *were* disposed to deny his claims (see Hobbs, 1924). Perhaps the most vivid criticism came from C. K. Mills: "If the craze for violent removal goes on, it will come to pass that we will have a gutless, glandless, toothless, and I am not sure that we may have, thanks to false psychology and surgery, a witless race" (Hobbs, 1924, p. 553).

As the controversy grew, the medical members of Trenton's Board of Managers began to fret about the likelihood and desirability of an outside evaluation of Cotton's achievements. Fearful that third parties would *impose* such an investigation, wholly independent of the hospital, they eventually decided, with Cotton's assent, to institute a review of their own, taking care to ensure that whoever was "selected should be . . . neutral or at least not unfriendly to [the] . . . work under consideration" and that the terms of reference be such as "to prevent the likelihood of anybody saying that Cotton was being 'investigated' " (Raycroft to Meyer, 30 June 1924, enclosing a memorandum dated 28 February 1924, Trenton State Hospital Archives, unpublished).

In the event, the governors elected to approach Adolf Meyer and ask him to undertake the task. Notwithstanding his eminence, this was, from a number of viewpoints, a curious choice. Cotton was, of course, Meyer's protégé, and had enjoyed a lengthy and close personal and professional relationship with him. Moreover, Meyer had provided a foreword to the published version of Cotton's Princeton lectures which the latter (and presumably not he alone) saw as a strong endorsement of his activities. Meyer had spoken there of "Dr. Cotton's substantial and not merely speculative work"; of the need to do "justice to the demands of a real cleansing". Attacking the physical basis of mental illness "without the wholesale elimination of vital functions, such as we experienced in the days of wholesale ovariotomies and the like," Cotton had made "an outstanding contribution [to] twentieth century medicine," one Meyer had followed "with interest and admiration" (Meyer in Cotton, 1921, p. v).[7] This was likely, then, to be an odd sort of impartiality.

In the event, Meyer declined to conduct the study himself, although he agreed to lend his name to it and exercise a general oversight of it. In his place, he sent Phyllis Greenacre, a Chicago MD who had been one of his assistants since 1916, and who later became a prominent New York psycho-analyst (Meyer to Raycroft, 10 July 1924, Trenton State Hospital Archives), taking time along the way to send reassurances to Cotton that he would "find her a very capable and judicious worker and a thoroughly cooperative personality" (Meyer to Cotton, 11 September 1924; Cotton to Meyer, 12 September 1924; Meyer to Cotton, 25 September 1924, Meyer Papers I/767/20). Beginning in late September 1924, Greenacre spent three days each week in Trenton, housed overnight in a converted closet in the nearby State Prison (Greenacre, 1983). On 8 September, Meyer himself had ventured on the scene, and his memorandum of the visit suggests that this was enough to raise serious qualms: "When I hear Dr. Cotton discuss his cases the problem seems to be absolutely nothing but one of focal infection . . . [but] the cases I saw this forenoon leave me troubled and uncertain" (memorandum of 8 September 1924, Meyer Papers I/767/20). Greenacre's interim reports soon removed the uncertainty. In her own words, the situation at the hospital proved to be "a nightmare". The statistical records, in the hands of a Mrs Rue, an ex-patient of Cotton's, were a shambles. The two 'social workers' assigned to undertake the necess-ary patient follow-up studies also turned out to be ex-patients, pathetically grateful for Cotton's detoxification work on themselves, so Greenacre felt compelled to do all the follow-up work herself. As she tracked her cases, both those discharged and those still in the hospital, it became apparent that vast discrepancies between published claims and actual results were somehow being overlooked by the entire professional staff (Greenacre, 1983). By December, Meyer had seen enough, confessing to his brother Hermann (A. Meyer to H. Meyer, 5 December 1924, Meyer Papers IV/3/229) that "The investigation of the material of Dr. Cotton discloses a rather sad harvest. His claims and statistics are preposterously out of accord with the facts."

Preposterous or not, it was to be a further year before Greenacre brought her elaborate study to a conclusion, and before that, the threat of a public scandal suddenly emerged from an unexpected quarter. A runaway state legislative committee, the Bright Commission, investigating governmental

---

7. A closer reading, however, reveals some typically Meyerian caveats, most notably some throwaway lines about the need for further controlled studies, and for Cotton to "run the gauntlet of professional criticism".

'waste', began poking about in the asylum's affairs, attracted in part by the higher costs associated with Cotton's aggressive therapeutics. One of its first witnesses was Cotton himself, who explained to an apparently credulous audience how his methods, which kept the operating room busy about four days a week, had increased the hospital's cure rate to some 87%, attracted large numbers of high-paying private patients, many from out of state, and saved New Jersey taxpayers well over a million dollars over seven years (*Trenton Evening Times*, 8 July 1925, p. 1).

But now the Bright Commission's hearings threatened to get out of hand. A parade of ex-patients, their families, and former asylum employees began to materialise, and over the next two months, their twice-weekly testimony provided lurid headlines in the local press about brutality by hospital attendants, unexplained deaths, patients dragged kicking and screaming into operating rooms where they were subjected to mutilating experimental surgery, and Cotton's lucrative private practice on the side, operating on paying patients in a proprietary hospital of his own elsewhere in the town. During this recital, Cotton's behaviour became increasingly erratic. He interrupted witnesses, attempted to prevent their testimony, and berated them privately after they had testified (*Trenton Evening Times*, 5, 12, 26 August 1925). Finally, shortly before he was to testify again on his own behalf, he became extremely agitated and dissolved into a confusional state that was to persist intermittently until the end of the year.

All during this period, Adolf Meyer's prime concern had been to avoid disclosure of Greenacre's findings to the state investigators. The existence of her study had been disclosed at an early stage in the proceedings, and, convinced she would be called to testify, Meyer began to coach her about her responses. Together, they agreed that she would "say that she has not seen any cruelty or neglect of the principle of getting permission for the operation from responsible relatives," and if asked "if the performance of the operations . . . [had] been justified," would respond that her investigation was not yet complete – a piece of duplicity they rationalised since "indeed it could not be considered finished until Dr. Cotton shall have had the opportunity to go over the report with us so as to draw our attention to any points that may have been overlooked" (Meyer to Raycroft, 15 September 1925, Trenton State Hospital Archives; Greenacre, 1983). In the event, the Bright Commission did not question her on the issue of efficacy, apparently assuming that her response would favour Cotton, so the subterfuge proved unnecessary; but for months afterwards, Meyer continued to reassure both the asylum authorities and Cotton's wife that he would suppress their findings as long as necessary, "as long as there is any hope that it can become helpful to Dr. Cotton" (Meyer to Mrs Cotton, 18 January 1926; Meyer to Raycroft, 18 January 1926, Meyer Papers I/767/ 24). To Cotton himself he wrote expressing his "great distress and regret" at "this terrible habit of our official America to institute public hearings of irresponsible people" (Meyer to Cotton, 25 September 1925, Meyer Papers I/767/21).

Meanwhile, the hospital managers, led by Joseph Raycroft, had covered up Cotton's breakdown as a physical illness, and aggressively rejected the charges made as the work of a few disaffected and incompetent former attendants and a handful of deluded ex-patients and well meaning but mistaken relatives. They secured the testimony of Royal S. Copeland, a physician, former Commissioner of Public Health, and US senator from New York, that "Trenton State Hospital is, without exception, the most progressive institution in the world in the treatment of the insane" (*Trenton Evening Times*, 23 September 1925, p. 1). Reiterating their own "sense of pride and satisfaction in the valuable and progressive work" being done at the hospital, and reminding the committee that "a policy of treating the mentally ill pays in dollars and cents," they urged that Cotton's splendid achievements be rewarded with an increase in salary. As Raycroft gleefully reported to Meyer two days later, their tactics were an overwhelming success (Raycroft to Meyer, 25 September 1925, Meyer Papers I/767/21). The Bright Commission, which had always had a number of Cotton's admirers in its midst, promptly ended its investigation of the hospital, and issued a report dismissing all the allegations made as malicious and ill-founded.

There remained, however, the awkward matter of Greenacre's findings. Cotton had been packed off to Hot Springs, Arkansas, to recover his mental equilibrium away from the state capital, and, aided, as he himself put it, by the extraction of three "dead and badly infected teeth," he eventually reported he had done so (Cotton to Meyer, 30 September, 23, 30 October, 17 December 1925, Meyer Papers I/767/23). At Meyer's suggestion (Meyer to Cotton, 23 December 1925, Meyer Papers I/767/23), Cotton met Greenacre and him in Baltimore in early January to spend several days going over her findings.

Inevitably, this would be an occasion fraught with tension. Greenacre's findings were devastating to Cotton's claims. In contrast to his claimed 87% cure rate, she had found a general rate of only 20%, and no better than 40% even in a series of cases specially selected by the hospital statistician. Moreover, "*the least treatment was found in the recovered cases and the most thorough treatment in the unimproved and dead groups,*" with the death rate among the treated group approaching 43%. "Of course," she continued, "it might be possible that a drastic treatment entailing a high death rate, might still be very effective in the case of those patients who survive, – in which case the treatment should not be wholly condemned, but every effort made to reduce the mortality." But further investigation removed even this possibility. "Consequently, it must be concluded that *thorough treatment, including abdominal operation, is not only dangerous to life, but ineffective in the cases of those who survive*" (Greenacre, 1926, pp. 24, 25, emphases in the original).

In the event, the meetings at which Cotton was confronted with

Greenacre's evidence and conclusions were extraordinary affairs. In Meyer's detailed record of their discussions, and in his subsequent report to Raycroft, Cotton's most ardent advocate on the Trenton Board of Managers, Cotton emerges as truculent and unyielding, if at times incoherent and verging on irrational. "Nobody," he informed Meyer, "should get him." Finally, in the midst of a weekend break in their discussions, Cotton's wife carted him back off to Trenton, his mental state once again precarious, to resume his duties as superintendent of the state hospital (see Meyer's notes of the meeting on index cards in the Meyer Papers I/767/25; Meyer to Raycroft, 18, 27 January 1926, Meyer Papers I/767/23). (Subsequently, she was to write to Meyer blaming the whole episode on Greenacre: "It was the presence of a third person that made the situation what it was, I think. After his years of experience and tremendous labours – you could not expect him to be told by a young woman of limited experience that his work was all wrong – and that he did his patients more harm than good – without developing on his part an attitude of defense. You – by yourself – would never have made such a statement (Mrs Cotton to Meyer, 25 January 1926, Meyer Papers I/767/23).)

Meyer had already decided that Cotton "needs some time now" to reconcile himself to the findings, and shortly thereafter, he received a vague promise from Raycroft "to find a formula which will harmonize two positions that seem now to be pretty divergent" (Raycroft to Meyer, 25 January 1926, Meyer Papers I/767/24). Months passed, with occasional communications from both Cotton and Raycroft indicating that a response refuting Greenacre's findings was in preparation. Finally, on 17 November, Cotton reappeared in Baltimore, bringing with him two new series, each of 500 cases, which he claimed decisively disproved Greenacre's findings. He at the same time advanced a slightly modified version of his theory, suggesting that "A certain amount of toxicity can be coped with but a relative overflow causes the outbreaks [of insanity]." Privately, Meyer confessed "My own feeling is in harmony with such a principle; but I want to replace plausibility by actual evidence." Cotton's own statistics were worthless, since "practically any discharge alive is counted as a recovery" (manuscript notes dated 18 November 1926, Meyer Papers I/767/27). Further discussion was deferred, but a follow-up meeting including Phyllis Greenacre, scheduled for 19 November, never took place, with Cotton once more retreating back to the hospital.

Six months later, Raycroft broke a long silence, noting that "The long delay in coming to some conclusion in this matter has been most exasperating but apparently under the circumstances unavoidable." He and Cotton were now prepared to meet Meyer once again. Before they did so, however, Greenacre was once more dispatched to Trenton, to go over Cotton's new series of 500 cases, and her report on her return drew an exasperated letter from Meyer: "The account Dr. Greenacre gave me makes me exceedingly doubtful as to whether any benefit from Dr. Greenacre's work and report was desired on the part of the hospital and whether any discussion is at all possible" (Meyer to Raycroft, 4 June 1927, Meyer Papers I/3215/2). Indeed it was not, and there the matter drew to a close. Meyer continued to refuse to allow Greenacre to publish her findings, and with her departure later in 1927 for New York, triggered when she discovered her husband Curt Richter was having an affair with one of his students (see A. Meyer to H. Meyer, 27 October, 17 November, 12 December 1927, Meyer Papers IV/3/239), the whole matter was swept under the rug.

In fact, Meyer went much further than this in concealing what he had learned of Cotton's activities at Trenton. In July of 1927, both he and Cotton left for Britain, to attend the meeting of the British Medical Association in Edinburgh. *En route*, Cotton visited the Rubery Hill Mental Hospital to visit and compare notes with T. C. Graves, his most active British disciple. Following Cotton's previous visit in 1923, Graves had succeeded in getting "a complete operating building" for his hospital, and he now proudly showed Cotton round the premises, introducing him to a number of therapeutic advances that had not yet occurred to his Trenton colleague: injections with antityphoid vaccine ("It produces a chill and a sharp rise in temperature, 103 to 105, which in an hour subsides . . . . The results were remarkably satisfactory"); and a superior method for diagnosing and treating sinus infections ("pushing a cannula through the nose, puncturing the sinus, withdrawing the contents and actually seeing the pus"). "The treatment was similar to ours as far as teeth and tonsils were concerned [though] it was rather astonishing to see them extract teeth without any local or general anesthetic . . . . The patients did not seem to object to this method of extraction" (Cotton, 1927, pp. 2–4).

From Birmingham, Cotton and Graves travelled north together to Edinburgh. Here, with Meyer in the audience, the whole session of the joint meeting of the Royal Medico-Psychological Association and the British Medical Association section on mental diseases was devoted to a series of papers lauding focal infection, opening with a paper by William Hunter, in which he proposed that the term 'functional psychoses' be changed to 'septic psychoses'. Hunter proceeded to cite Meyer as "the most judicial [*sic*] opinion" in support of focal infection theory (quoting from his introduction to Cotton's book), and called for the removal of "all septic foci . . . as a matter of urgency." That many people suffered from rotting teeth and infected tonsils without going mad demonstrated only that there was considerable variation in the susceptibility to focal sepsis, but "however much ordinary people in health may be able to resist, and do successfully resist, the deleterious action of . . . similar sepsis . . . the sufferer from mental disorder *cannot afford to have any such sepsis unregarded*. He is playing for the highest stakes – the preservation of his brain power." Cotton's great achievement had been to recognise this and to begin "from 1918 onwards a desperate frontal attack with horse, foot and artillery – namely medical recognition of the importance of oral and focal sepsis, surgical help for its removal, and bacteriological support for both . . . in the teeth, the tonsils, nasal sinuses, stomach, intestine and colon, and the genito-urinary tract." His splendid example was a pattern for all psychiatry to follow, and one must forthwith equip all mental hospitals with operating facilities, dentists, and a variety of surgeons, radiologists, and bacteriologists (Hunter, 1927).

A parade of the eminent followed him to the podium to add their endorsements: Sir Berkeley Moynihan, President of the Royal College of Surgeons, G. M. Robertson, Professor of Psychiatry at Edinburgh and past president of the RMPA, and Chalmers Watson, also of the university. Cotton then briefly reviewed his astonishing achievements at Trenton, followed by Graves, who made almost equally extravagant claims for his work at Rubery Hill. In the discussion that followed, only D. K. Henderson broke with the atmosphere of mutual self-congratulation, and his invocation of Kopeloff and Kirby's critique of Cotton was promptly dismissed by Hunter: Kopeloff had failed because he had made only token efforts to remove the sources of sepsis. His one recovery had come in a case where he had extracted 30 teeth, instead of the two or three he usually remained content with. Besides, "Kopeloff was not even a doctor; he was a bacteriologist. He did not think psychiatrists need worry about Kopeloff's work" (*Journal of Mental Science*, 1927, p. 726; see also Hunter, 1929).

In his private record of the Edinburgh proceedings, Cotton noted, as one indicator of the eminence of his supporters in Britain, that following their speeches endorsing his work, both Hunter and Moynihan had been awarded honorary LLD degrees by Edinburgh University. He added, "It is to be hoped that recognition of this work by the British Medical Association will do much to overcome the apathy and opposition which has been so evident in this country" (Cotton, 1927, p. 11).

Buoyed by such influential support, Cotton returned to his labours at Trenton with renewed vigour. He had now modified his stance on bowel surgery, much to his wife's relief, and fortunately for the mortality statistics at Trenton, since he had now discovered that 80%, not the 20% he had diagnosed in the early '20s, "will be found to have intestinal stasis and toxemia." Instead of full-fledged colectomies, he opted for less drastic surgical interventions suggested by the British surgeon, Sir Arbuthnot Lane, designed to prevent "adhesions," and supplemented these "by means of physiotherapy which consists of massive colonic irrigations, 15–20 gallons in a treatment, and diathermy and Morse Sine Wave" (Cotton, 1930, p. 2). Writing to Meyer, Cotton's wife noted: "In regards to colon removals, you know that this was long a source of great distress to me and a topic on which my husband and I finally were unable to speak. But I respected his attitude and lived in hope and now my hopes have been rewarded and I see him learning new methods and ways of treating the colon – by physiotherapy etc. so that only in extreme cases will he in future resort to its removal. His eagerness to always go on and try new ways wins my admiration" (Mrs Cotton to Meyer, 25 January 1926, Meyer Papers I/767/23). Others, a little closer to the action, could not always sustain such patient stoicism: "It was awful to work there; he was going much too far with his operating. There was a young girl, she worked in the office right by the door where they had to roll the baskets past that carried the bodies and organs and stuff. One day she ran out screaming, she couldn't stand it any more" (Mrs Agnes Trier, a former hospital employee, quoted in Leiby (1967, p. 186)).

In other respects, though, his drive to eliminate sepsis became even more aggressive than before. Deploring the "conservatism" of the dental profession, he noted that "Many dentists would hesitate to extract vital teeth and for some years we followed this practice. But we have found within the last year that many of our failures were due to the fact that we allowed vital teeth to remain in the mouth although we had extracted a large number of teeth which were infected. It has become the rule now that if a patient is found to have a considerable number of infected teeth complete extraction must be done to eradicate all infection in the mouth . . . we have by necessity become more radical . . . . We have yet to have any regrets when we have ordered complete extractions in our patients and no patients when they have recovered have ever blamed us for extracting the teeth . . . [on the contrary] it is a source of satisfaction to know that the infection has been entirely eliminated and there is no prospect for any further trouble" (Cotton, 1929, pp. 4, 10).

Others had a very different reaction. Reporting on a visit to Trenton in which he was taken on rounds by Cotton, Katzenelbogen (1930) commented "First of all, I felt sad, seeing hundreds of people without teeth. Only a few have sets of false teeth. The hospital takes great care as to the pulling out of teeth, but does not provide false teeth . . . . While in the hospital they suffer from indigestions, I was told, not being able to masticate the ordinary food which they get there. At home, recovered, these poor people have the same troubles, not being in a position to choose food which they would be able to eat without teeth. In addition, they are ashamed to be without teeth, since in their communities it is known to be a token of a previous sojourn in the State Hospital."

Meyer meanwhile elected to let sleeping dogs lie. Invited to the dinner celebrating Cotton's 20th anniversary at Trenton, he declined "with very great regret . . . . It is a splendid and well deserved thing to celebrate the twentieth anniversary of what has been a most creditable and noteworthy period in psychiatric activity. I remember with great satisfaction having had an opportunity to encourage Dr. Cotton to accept his position, and following step by step the many valuable innovations he has brought about . . . hence my pleasure in conveying my expressions of highest appreciation through you" (Meyer to Raycroft, 1 December 1927, Meyer Papers I/767/ 29). Three years later, he intervened at Cotton's request to secure his oldest son's admission to Johns Hopkins Medical School, where he planned to train to follow his father into psychiatry. Meanwhile, Cotton kept Meyer abreast of his latest progress in the war on sepsis, including the series of 30 abdominal operations he had performed on private patients in 1932, and his fight to reinstitute the use of colectomies at the state hospital, without drawing as much as a word of remonstrance from his mentor (e.g., Cotton to Meyer, 29 April, 8 May 1933; Meyer to Cotton, 6 May 1933, Meyer Papers I/767/31, 32). And when Cotton unexpectedly dropped dead on 8 May 1933, Meyer was his obituarist in the *American Journal of Psychiatry*.

The obituary is an extraordinary document, revealing no hint of what Meyer actually knew of Cotton's activities at Trenton. On the contrary, his work there is described as "a most remarkable achievement of the pioneer spirit . . . an extraordinary record of achievement [by] one of the most stimulating figures of our generation." Meyer acknowledged (as how could he not?) that Cotton's work had been controversial, especially among "non-surgically inclined colleagues in the rising wave of variously inclusive psychogenic interpretations." But this only made the more tragic the "outstanding and unexpected and premature" loss the profession had suffered when Cotton died with his research programme "only partially fulfilled" (Meyer, 1934, pp. 921–923). He also wrote a brief note to Mrs Cotton on hearing of "the abrupt and deplorably premature" death of her husband: "A remarkable and noble life and then end like that of the soldier in action. [Cotton had actually died while lunching at his Trenton club, but Meyer was presumably referring here to his campaign to expand the surgical programme at Trenton, about which Cotton had kept him informed, apparently with expectations of enlisting his support.] A life and work that will live on and will lead to more fruitions" (Meyer to Mrs Cotton, 10 May 1933, Meyer Papers I/767/32).

Others shared Meyer's regret at Cotton's untimely death. The *Trenton Evening Times*, in a fulsome tribute to the world-famous figure who had done so much for the mentally ill of the state of New Jersey, reminded its readers that "Thousands of persons who have suffered mental affliction owe him an enduring debt of gratitude for . . . displacing confusion and despair with hope and confidence. [All must lament the loss of] this great pioneer whose humanitarian influence was, and will continue to be, of such monumental proportions" (9 May 1933, p. 6; see also Graves, 1934). And indeed his influence *did* continue. For Cotton's departure from the scene did not spell the end of Trenton's infatuation with focal infection. The reign of his assistants as the hospital's superintendents lasted until the retirement of Harold Magee,[8] in 1960, as did the employment of Ferdearle Fischer, the

---

8. In succession, the superintendents were Robert Stone (1930–44), who throughout the '20s had done the bulk of the tonsillectomies and gynaecological surgery under Cotton's supervision; J. B. Spradley (1944–48) whose resignation for reasons of health was followed immediately by his appointment to the hospital's Board of Management; and Harold Magee (1948–60), whose particular enthusiasm was for the transorbital lobotomy. Further continuity with the Cotton regime was provided by the continued presence, as the medical representatives on the hospital's Board of Managers, of Drs Raycroft and McCray, Cotton's key supporter throughout the 1920s. Both were succeeded in this role by their sons, with Paul McCray Jr continuing as a member of the Board until 1978.

dental surgeon whom Cotton had hired in 1918. Annually, the hospital's reports announced that "Sepsis is carefully searched for and eliminated in all cases" (Trenton State Hospital *Annual Report*, 1955, p. 2).[9] Local newspaper articles continued to celebrate their hospital's role as the pioneer in this valuable assault on the nightmare that was madness (see, for example, the lead article in the *Trenton Sunday Times Advertiser*, 26 September 1948, on the occasion of the 100th anniversary of Trenton State Hospital, which includes a photograph of the operating theatre of the oral department). Of course, to the colonic irrigations, the pulling of teeth, and the extraction of tonsils, there were added a host of other wondrous means of restoring the mad to sanity: insulin shock, hypothermia therapy, camphor and metrazol-induced convulsions, histamine shock, inoculation with malaria, electro-convulsive therapy in a variety of forms, anectine, and lobotomy – in both its transorbital and standard forms. Through it all, though, Cotton remained the hospital's guiding genius and patron saint, his contribution symbolically recognised each year by the award to the outstanding member of staff of the "Cotton Award for Kindness".

References

ABBOTT, E. S. (1902) The criteria of insanity and the problems of psychiatry. *American Journal of Insanity*, **59**, 1–16.

AMERICAN JOURNAL OF PSYCHIATRY (1922) Discussion – functional psychosis. *American Journal of Psychiatry*, **79**, 195–210.

BARKER, L. (1920) Oral sepsis and internal medicine. *Journal of Dental Research*, **2**, 43–58.

BILLINGS, F. (1916) *Focal Infections*. New York: Appleton.

BRUCE, L. (1906) *Studies in Clinical Psychiatry*. London: Macmillan.

CLARK, M. J. (1981) The rejection of psychological approaches to mental disorder in late nineteenth century British psychiatry. In *Madhouses, Mad-doctors, and Madmen: The Social History of Psychiatry in the Victorian Era* (ed. A. Scull), pp. 271–312. London: Athlone; Philadelphia: University of Pennsylvania Press.

COKENOWER, J. W. (1904) A plea for conservative operations on the ovaries. *Transactions of the Section on Obstetrics and Diseases of Women of the American Medical Association*, **1**, 293–300.

COTTON, H. A. (1919) The relation of oral infection to mental diseases. *Journal of Dental Research*, **2**, 269–313.

—— (1921) *The Defective Delinquent and Insane: The Relation of Focal Infections to Their Causation, Treatment and Prevention*. Princeton: Princeton University Press; London: Oxford University Press.

—— (1922a) The etiology and treatment of the so-called functional psychoses. *American Journal of Psychiatry*, **79**, 157–194.

—— (1922b) Oral diagnosis: an essential part of medical diagnosis. *Journal of Oralogy*, **1**, 3–11.

—— (1923) The relation of chronic sepsis to the so-called functional mental disorders. *Journal of Mental Science*, **69**, 434–465.

—— (1925) Relation of focal infections to crime and delinquency. *Proceedings of the 49th Annual Session of the American Association for the Study of the Feeble Minded*. Raleigh, North Carolina.

—— (1927) European rambles of a psychiatrist. Unpublished typescript, Trenton State

9. The last reference of this sort I was able to trace is in the annual report for the following year, 1956, though whether this actually spelled the demise of the treatment is unclear.

Hospital Archives, Trenton, New Jersey.
—— (1930) Gastro-intestinal stasis in the psychoses. *Proceedings of the Fifth International Congress of Physiotherapy*, Liege, Belgium. 14–18 September.
—— & DRAPER, J. W. (1920) What is being done for the insane by means of surgery: analysis of one hundred and twenty five laparotomies; importance of preventive psychiatry. *Transactions of the Section on Gastro-Enterology and Proctology of the American Medical Association.*
—— & LYNCH, J. (1920) Intestinal pathology in the functional psychoses: preliminary report of surgical findings, procedures, and results. *Medical Record*, **97**, 719–742. (Reprinted as a separate pamphlet.)
FRANKEL, E. (1932) Study of 'end results' of 645 major operative cases and 407 non-operative cases treated at Trenton State Hospital 1918–1932. Unpublished report, State of New Jersey, Department of Institutions and Agencies.
GRAVES, T. C. (1923) The relation of chronic sepsis to so-called functional mental disorder. *Journal of Mental Science*, **69**, 465–471.
—— (1927) Chronic sepsis and mental disorder. *Journal of Mental Science*, **73**, 563–566.
—— (1934) Obituary: Henry Andrews Cotton, M.A., M.D. *Journal of Mental Science*, **79**, 178–180.
GREENACRE, P. (1926) Trenton State Hospital Survey – 1924–1926, made with the co-operation of Dr. Adolf Meyer. Unpublished typescript, Trenton State Hospital Archives.
—— (1983) Interview with the author, 23 December. New York City.
GROB, G. (1983) *Mental Illness and American Society, 1875–1940.* Princeton: Princeton University Press.
HILL, C. G. (1907) How can we best advance the study of psychiatry? *American Journal of Insanity*, **64**, 1–7.
HIRSCH, (1966) *Frank Billings: The Architect of Medical Education.* Chicago: University of Chicago Press.
HOBBS, A. T. (1924) A survey of American and Canadian psychiatric opinion as to focal infections (or chronic sepsis) as causative factors in functional psychoses. *Journal of Mental Science*, **70**, 542–553.
HUNTER, W. (1900) Oral sepsis as a cause of disease. *British Medical Journal*, ii, 215–216.
—— (1927) Chronic sepsis as a cause of mental disorder. *Journal of Mental Science*, **73**, 549–563.
—— (1929) The relation of focal infection to mental diseases. *Journal of Mental Science*, **75**, 464–466.
JOURNAL OF MENTAL SCIENCE (1923) Notes and news: minutes of the Medico-Psychological Association annual meeting, session on 'chronic sepsis and mental disorder'. *Journal of Mental Science*, **69**, 552–559.
KATZENELBOGEN, S. (1930) The Trenton State Hospital. Unpublished manuscript, Adolf Meyer Papers, Chesney Archives, Johns Hopkins Medical School, Baltimore, Maryland.
KOPELOFF, N. (1923) Is the stomach a focus of infection? *American Journal of the Medical Sciences*, 2nd series, **165**, 120–129.
—— & CHEYNEY, C. O. (1922) Studies in focal infection: its presence and elimination in the functional psychoses. *American Journal of Psychiatry*, **2**, 139–156.
LARSON, M. S. (1977) *The Rise of Professionalism: A Sociological Analysis.* Berkeley: University of California Press.
LEIBY, J. (1967) *Charity and Correction in New Jersey: A History of State Welfare Institutions.* New Brunswick, New Jersey: Rutgers University Press.
LEWIS, B. G. (1922) The winning fight against mental disease. *Review of Reviews*, December.
MEYER, A. Unpublished papers. Chesney Archives, Johns Hopkins University Medical School, Baltimore, Maryland.
—— (1934) In Memoriam: Henry A. Cotton. *American Journal of Psychiatry*, **90**, 921–923.
MITCHELL, S. W. (1909) Address to the American Neurological Association. *Transactions of the American Neurological Association*, **35**.
ROBINSON, N. (1729) *A New System of the Spleen, Vapours, and Hypochondriack Melancholy, to which is Subjoined, a Discourse upon the Nature, Cause, and Cure of Melancholy, Madness, and Lunacy.* London: Bettesworth.
ROSENOW, E. C. (1919) Studies on elective localization: focal infection with special reference to oral sepsis. *Journal of Dental Research*, **1**, 205.

SHAW, A. (1922) Physical treatment for mental disorders: a summary of expert commentary upon Dr. Cotton's work at Trenton. *Review of Reviews*, December.

SICHERMAN, B. (1967) The quest for mental health in America, 1880–1917. Unpublished PhD dissertation, Columbia University.

STARR, P. (1984) *The Social Transformation of American Medicine*. New York: Basic Books.

TAYLOR, E. W. (1908) The attitude of the medical profession toward the psychotherapeutic movement. *Journal of Nervous and Mental Diseases*, **35**, 420.

UPSON, H. (1907) Nervous disorders due to the teeth: a preliminary report. *Cleveland Medical Journal*, **6**, 458–459.

—— (1909) Dementia praecox caused by dental impaction. *Monthly Cyclopedia and Medical Bulletin*, November, 648–651.

—— (1910) Serious mental disturbances caused by painless dental lesions. *American Quarterly of Roentgenology*, **11**, 223–243.

WATSON, C. (1923) The role of auto-intoxication or auto-infection in mental disorders. *Journal of Mental Science*, **69**, 52–77.

WHITE, W. A. Unpublished papers. Records of St Elizabeth's Hospital, National Archives, Washington, DC: Record Group 418.

11 Rich and mad in Victorian England

TREVOR TURNER

Case history

In July 1875 a 31-year-old Barrister at Law, Charles T, was transferred from Brook House, Clapton, to Ticehurst House Asylum in Sussex. He had been in Brook House for about two months, his first admission, diagnosed as having "melancholia". His certificates mentioned his incoherent conversation, and his various delusions about himself and others. It was also noted that he had a strong desire to be dead, had made suicidal attempts, was refusing food, and had been violent to himself and other people. A description was given of his alternating depression and excitement of mind, his obstinacy and his restlessness at night; it was uncertain whether or not there was a "hereditary tendency". An admission note described him as being "well made and 6'1" tall". As well as having a "nervous and suspicious way of looking about", he did not "like to be touched", and "will not speak".

Over the next few months he could not "collect his ideas", was occasionally violent at dinner, and had to be fed because he would not take his food appropriately. He was described as talking nearly all night with his "voices", as listening to something beneath the floor, and as "eccentric and suspicious in manner". By 1876 his "great mental enfeeblement" and "muddled ideas" are again noted. He is quoted as saying "I know that the voices are right", and during conversations he would suddenly "break off and stand silent as if listening to voices". It seems that "under the influence of his delusion he shouted to everyone of his past life, and repeatedly demanded to see the First Lord of the Admiralty at the Spithead review", but this was refused. In a letter from Dr William Gull, he is described as having "a mind preoccupied by delusions associated with the hearing of voices". Despite treatment with mustard baths, and the routines of diet, exercise and example, he was transferred to Brislington House, "not improved", in 1878. However, he was subsequently re-admitted, in February 1879, in "good bodily health", but now deemed to be suffering from "chronic mania and aural hallucinations". He continued to hear and answer the voices, particularly noises under the floor. He was felt to be a danger, and a certain Captain H was appointed his gentleman companion. By January of 1880 his "improved moral conduct" was noted, but

170

now a Captain C was looking after him. Still thought to be "suspicious at times", in September 1880 he escaped. He seems to have fled to Newhaven, taken a boat to Dieppe, and then to have set off inland. His story ends sadly. He was found dead with "a bullet in his brain on the Rouen road".

Although given here in its bleak essentials, Mr T's case is typical, in its language of description and psychopathology and treatment approach, of a routine admission to the most expensive of Victorian private asylums. It is atypical, in that only three out of over 600 admissions ended in completed suicide, and personally striking since the patient was the son of a Harley Street physician, a Dr T. Turner.

There seems little doubt that there is now a considerable divergence between the history of psychiatry and the history of madness. The former has concentrated on the lives of physicians devoted to the care of the mentally ill, the diseases and symptoms with which they had to deal, the treatments and institutions deemed appropriate for their patients, and a general perspective of scientific progress (e.g. Zilboorg, 1941; Leigh, 1961). The latter is concerned more with the social impact of insanity, the light thrown on contemporary society by the management of the mad, and has remained sceptical as to the reality of a true advance in understanding (e.g. Scull, 1979; Porter, 1987). Such disparity is not surprising. Clinicians wish to understand the past largely for amateur reasons. They wish to diagnose famous men, to add their understanding to the insights of historical research. They also need to know the course of a disease, uncomplicated by modern interventions, so as to clarify their therapeutic approach. A good history in both senses of the term is the basis of clinical activity. By contrast, historians are much more single minded. They need to know exactly what happened, the real story. Using primary sources and avoiding the interpretations of hindsight, they have developed a rich matrix of ideas concerning the past of both psychiatry and madness. Recent lectures in this series by William Bynum (Ch. 8), Roy Porter (Ch. 9) and Andrew Scull (Ch. 10) have opened our eyes to the importance of mental illness in understanding a culture.

The present debate about community care, the 'Irish Question' so to speak of modern psychiatry, has generated a renewed puzzlement as to why the Victorians built so many asylums. It has been suggested that this was largely the result of social factors (e.g. Foucault, 1965; Doerner, 1981; Busfield, 1986). Increasing urbanisation and industrialisation led to the need to segregate a group of people unable to cope for themselves in such an organised world. The mopish villagers of 17th-century England could not be expected to deal with the regulated working hours of the 19th-century factories. Furthermore, an increased sympathy towards the insane, generated by the Quakers and the emergent evangelists, added to the switch from supernatural or religious versions of madness to a medical and pathological model, further promoted, it is said, an enlightened hospital care system. There are more contentious views. E. F. Torrey (1980) and Edward Hare

(1983) have postulated a genuine increase in schizophrenic illness, possibly mediated by a toxic or viral agent. Andrew Scull (1979) has suggested a lowered threshold of acceptability for mad behaviour. Whatever the reasons, there is no doubt that the proportion of the population deemed suitable for asylum care went on rising, reaching its apogee in the first half of the 20th century (Jones, 1972).

Clinical psychiatrists are limited in terms of their useful contribution to these learned discussions. The standard histories, such as that written by the zealous Freudophile Gregory Zilboorg (1941), have concentrated on psychiatric textbooks and similar writings. The work of Richard Hunter and Ida Macalpine has been more scrupulous in using primary sources, for example their study of Friern Hospital in *Psychiatry for the Poor* (Hunter & Macalpine, 1974); but even this was based upon annual reports rather than working case notes. While there are many detailed individual cases written up by 19th-century medical men, there still seems room for a consistent series of reports describing the mental state of an asylum population.

Unless we know what sort of people were put in them, it will continue to be very difficult to understand why the asylums were created in such numbers. From the evidence we have, it seems likely that the vast majority of patients were suffering from psychotic illnesses, brain diseases, physical disease presenting with behavioural disorder, and mixtures of the three. It has been suggested that up to 20% of asylum inmates had general paralysis of the insane (Hunter & Macalpine, 1963).

Yet such assumptions did not go unchallenged even in the 19th century. In the years preceding the 1890 Lunacy Bill there was considerable concern that alienists were locking up strangely sane individuals. Such anxieties were most rife in the semi-secret private sector, where the fortunes of innocent heiresses (and heirs) were deemed at risk from the unjustified certifications of unscrupulous mad doctors. Popular novels such as *Valentine Vox* (Cockton, 1854) and *Hard Cash* (Reade, 1863) caused a considerable outcry, even in the staid *Journal of Mental Science*. In 1877 a commission of inquiry into lunacy law investigated in detail the allegations of a certain Mrs Lowe, who subsequently published a book entitled *The Bastilles of England* (1883). A strong believer in spiritualism, she was for a while confined in Lawn House, the small private asylum in Hanwell run by John Conolly, and then by his son-in-law, Henry Maudsley. Despite conversations "night after night . . . ", at first, Maudsley seems to have become exasperated and eventually transferred her because she kept running off and was "not an agreeable inmate of one's house" (Select Committee on Lunacy Law, 1877, p. 322). Whatever actually happened, considerable doubts have been expressed both then and now, as to the purpose and effect of commitment to an asylum (e.g. Szasz, 1962; Kosky, 1986). Were such institutions more a reflection of family dissensions and non-conformist behaviour than a therapeutic response to the better recognition of disordered mental states?

Another aspect of Victorian psychiatry that has been poorly explored is the true nature of the asylum doctor. What kind of medical man chose such a career? A modern social historian, E. S. Turner (1958), has written, "there were posts in asylums, both public and private, for those who were willing to take the risk of being clubbed or strangled, and who did not shrink from the peculiar tensions of dance nights and amateur dramatics behind locked doors". He also suggested that asylum doctors worked under social and financial disadvantages, by contrast with other specialists who could look forward "to some public recognition of their status by being appointed, as an honorary distinction, to the public medical charities and other institutions" (p. 213). Furthermore, asylum doctors had no control over admissions, never saw patients before they came in, and could only advise when a patient was well enough to be discharged (Hunter & Macalpine, 1974). Responsible for medical and moral treatment, diet, exercise, occupation and amusement, they also classified patients to the appropriate wards.

It is noteworthy that the main writers on mental disease in 19th-century England spent very little time working as asylum doctors. Conolly stayed only four years at Hanwell, Maudsley a bare three and a half at Wakefield and Manchester, and D. H. Tuke spent little more than three years at the small and somewhat special Retreat at York. While detailed research is needed, there is little suggestion that the average asylum doctor was regarded as an outstanding member of the medical profession. Which enhances the view that there may have been considerable flaws in the practice of psychiatry at the time.

One of Maudsley's contemporaries was a Dr Herbert Hayes Newington, who was president of the Medico-Psychological Association (MPA) 1889–90, and subsequently became its treasurer for many years until his death in 1917. He ran the "mecca of private asylums", at Ticehurst in Sussex. In fact it had been run by his family since its opening in 1792, and during the second half of the 19th century was the most expensive establishment in England. Its clientele were by definition rich, and social factors in their admission have been elegantly analysed by Charlotte McKenzie (1985); their fees enabled the Newingtons to provide an extraordinary range of diversions. Not only were there graded walks, a cricket pitch and a croquet lawn, but excursions to the seaside, picnics, whist drives, entertainments, and weekly concerts were included in the regular activities. Horses and carriages, a pack of harriers, with which the gentlemen could go hunting, and the numerous attendants, servants and companions, provided a veritable therapeutic community. The patients were outnumbered two to one, and the whole Newington family, as well as assistant medical officers, took part in their care.

More importantly, from the modern point of view, there are excellent and detailed case books which have been preserved, and are now kept in the Archives of the Wellcome Institute for the History of Medicine. Since, to quote a present professor of psychiatry, "most people never think about things that psychiatrists think about", it seemed worthwhile to assess these materials from a diagnostic point of view. If recognisable symptoms and behaviour emerged therefrom, it might usefully clarify aspects of Victorian asylum practice. An absence of such symptoms would have been perhaps more intriguing to the historian, and especially to those enamoured of the works of Dr Thomas Szasz, but the recognisability, severity, and physicality of the syndromes that did emerge from these notes, soon led to the formulation of another question. How could this information, the perspective of modern diagnoses, aid in our historical understanding? Could such insights also have a modern usefulness?

Method

Looking at Victorian case books is not unequivalent to the task of the histopathologist. Much of the language becomes a form of routine cellular structure; phrases such as 'labouring under delusions', 'unpardonable sins', 'no change' and 'of neuro-sanguineous temperament', provide the connective tissue between which exist pockets of extraordinary psychopathology. The first task with the Ticehurst material was to extract the significant details of each patient. Between 1845, when the existing clientele were hurriedly written up in half a dozen lines, and 1890 when a standardised format had emerged, over 600 admissions were recorded. A number of patients were re-admitted on several occasions, for reasons that will become clear. Thirty-two case books, varying in length from 150 to 300 pages, covered this period, which is conveniently located between the two major legislative years of Victorian psychiatry, namely 1845 (the Asylum Act) and 1890 (the Lunacy Bill).

Apart from basic demographic data, such as age, marital status and sex, details of the presenting physical and mental state, the previous and family history, and daily, weekly and monthly notes of the patients' behaviour and progress were all recorded, in long hand. But the Newingtons were not naive as to their patients' qualities. Describing the history and practice of the establishment, in a paper delivered in 1901 at Ticehurst, they remarked: "hereditary predisposition is a hopelessly unknown quantity. We get in time to hear of the history, in many cases, which has been denied unblushingly on admission. With us mendacity is added in probably a greater degree to ignorance of family history than is usual in most institutions" (Medical Superintendents, 1901).

The key feature of this material is the repetitive detail. For example, by contrast to the two or three pages customary in the Bethlem notes, many patients take up some 20 to 30 pages, across several case books. Newspaper cuttings, letters, drawings, the odd poem, go far beyond the skeletal data seen today in many hospitals. Appetite, sleep, social interaction, quirks of behaviour, characteristic remarks, clothing, and forms of exercise dominate the descriptions. Using the Research Diagnostic Criteria (Spitzer *et al*, 1975) it was generally not difficult to make a diagnosis, and five broad categories were outlined (see Table 1) including one called 'indefinite' so as to avoid the pitfalls of forced choices.

Especial note was taken of delusions and the way in which they were described, hallucinations in all modalities, and other evidence of psychopathology, such as formal thought disorder, flight of ideas, and catatonic behaviour. Examples of unusual syndromes, such as the Capgras, were noted in particular detail, as was the prevalence of certain behaviour, including forms of movement disorder, violent outbursts, the use of restraint, masturbation (also known as self-abuse), and suicidal attempts.

Treatment approaches, such as stomach pumps and the use of mustard baths, were also enumerated.

Descriptive results

Clearly, words like 'delusions' and 'hallucinations' may not present similar phenomena to those defined as such today. By and large the detail attached to such terms was sufficient to justify their use; thus Mrs Francis H, "fancies herself the Queen of England and Empress of China", and was described as having delusions of identity, place and position. Mr Henry R, a 36-year-old unmarried snuff manufacturer, was "labouring under grandiose delusions". He was quoted as saying that he was "an enormously strong man, he has copulated with 300 women in one night and that if his parts fail him it is his intention to get a little steam engine and insert it up his anus".

Likewise, reasonable reports of hallucinatory experiences, often described as voices, visions, or smells, were detailed for at least 128 patients, over 21% of the whole cohort. Thus Henry M "imagined he heard voices outside his bedroom door reproaching and taunting him about filthy acts", and believed he was surrounded by a mob. Henry H not only talked incoherently to himself but also "carried on communication with the spirit land and believed in unseen agencies". Asking the medical officer "don't you think they [the voices] are making the air too pungent", he was described as "talking as though there were several persons in the room with him". Others claimed they were being tormented by galvanism, one patient insisting that "persons whom he could not see proceeded to frig him through the influences of electricity and galvanism".

Visual experiences were also common. A Mrs D claimed she saw her tormentors looking down from the bed. A Dr Samuel H, an asylum superintendent from Yorkshire, "spoke of birds that had been flying about and whistling", while in a state of alcohol withdrawal. A Mrs Constance O was "full of optical delusions and hallucinations", and "sees devils, fancies persons change colour, and imagines she sees all sorts of objects that do not exist". A particularly detailed account of second- and third-person auditory hallucinations was given in a letter written by a Mrs Sarah F. She wrote to her niece as follows: "Dear Julia, when I was in the village this afternoon I heard a voice say 'how very unkind of you aunt Sarah'. I feel certain that it was your voice but how came you here in Ticehurst". She then went on to insist that she could "hear her relatives in the village talking" about her and "thinks it must be telephonic". Furthermore, hallucinations in the context of a depressive illness were quite common. For example, "she hears persons speaking to her from the ceiling and corners of her room, who tell her she is to be starved for the crime she has committed". A Mr William D felt that "the evil one whispers deplorable words and sentiments", and believed that his inside was "full of demons". But there was also a discussion as to the form of such experiences. Mrs Emma E had a significant puerperal depression, but it was thought that "she hears noises and it does not appear that she hears voices," and later, "she does hear noises at night but misinterprets them".

A particular feature was the extraordinary prevalence of abnormal movements and postures. Terms like 'grimaces', 'fidgets', 'jerkiness' and 'twitching' recur constantly. Mrs B turned "round and round like a little dog". Mrs T made "hideous grimaces". Mr K indulged in "pugilistic manoeuvres". Mr J was "attitudinising before his mirror", and had a "ceaseless habit of gesticulating and grimacing". Edward B "was wriggling himself about in a most absurd fashion" and "moving his mouth about a good deal as if he were in a slight epileptoid condition". Nor did these movements seem to be of neurological origin. William F played golf twice with Dr Newington despite being "unable to sit still" and "making grimaces in a senseless way". Mr Henry B, although "clownish and eccentric when at the wickets, putting himself in absurd attitudes", was "improved very much in his play and an active and willing fielder". Others were described as "sitting for hours in the same attitude". The Countess D

TABLE 1
Modern diagnosis (RDC[1]) of patients in Ticehurst House Asylum, 1850–89

Year of admission	Total no.	Schizo-phrenia (%)	Manic–depressive illness (%)	Organic (%)	Neurotic (%)	Indefinite (%)
1850–54	25	12 (48)	6 (24)	2 (8)	1 (4)	4 (16)
1855–59	22	6 (28)	11 (50)	2 (9)	2 (9)	1 (4)
1860–64	58	19 (33)	22 (38)	7 (12)	3 (5)	7 (12)
1865–69	84	20 (24)	31 (37)	21 (25)	2 (2)	10 (12)
1870–74	69	22 (32)	24 (35)	11 (16)	4 (6)	8 (11)
1875–79	90	21 (23)	47 (52)	9 (10)	6 (7)	7 (8)
1880–84	96	16 (17)	46 (48)	19 (20)	7 (7)	8 (8)
1885–89	71	26 (37)	28 (39)	7 (10)	1 (1)	9 (13)
Total	515	142 (28)	215 (42)	78 (15)	26 (5)	54 (10)

1. Research Diagnostic Criteria (Spitzer *et al*, 1975).

displayed a "rigid and resisting condition and sat for hours doubled up and head bent forward vacantly staring". Since she also tried to bite the attendant, gesticulated, and was talking to herself, terms like "silly" and "impulsive" were employed. Often violent behaviour ensued. Henry M "stood for some time in the same position", but later "knocked the MO down". More obviously catatonic features were also apparent. Mrs Isabella S was in "a state of cataleptic rigidity, mute and statuesque at times", as well as "addicted to making grimaces when reading, and 'pirouetting' among the guests". Miss Henrietta B "remains in one position without moving or speaking". Sometimes she fancied "she is a tiger and acts in accordance with that animal", and "if her arm is raised it remains in that position". The modern diagnoses of patients admitted between 1850 and 1889, based on this case-book material, are outlined in Table 1, by quinquennia.

Contemporary diagnostic terms used at Ticehurst

The business of diagnostic classification flourished in the 19th century. However, the most important English-language textbook, the *Manual of Psychological Medicine* (Bucknill & Tuke, 1858), was rather sceptical of such schemes, admitting that "very different arrangements have been made by different writers grouped upon somewhat opposite principles" (p. 89). As can be seen from Tables 2–5, the details of the relationship between contemporary and modern diagnoses indicate several general themes. Most striking is the variety and looseness of the terms, particularly in regard to the schizophrenic group (Table 2). There is also a progressive development, towards a wider variety of categories, and a significant number of non-diagnoses.

The least coherent group is that fulfilling modern criteria for schizophrenia. At Ticehurst the word 'delusions' predominates, declining over time. The word 'hallucinations' attains significance by the 1880s, but the

TABLE 2
Diagnostic terms for patients fulfilling RDC for schizophrenia, Ticehurst House Asylum 1850–89, by percentage

	1850–59	1860–69	1870–79	1880–89	Total
'Delusions'					
(± phrase)	83.5	41	62.8	26.2	48.6
'Dementia'	5.5	5	2.3	4.8	4.2
'Hallucinations'					
(aural/auditory)	0	2.5	0	16.7	5.6
'Mania'					
(± phrase)	0	20.5	16.3	38.0	21.8
Melancholia	0	0	4.7	7.1	3.5
Others/nil	11.0	31	13.9	7.2	16.3

TABLE 3

Diagnostic terms for patients fulfilling RDC for manic–depressive disorder (mania or major depression), Ticehurst House Asylum 1850–89, by percentage

	1850–59	1860–69	1870–79	1880–89	Total
'Delusions' (± phrase)	64.7	35.8	32.4	9.4	27.8
'Mania' (± prefix)	23.5	24.5	29.6	44.4	33.0
'Melancholia'[1] (not subordinated)	11.8	11.3	25.3	36.4	24.6
Others	0	7.6	12.7	8.4	9.1
Nil used	0	20.8	0	1.4	5.5
	(100)	(100)	(100)	(100)	(100)

1. Terms such as 'delusions with melancholia' are included in the 'delusions' category.

only other formal category used at all heavily is 'mania', especially 'chronic mania'. Only about a third of the cases were attributed to any accepted diagnosis, which contrasts with other groups.

The manic–depressive group (Table 3) is, in addition, more coherent in other ways. The words 'melancholia' and 'mania' progress to take up 80% of the diagnoses by the 1880s (while the term 'delusions' is used less and less). Not only is there agreement between the 19th-century use and the modern use of such terms, but contemporary coherence of diagnosis is obvious. We thus seem to be seeing, in a small way, the development of a clear diagnostic category that has survived in robust form to the present day. From being general terms, defining over- and under activity within the broad compass of insanity, melancholia and mania become increasingly mood-specific disorders, distinct from other functional psychoses. Further-more, additional diagnostic language, such as the prefixes 'paroxysmal' or 'senile', is rarely needed.

Implications of diagnoses

The relationship between diagnosis and asylum management may thus be seen as dynamic and coherent rather than casual. It also appears that the process of honing diagnostic clarity had a strong social pressure behind it. To project an asylum with a good record of cured patients it may have been important to know the clientele and the prognosis of the conditions accepted. The re-admissions at Ticehurst were largely female, middle-aged manics, some admitted four or five times but recovering fully on each occasion. Unlike a large public asylum, receiving admissions from lay magistrates, private establishments were perhaps able therefore to use medical criteria more purposefully in controlling admissions.

An alternative view, that the proportion of diagnoses seen in Ticehurst

TABLE 4
Diagnostic terms of patients having an 'organic' diagnosis, Ticehurst Asylum 1850–89

	1850–59	1860–69	1870–79	1880–89	Total	%
Delusions	1	9	9	2	21	26.9
Dementia	1	3	0	0	4	5.2
Mania	0	1	3	7	11	14.1
Melancholia	0	2	1	3	6	7.7
General paralysis	0	3	0	11	14	17.9
Dipsomania/ DTs	0	2	0	0	2	2.6
Others	2	3	5	1	11	14.1
Nil used	0	5	2	2	9	11.5
Total	4	28	20	26	78	

merely reflected admissions as a whole in Victorian England, cannot as yet be justified by the available data.

It is important to note that the pattern of diagnoses for the organic group (Table 4) does not resemble any of the others. It is therefore unlikely that we are seeing physical conditions masquerading as mental illnesses. (The neurotic group are few in number and loosely defined. Never violent or disinhibited, this is probably an unsatisfactory category, based partly on absence of symptoms. There is a hint though that these less disturbed forms of illness also lacked a clear diagnostic consensus.) The 'indefinite' group (Table 5) is likewise very variable in its range of contemporary terms. That it may largely represent a chronic schizophrenic category is discussed below.

As a whole the process of diagnosis is not very precise, and equating 19th-century terms with modern ones is often unjustified. Close attention to physical signs was required to check for general paralysis of the insane (GPI) behind obviously affective presentation. The manics, in particular, were a group that could recover fully or slide into dementia and death. Thus from the treatment perspective new drugs, mustard baths, electricity and hydrotherapy, vigorous physical exercise and dietary innovations could not be ignored once they had been associated with just one or two

TABLE 5
Diagnostic terms for patients proving 'indefinite' on RDC, Ticehurst Asylum 1850–89

	1850–59	1860–69	1870–79	1880–89	Total	%
Delusions	3	4	1	2	10	18.5
Dementia	0	3	1	3	7	12.9
Mania	1	2	6	7	16	29.6
Melancholia	0	0	2	2	4	7.4
Moral insanity	0	0	0	2	2	3.8
Others	1	3	4	1	9	16.7
Nil used	0	5	1	0	6	11.1
Total	5	17	15	17	54	

TABLE 6
Length of stay of Ticehurst patients, 1850–89, according to diagnosis and outcome

	Less than 1 year	1–5 years	More than 5 years
Total	280	127	105
Average age on admission (years)	45.5	45.1	41.76
Male:female ratio	132:148 (0.89)	78:49 (1.59)	54:51 (1.6)
Single:married ratio	134:146 (0.92)	71:56 (1.27)	72:32 (2.25)
Diagnosis (%)			
Schizophrenic	17.5	22.0	60.0
Manic–depressive	52.9	38.6	16.2
Organic	15.0	24.4	8.6
Neurotic	7.1	4.7	0
Indefinite	7.5	10.3	15.2
Outcome (%)			
Died	12.1	32.0	82.8
'Recovered/cured'	53.6	20.3	1.0
'Relieved'	15.4	21.9	5.7
'Not improved', etc.	18.9	25.8	10.5

recoveries. The prognosis after one year seems to have been very gloomy, as the relationship between length of stay, diagnosis and outcome (Table 6) clearly indicates.

Such recoverability seems also to have led to the early establishment of a robust empirically derived diagnostic category. This was manic–depressive psychosis, its active management highlighting the relative lack of interest in other forms of psychotic illness. For those neither dying nor recovering there was no commercial or professional impetus towards improving diagnosis or treatment. Such illnesses, described by Clouston (1888) in his presidential address to the MPA as "the great lowering agency in our asylums", provided a regular clientele for both public and private establishments. The latter, however, could not afford to let its establishments silt up with chronic incurables. To quote Parry-Jones (1972), "continued success . . . depended to a large extent on the personal reputation of the proprietor and the public confidence he held" (p. 85). The methods by which the Newingtons organised their establishment, selecting and training their own attendants, inventing a machine for clocking in and out of work, designing measured walks in the grounds, using their own version of the stomach pump (MacKenzie, 1985; Turner, 1985) all reflected such a pragmatic approach.

Delusions and hallucinations

Broadly speaking, it appears that delusions, in the Ticehurst material, were the key symptom of insanity, the marker of a sufficient severity of mental illness. Hallucinations on the other hand seem to have been more related to the course and outcome of the admission, their development seen as predictive of chronicity rather than indicative of severity. A letter from Henry Maudsley (in case book 30), dated 21 June 1886, describes one patient as "afflicted with hallucinations of hearing . . . of significance not only because they are so often permanent in their nature". Furthermore, the increased use of the term 'hallucinations' in the schizophrenic category (Table 2) is in marked contrast to its absence elsewhere. Again, in a small way, the rudiments of modern diagnosis seem to be emerging from the terminology. Yet, at least 21% of the whole cohort, from 1845 to 1890, had hallucinations. Why was it not used more often therefore as a diagnosis?

It is perhaps necessary to remember that while the meaning of the term, as defined by such influential authors as Esquirol (1845), De Boismont (1859), and Bucknill & Tuke (1858), concurs with its modern meaning, of "a perception in the absence of a stimulus", they also stressed a distinction between hallucinations coexisting with sanity and pathological halluci-nations. Encouraging the reader "not to forget that hallucinations may exist without insanity", they quote the experiences of Samuel Johnson and Napoleon Bonaparte, and give a considerable list of conditions in which such phenomena occur. Thus while it is clear that the condition embraced by Research Diagnostic Criteria, and known in modern terms as schizo-phrenia, existed in a remarkably similar form in the second half of the 19th century, it is also likely that it was less distinctive amid other contemporary psychopathology.

Hallucinations seem to have been commonplace, across a wide variety of physical and mental illnesses. Among a host of individuals and conditions they were not seen as necessarily diseased. They start to emerge in the Ticehurst notes as phenomena worth detailing and using for diagnoses in the later part of the period, but until the tide of paralytic, febrile, nutritional and other causes had gone down, they could not presumably be regarded as a distinctive marker. Furthermore, they shared, with delusions, a much more prominent place among the symptoms of what is now termed 'manic–depressive illness', and this is most likely due to such disorders being more severe, often psychotic, and liable to be complicated by GPI.

It should not therefore be seen as puzzling that Victorian alienists, at least in England, did not seem to make any significant diagnostic advances. Faced by a wider range of conditions with often indistinguishable symptoms, their attention to diet and so forth would have enhanced chronicity without clarifying nosological entities. On the other hand, such activity was chronologically essential for the Kraepelinian analysis, which was based on looking at the course of mental illness as much as the symptoms. This latter task, requiring the prolonged asylum care of numerous patients, was the natural offspring of the asylum process. Thus there is no evidence, in Ticehurst, of schizophrenia providing an increasing proportion of the clientele, but there is a growing recognition of a chron-ically deluded and/or hallucinated cohort that did not die and did not get better. Such a recognition may in itself have played a part in the contemporary concern that insanity was on the increase (Hare, 1983). Asylum doctors would have found themselves increasingly surrounded by schizophrenics, as the tide of other pathologies were discharged or went to their deaths. There is probably little doubt that a Parkinson-like law, namely "lunatics increase to fill the number of spaces available for them", informed the asylum era. But, along with structured working hours, increasingly nuclear families and increased physical health, prolongation of chronic illness and an increased professional acquaintance and recognition of schizophrenia-like disorders led to perceptions of an increased proportion of insanity.

Movement disorder

Perhaps one of the most unexpected findings in this study was the high prevalence of various forms of disordered movement, unusual postures, and typical catatonic phenomena. In fact, patients showing these characteristics had a particular behavioural and diagnostic profile. Not only did they, in more than half of the cases, stay for more than five years, but their prognosis was very poor. Less than one in five were 'relieved', or 'recovered'. Their tendency to violence, their single status and their almost uniquely

TABLE 7

Modern diagnoses of Ticehurst House patients, 1845–90, relating them to length of stay, outcome, sex, mental state, movement/posture disorder, violence and masturbation

	Schizophrenia	Manic–depressive	Organic	Neurotic	Indefinite
Length of stay (%)					
Total	26	36	15	5	18
Less than 1 year	35	69	51	77	42
1–5 years	20	23	38	23	26
More than 5 years	45	8	11	0	32
Overall outcome (%)					
Died in asylum	38.6	16.8	59.8	7.7	40.0
Cured/recovered	18.6	52.8	21.9	42.3	18
Relieved	10.7	17.3	7.3	46.2	14
Discharged/not improved	32.1	13.1	11.0	3.8	28
% Male	50.7	40.7	84.1	42.3	48
% Female	49.3	59.3	15.9	57.7	52
% Single	71.4[1]	42.5	45.1	30.8	80
% Married	27.9	57.5	54.9	69.2	20
% Having movement/ posture disorder	28.5	0.5	3.6	0	22.0
% Described as masturbating	28.6	7.5	4.9	0	20.0
% Described as violent	35.7	23.8	15.9	0	40.0

1. One schizophrenic had no recorded marital status.

schizophrenic or indefinite diagnoses (see Table 7) further marked them out as being a core group of patients who were difficult to manage and had severe illnesses. Given the rarity of movement disorder in other diagnostic groups, it is difficult not to form the conclusion that many of the 'indefinite' group had a similar condition to those given a schizophrenic diagnosis.

Whatever the category, the face and arms were predominately affected, and the terms 'grimace', 'fidget' and 'jerky' were the common descriptions. Over a quarter of the whole schizophrenic cohort was thus described, and it seems likely that many of these patients had something akin to tardive dyskinesia. Such a prevalence is in accord with the range of prevalence in modern studies of tardive dyskinesia (e.g. Owens *et al*, 1982). The exact date of onset of symptoms in the Ticehurst cohort could not be clarified in most cases, but the condition was largely seen in the long-stay group. All of which seems to indicate that dyskinesia, of some form, was an intrinsic sign of chronic schizophrenic illness.

Alternative hypotheses would be that the medication at Ticehurst included agents having similar properties to modern neuroleptics, or that this cohort has been falsely diagnosed and in fact consisted of patients suffering from primary neurological movement disorders. The former is unacceptable, while the latter is contradicted by the lack of such signs of dyskinesia among the known organic group, who often had GPI, a disorder causing widespread and various cerebral and peripheral neurological lesions.

However, it should really come as no surprise that grimacing and posturing formed such a prominent part of the clinical picture. The traditional description of dementia praecox by Emil Kraepelin (1913), included "making faces or grimacing, and a fine muscular twitching in the face" (p. 24). Impulsive actions, postures and "catalepsies" were also typical. Likewise Thomas Clouston (1904), although somewhat dismissive of Kraepelin's ideas, does mention that "in many forms of insanity there are chorei-form and rhythmical movements that may be called ideomotor" (p. 505). He mentions a patient with "excited melancholia, who makes the most extraordinary chorei-form faces and grimaces in a sort of automatic unthinking way", and goes on to state quite blandly that "this sort of movement is common among the insane", and that he looked on it as being in many of them closely allied to chorea. Earlier, in the 19th century, Griesinger (1867) devoted a section of his textbook to the "Elementary disorders of movement", distinguishing partial or general convulsive states from those due to paralysis. He wrote, "the persistent automatic grimacing, painful convulsions of the muscles of the neck – those confused compulsive movements of the extremities which cause the patient often to walk irregularly . . . are all phenomena of serious signification, and their continuance usually indicates a transition into the state of incurability" (p. 104).

The modern literature seems to be moving towards just such a view, despite the standard teaching that insists that tardive dyskinesia is a side-effect of antipsychotic medication. Thus a recent editorial stated "the pre-eminent challenge in the field of tardive dyskinesia research is to discover an antipsychotic drug which does not cause tardive dyskinesia" (Stahl, 1986). Yet a large cohort of chronic schizophrenics (Owens *et al*, 1982), including 47 who had never been exposed to neuroleptic medication (because of a bravely different approach by one of the consultants in the mental hospital used for the study), concluded that spontaneous involuntary disorders of movement can be a feature of severe chronic schizophrenia, unmodified by neuroleptic drugs. Likewise Waddington (1987) in a detailed review suggested it was "extremely difficult to demonstrate any general relationship between increasing drug exposure and the emergence of the syndrome", yet pointed to a "striking consistency in the association with cognitive dysfunction and negative symptoms". Accepting that "recourse to the historical literature, from the pre-neuroleptic era, offers little quantitative guidance in the absence of systematic studies", he supported the findings of Rogers (1985) "that mental and motor disorder might both be an expression of a unitary cerebral disorder", and concluded that neuroleptic treatment "interacts, in some as yet unknown way, to hasten the appearance of dyskinetic movements in individuals with the greater likelihood of ultimately having such movements spontaneously as cerebral deterioration proceeds".

An interesting sideline to this discussion is the work of Richard Hunter, one of the earliest authors (Hunter *et al*, 1964) to comment on this "new syndrome", which *he* attributed to phenothiazines. While admitting that "the agitation and restlessness of these patients and their obvious distress may be mistaken for manifestations of the illness", for example psychotic mannerisms and stereotypies, the cohort upon which he reported all had definite brain damage. Given his detailed acquaintance with primary historical sources, it seems strange that he should have so readily differentiated tardive dyskinesia as a drug-induced event, particularly when in *Psychiatry for the Poor* (Hunter & Macalpine, 1974) there is much detailed comment on movement and posture. In fact, when discussing long-stay patients in this work, he wrote "the usual story is that they came in with an abnormal mental state and developed an abnormal motor state", which included "abnormal movements from tremor to choreoathetosis or a mixture of both, from simple facial and respiratory tics, including hemispasm and torticollis, to complex grimaces and mannerisms" (p. 225). Unlike the present study, Hunter's work at Friern was based largely on annual reports, the case notes being usually too sparse (one line written up annually in the examples given) to provide a pervasive picture of this disorder. This may have obscured the clinical details. Given that the historical study was written some years later than that on tardive dyskinesia, it may have been that he altered his views. Perhaps this puzzling discrepancy is just an excellent illustration of the urgent need for modern psychiatrists to know their clinical history, in both senses of the term, in particular the manifestations of unmodified, chronic, schizophrenic illness.

Masturbation

The impact of the 'masturbatory hypothesis' on Victorian practice has been fully described by Hare (1962) and the Ticehurst material fills out his analysis. At least 70 patients were described as masturbating or abusing themselves. Initially seen as a cause of insanity, subsequently its effects on physical health, its secondary effects on behaviour and the mental state, and it presence as a marker of illness become the predominant usage. It is often called a 'habit' to which patients are 'addicted'. It became of increasing concern to the Ticehurst physicians as the century progressed, but it must remain uncertain as to whether there was a true increase in its prevalence. There was a very strong association with a schizophrenic or indefinite diagnosis (see Table 7), enhancing the likelihood that these may have been similar conditions.

Various physical effects were attributed to this behaviour. Mr Ramsey J had "dyspepsia, probably owing to masturbatory practices". Frederick B was "very haggard", thus "evidently up to his old tricks of masturbation". Alfred H had an "aspect and history that betoken imbecility from self abuse", and James B was "restless and noisy owing to his bad habit of masturbating".

It was also seen as a marker of illness. Miss Kate P was "pulling up her clothes and abusing herself before the attendant" due to "pressure of the voices". Not surprisingly, a range of treatments ensued; particularly popular were Lotio Alum and Liquor Epispasticus (drying agents applied to the genitals). Others were given "Morphia per anum" or a "Metal Pessary". Bertha M was "syringed out with Alum lotion, having behaved in a very disgusting manner with some puppies." The experience of William S sums up much of this approach. Described as "laughing to himself" and therefore "from his expression he has evidently been masturbating", it appears that "he always masturbates after being in the company of ladies", so "before going to bed his penis was blistered".

Unusual diagnoses

There were 15 cases of Capgras syndrome. Thus Captain Arthur B "entertained strong delusions with regard to some of his relatives whom he says are not his relatives but persons who represent them" and "that his own relatives have been dead for years". Eliza W said that "Mr. W was someone else" and had delusions that persons "have passed off as herself". George F claimed that "the person who called yesterday was not his brother", while

Diana F insisted that "the letter is not from her mother but from another person". Mr Samuel N, a paranoid schizophrenic who circulated a pamphlet entitled "The Protophantasmist – an autobiography by Skate-brain" imagined his niece to be an embodiment of his late wife's spirit. John M claimed that "servants had the power of assuming different forms so the real person may be miles away, and this is done on purpose to deceive him so that they may skulk their work. He cannot say whether Mrs. M. is Mrs. M. or another person". He also declared that "his attendant assumes two or three forms and has a double", while "his children at home are not his".

Nihilistic delusions abound. At least 14 cases were clearly identified, and six required feeding with a stomach tube. Joseph J had no gullet, Colonel H said "there was no passage through his gullet or rectum", and the Reverend William T said "he had no stomach, it being full of worms and eaten alive by them". Thomas P insisted "he is dead" with "no spine, no inside and is made of wood". Anne F claimed "her head is cut off" and "she has no body and no feet". The physician in her case also wrote "when I pointed to them, she said they were not hers".

Eating disorders were rather rare. Three possible anorectics had primary psychotic illnesses, two being clearly depressed and one schizophrenic. Thus Catherine M had amenorrhoea, was "refusing food saying she weighs tons", and had "a delusion her throat was too long". Only two clear episodes of bulimic behaviour were noted; Miss Francis H for example, threw herself on the ground and was seen to place her fingers in her throat to vomit up her food.

Hysterical mania

It is noteworthy that only a very small group of patients, all women, 16 in all, were diagnosed as having "hysterical mania". With an average age of 34 years, significantly younger than the remainder in Ticehurst, most of them stayed for less than a year.

A considerable degree of violence was recorded, in eight out of the sixteen patients, and only five had an outcome defined as "cured". Overall the picture is not especially coherent and the outcome not promising. Good recovery was confined to those with a modern diagnosis of mania (five out of seven cases), but the nature of their overall behaviour is clear. In essence it did not conform to the expected symptoms or severity of the disease. Words such as 'wayward', 'fanciful', and 'capricious' were in constant use.

One patient pretended to be unconscious, and was "addicted to com-plaining and mischief making". Another constantly begged for chloroform ("Chloroform me, why will you not give me chloroform, I'm in burning pain all over"). However, she did have "good nights with only coloured draughts" of placebo medication. Impulsive acts and various fits were also common (a Miss Eliza A being reported as having had "slight attacks of an epileptoid character"), while screaming and masturbation were also regularly recorded.

However, no special treatments were employed, and no particular aetiology was accepted. If anything this cohort reflects a considerable uncertainty as to the use of the words 'hysterical' or 'hysteria' by the Ticehurst physicians. In fact, there was a startling absence of rich young hysterical women in Ticehurst at this time, and this accords with Bucknill & Tuke's (1858) statement that "hysteria is not insanity, but there is a form of mental disease in which aggravated hysteria constitutes a prominent symptom". If anything hysterical clients were unwelcome guests in Ticehurst, in view of their difficult behaviour, poor outcome, and limited treatability, and this evidence does not support the feminist criticisms (e.g. Showalter, 1981) of Victorian asylum practice.

Treatment approaches

These are well illustrated by the case of the Reverend Joseph J, who was admitted in June 1869, in a "despondent and agitated state". It seems that some two years previously he had altered in his behaviour, becoming more reserved and irritable. According to his certificates he now thought he was ruined, he was not answering questions readily, and was refusing all food. His condition was "evident by gesture and expression more than by utterance". Described as "pacing the room" and "wringing his hands", it seems he was also in the custom of sitting in a chair in a "listless self-absorbed condition". Physical examination described a man whose head was "of normal configuration", whose features were "coarse", and whose pupils were deemed to be, possibly, unequal. He was gloomy, dejected, and was noted to have a delusion that his bowels were "completely full and that the whole place would be destroyed by the quantity". His claim that he "never sleeps at night" was also regarded as a delusion, and by July he had to be fed via the stomach pump because he was refusing food. Suitable ingredients for this, apparently, were turtle soup and champagne, and he also received two glasses of stout and four glasses of brandy every 24 hours.

By December 1869 it was noted that he had increased his weight from 126 lb to 131 lb in about a month. However, his bowels not having been opened for at least 10 days it proved necessary manually to extract hard faeces (scybala). Work on his bowels continued over the next two years, and included injections, olive oil, aloes, castor oil, and croton oil. During all this time he was fed via the stomach pump. In 1872 his weight was only 122 lb, so his diet was changed. By September of that year he had increased his weight to 132 lb and this was maintained until the next year. Numerous enemas, as well as repeated manual extractions, were needed.

In December 1873 it was reported that since July 1869 (his admission) "he has been fed 7,584 times". In 1874 it was noted that he was still very irritable, yet reading the Bible. "He persists that he has no gullet and never eats anything. He says there is not such a thing as mutton, beef, beer or any food in the world. He is fed with the spoon at various times to show him he can swallow". By March 1874 he had been fed 7647 times with "no injury to the fauces via the stomach tube". The time occupied in feeding was 40 seconds, 15 of these taken up in-filling the stomach. The Reverend J was rather offensive though, and claimed that he was so poor he could not pay his taxes. The diet persisted. It was reported that it became quite regularised so that at 9 a.m. he would receive milk, egg yolk and brandy, at 1 p.m. beef tea, olive oil and brandy, at 5 p.m. soup, olive oil, and brandy, and same at 9 p.m. In September 1877 he was still claiming he had no stomach, and in June he still had delusions about food after 15 159 feedings. He eventually died at the end of July 1880, after a collapse following "derangement of the alimentary system". At that time he had been fed 17 160 times.

Mustard treatment

From 1865 onwards, mustard was used intermittently in the treatment of restless and overactive patients who needed sedation. In fact Samuel Newington wrote a letter to the *Lancet* on 10 June 1865 (Newington, 1865) describing "a new remedial agent in the treatment of insanity and other diseases". Applied either as a paste spread upon a sheet of brown paper sufficiently large enough to cover the whole abdomen, a piece of muslin being interposed to keep the skin clean, or via a thick towel wrung out as an infusion, or as a mustard bath, an ordinary warm bath into which had been thrown five or six handfuls of crude mustard, it was used in at least 40 cases. The Newingtons felt that the mustard pack was most useful, but needed to be applied for some hours. By 1901 the new rules of the Commissioners limited the continued use of the pack to just two hours, so they had been unable to use it as they wished (Medical Superintendents, 1901). They felt the mustard bath was not so powerful, on account of the shorter time to which the patient could be subjected to it. Apparently the time of immersion varied from 10 minutes to 30 minutes, according to the susceptibility of the skin.

Other physical approaches included the application of croton oil to the scalp, after closely cropping the hair, and various electrical procedures. These were often used for people who were slowed down or rigid; thus Leon L was "given the electrical battery for his cataleptic trance", while Henry C received the electric battery to the head and neck for his "slow cerebration".

Cricket

Although walking exercise was constantly recorded as the most prominent activity, cricket seems to have been played both for assessment and for occupational therapy. For example James C "plays at cricket generally twice a day; he says it relieves him in some degree from his agony". Less encouragingly Lord Frederick H "went into the cricket field but refused to play", while James M "was expelled from the cricket field for 1 week for manner and language habitually disgusting". Samuel W was "quarrelsome and abusive on the cricket ground", a behaviour not unknown today.

It was also clear that symptoms need not inhibit activity. Edward B "was unable to sustain any conversation but 'plays at cricket and is very active in the field' ". Frederick P "played today in the annual cricket match and made 56 runs not out. He seems much pleased with his success. The voices still trouble him on first going to bed". Edward F had "delusions of not existing", but still was keen on "playing cricket every afternoon". These were perhaps unrepresentative cases, since according to the Newingtons (Medical Superintendents, 1901), only "a fair number" take a "more or less perfunctory interest in cricket". But they did find that "some patients had a very decided liking for bicycle polo. This latter is a really valuable agent, as it needs such skill and direct attention to the game that their mental idiosyncrasies had little scope for action for the time being".

Discussion

One small and very exceptional asylum may seem a rather thin base on which to take a broad overview of Victorian psychiatry. Yet the relationship between wealth and forms of mental illness has never been clearly defined, and the comings and goings to and from other asylums, both public and private, indicated that Ticehurst was part of an integrated network, dealing with the same sorts of people. If anything, given its fine fabric and extensive extras, it was less able to deal with the dirt and violence so prevalent in those times.

Certain broad conclusions seem inevitable. Most striking is the sheer recognisability of the cases recorded, in that over 80% have a significant modern diagnosis (see Table 1). Even the 'indefinite' are not strange or novel in their presentations; in most instances they are simply lacking the positive symptoms required of modern criteria. Similar recognitions have emerged from previous studies, looking for example at the textbook cases of Emil Kraepelin (James & May, 1981), at the Bethlem case books (Klaf & Hamilton, 1961) and at Australian asylum records (Krupinski & Alexander, 1983). This work extends and reinforces such approaches, showing the extraordinary consistency of certain symptom patterns over the last 140 years. In fact it is something of a mystery that the wealthy bourgeoisie of Victorian Sussex should have symptoms indistinguishable from those seen at modern, inner-city clinics. Foucault's notion (1965) that "we are not dealing with the same madman" finds little support.

The severity of symptoms protrayed was also quite frightening. Depressive and manic states were characterised by delusions and hallucinations, and chronic psychotic illness was accompanied by violence, incontinence of urine and faeces, disgusting habits of eating, and overt masturbation. Although such behaviours are well recognised by modern clinicians, their accumulation and persistence in one establishment is becoming a thing of the past. Writing of his personal experiences in a 1929 asylum, Parfitt (1985) described admissions as "far gone, roughly the worst fifth of modern admissions, with bizarre delusions and riotous hallucinations patently intolerable in the community".

Certainly at Ticehurst physical illness was very common, and at least 15% of the cases quite clearly had an organic diagnosis. Given the similarity of symptoms between manic–depressive illness and the early stages of GPI it is likely that a number of patients discharged 'relieved' or 'recovered', from what seemed to be typical affective disorders, may have gone on to develop overt paralytic disease. The extent to which tuberculosis, rickets and chronic infectious illness also influenced presentation is uncertain. The incidence of such disorders was probably much less than seen in a pauper asylum population, supporting the view that such extreme states of mental illness cannot have left the caring personnel unaffected. Incoherent language and eccentric behaviour would have been inextricably associated with disordered bowels, physical infirmity and other practical nursing needs. Washing, feeding, dressing and administering medicines were the necessary accompaniments to 'moral' treatments and appropriate behavioural examples.

Is it then surprising that the medical profession should have taken over the management of madness? It was not a particularly rewarding business, and if anything was heavily stigmatised. There is no sense in which a medical model, at least in Ticehurst, seems to have been imposed on those who were merely deviant from a social point of view or harmlessly eccentric. The picture seen here is one of medical powerlessness. Patients come and go at the will of families, possibly for economic reasons, and are more often 'relieved' or 'unimproved' than 'cured'. Despite all their accoutrements of measured walks, generous diets, numerous attendants and physical therapy, the Newingtons had to deal with constant disappointment. They and their attendants, whose role was formally defined as that of valets, were assaulted and abused. They had to cope with the sordid business of nursing demented paralytics through months of increasing inanition and incontinence. A residue of chronic incurables lived on in the asylum, playing cricket, attending concerts, going to the seaside, but not getting better. The public views of asylums and their doctors were not much more than grudging, and the need for sheer practical energy, as evidenced in the lifestyle of Hayes Newington (Anonymous, 1917), must have been paramount. It is also clear that the symptoms and behaviour noted in the case books are often left to stand for themselves instead of forming a diagnosis. This has a close parallel in the practices described at the York Retreat (Digby, 1985) where "during much of the second half of the 19th century medical labelling of patients seems to have been honoured more in the breach than in the observance".

For example, the contentious label 'moral insanity' was only used for three admissions in this period. In one case it is actually the basis for removal from the asylum. Few attempts were made at classification, psychological speculation or aetiological concern, and such linguistic barrenness is in considerable contrast to the rich details of management and organisation that made the asylum work. This emphasis on practical matters must have significantly affected contemporary views of alienists. Expecting asylum doctors and mental specialists to be learned philosophers of the mind, able to discuss mind–brain physiology and sophisticated diagnoses, Victorian highbrows may have been puzzled by the discrepancies between theory and practice, and disappointed at the concentration on administration and physical approaches. Yet the importance of the physician's personality, of the personnel attending on the patients, and of the social networks as provided, seems over-riding. Coping with the demands of the insane in Victorian Sussex required skills more associated with army logistics than a university common room.

Nevertheless, the power and intimacy of the clinical interview and the alluring possibility of curing insanity by persuasive eloquence and psychological insight was not entirely ignored. Among these case notes is the formal description, by Hayes Newington, of an interview in 1886 with a 26-year-old coffee planter, Mr Frederick P. Although more Conan Doyle or even John Buchan than Freud or Jung, it has a common touch:

> "I took the first opportunity of examining his mental state thoroughly; he told me that with the exception of the previous night he had slept and that his bowels were open. He told me that 'I and others were his enemies; that I and others, Miss V. for instance, cough at him' – 'That I was greedy' – 'Of what' I asked, 'of lives, and you want mine' (he replied). He told me deliberately, and again on being pushed further that he had no thought of taking his own life and that his only fear was for his own being taken by others . . . . I spent some time in showing him the absurdity of his ideas. I pointed out that the worry which he confessed to having seen me undergo over the previous fortnight was due to the death of another patient. I pointed out also that he knew me well enough to understand that if I had anything disagreeable to say I had the courage to say it openly and not cough or whisper it at him. I also told him that his condition made *me* feel very uncomfortable. He went on to my house and finished some work, lit his pipe and at the next meal took his sherry as usual, and since then has been quite different, cheerful, and ready to talk or do anything."

Acknowledgements

I am indebted to Charlotte Mackenzie, William Bynum and Michael Neve for their professional help and personal support during the research for this paper, and to Ursula Phillips and Maureen Taylor for typing the manuscript.

References

ANONYMOUS (1917) Herbert Francis Hayes Newington. F.R.C.P. Edin., M.R.C.S. Eng. *Journal of Mental Science*, **63**, 461–467.
BUCKNILL, J. C. & TUKE, D. H. (1858) *A Manual of Psychological Medicine*. London: John Churchill. (Facsimile edition 1968, New York and London: Hafner.)
BUSFIELD, J. (1986) *Managing Madness: Changing Ideas and Practice*. London: Hutchinson.
CLOUSTON, T. S. (1888) Presidential address. *Journal of Mental Science*, **34**, 325–348.
—— (1904) *Clinical Lectures on Mental Diseases* (6th edn.). London: J. and A. Churchill.
COCKTON, H. (1854) *Valentine Vox – The Ventriloquist*. London: George Routledge.
DE BOISMONT, A. B. (1859) *On Hallucinations* (trans. R. T. Hulme). London: Henry Renshaw.
DIGBY, A. (1985) *Madness, Morality and Medicine. A Study of the York Retreat 1796 – 1914*. Cambridge: Cambridge University Press.
DOERNER, K. (1981) *Madness and the Bourgeoisie* (trans. J. Neugroschel & J. Steinberg). Oxford: Basil Blackwell.
ESQUIROL, J. E. D. (1845) *Mental Maladies: A Treatise on Insanity*. Philadelphia. (Facsimile edn. 1965, New York: Hafner.)
FOUCAULT, M. (1965) *Madness and Civilisation; A History of Insanity in the Age of Reason* (trans. R. Howard). New York: Random House.
GRIESINGER, W. (1867) *Mental Pathology and Therapeutics* (trans. C. L. Robertson & J. Rutherford). London: New Sydenham Society.
HARE, E. H. (1962) Masturbatory insanity: the history of an idea. *Journal of Mental Science*, **108**, 1–25.
—— (1983) Was insanity on the increase? *British Journal of Psychiatry*, **142**, 439–455.
HUNTER, R., EARL, C. J. & THORNICROFT, S. (1964) An apparently irreversible syndrome of abnormal movements following phenothiazine medication. *Proceedings of the Royal Society of Medicine*, **57**, 758–762.
HUNTER, R. & MACALPINE, I. (1963) *Three Hundred Years of Psychiatry 1535–1860*. London: Oxford University Press.
—— & —— (1974) *Psychiatry for the Poor*. London: Dawsons.
JAMES, R. L. & MAY, P. R. A. (1981) Diagnosing schizophrenia: Professor Kraepelin and the Research Diagnostic Criteria. *American Journal of Psychiatry*, **138**, 501–504.
JONES, K. (1972) *A History of the Mental Health Services*. London: Routledge and Kegan Paul.
KLAF, F. S. & HAMILTON, J. G. (1961) Schizophrenia – a hundred years ago and today. *Journal of Mental Science*, **107**, 819–827.
KOSKY, R. (1986) From morality to madness: a reappraisal of the asylum movement in psychiatry 1800–1940. *Australian and New Zealand Journal of Psychiatry*, **20**, 180–187.
KRUPINSKI, J. & ALEXANDER, L. (1983) Patterns of psychiatric morbidity in victoria, Australia, in relation to changes in diagnostic criteria 1848–1978. *Social Psychiatry*, **18**, 61–67.
KRAEPELIN, E. (1913) *Lectures on Clinical Psychiatry* (3rd edn) (ed. T. Johnstone). London: Bailliere, Tindall and Cox.
LEIGH, D. (1961) *The Historical Development of British Psychiatry, vol. 1–18th and 19th Century*. New York: Pergamon Press.
LOWE, L. (1883) *The Bstilles of England; or The Lunacy Laws at Work*. London: Crookende.
MACKENZIE, C. (1985) Social factors in the admission, discharge, and continuing stay of patients at Ticehurst Asylum, 1845–1917. In *The Anatomy of Madness, Vol. II, Institutions and Society* (ed. W. F. Bynum, R. Porter & M. Shepherd), pp. 147–174. London: Tavistock.
MEDICAL SUPERINTENDENTS (1901) Some incidents in the history and practice of Ticehurst Asylum. *Journal of Mental Science*, **47**, 62–72.
NEWINGTON, S. (1865) On a new remedial agent in the treatment of insanity and other diseases. *Lancet*, **i**, 621.

OWENS, D. G. C., JOHNSTONE, E. C. & FRITH, C. D. (1982) Spontaneous involuntary disorders of movement. *Archives of General Psychiatry*, **39**, 452–461.

PARFITT, D. (1985) Asylum 1929. *British Journal of Clinical and Social Psychiatry*, **3**, 3–5.

PARRY-JONES, W. L. (1972) *The Trade in Lunacy*. London: Routledge and Kegan Paul.

PORTER, R. (1987) *A Social History of Madness*. London: Weidenfeld and Nicholson.

READE, C. (1863) *Hard Cash: A Matter of Fact Romance*. Serialised in *All the Year Round* (ed. C. Dickens).

ROGERS, D. (1985) The motor disorders of severe psychiatric illness: a conflict of paradigms. *British Journal of Psychiatry*, **147**, 221–232.

SCULL, A. (1979) *Museums of Madness*. London: Allen Lane.

SELECT COMMITTEE ON LUNACY LAW (1877) *Minutes of Evidence*, pp. 320–327. London: HMSO.

SHOWALTER, E. (1981) Victorian women and insanity. In *Madhouses, Mad-Doctors and Madmen: The Social History of Psychiatry in the Victorian Era* (ed. A. Scull), pp. 313–336. London: Athlone Press.

SPITZER, R. L., ENDICOTT, J. & ROBINS, E. (1975) *Research Diagnostic Criteria*. New York: New York State Psychiatric Institute.

STAHL, S. M. (1986) Tardive dyskinesia: natural history studies assist the pursuit of preventive therapies. *Psychological Medicine*, **16**, 491–494.

SZASZ, T. (1962) *The Myth of Mental Illness*. London: Secker and Warburg.

TORREY, E. F. (1980) *Schizophrenia and Civilisation*. New York: Jason Aronson.

TURNER, E. S. (1958) *Call the Doctor: A Social History of Medical Men*. London: Michael Joseph.

TURNER, T. H. (1985) The past of psychiatry: why build asylums? *Lancet*, **ii**, 709–711.

WADDINGTON, J. L. (1987) Tardive dyskinesia in schizophrenia and other disorders: associations with ageing, cognitive dysfunction and structural brain pathology in relation to neuroleptic exposure. *Human Psychopharmacology*, **2**, 11–22.

ZILBOORG, G., WITH HENRY, G. W. (1941) *A History of Medical Psychology*. New York: W. W. Norton.

12 Memory and the cognitive paradigm of dementia during the 19th century: a conceptual history*

GERMAN BERRIOS

This lecture, based on a historiographical approach which will here be called 'conceptual', means to illustrate the power of the history of psychiatry to explain clinical conundrums. When doing so, however, the historian must avoid compromising standards of historical research (Berrios, 1988a).

Work on the neurobiology of the dementias is going through exciting times. Because basic scientists obtain their research material from clinicians, the latter need to collect patient samples with a homogeneous diagnosis, and properly quantified signs and symptoms. Such a task depends on the availability of sensitive and specific definitions of dementia, and of reliable and valid evaluating instruments.

Current definitions of dementia are variations of what will henceforth be called the 'cognitive paradigm', that is, a model of the disease that gives preferential attention to intellectual, particularly mnesic, deficits (Berrios, 1989a; Branconnier & DeVitt, 1983). Now, it has been known for some time that such definitions generate, particularly on cross-sectional usage, a fair number of false positive and false negative diagnoses (Marsden & Harrison, 1972; Nott & Fleminger, 1975; Ron et al, 1979; Smith & Kiloh, 1981; Martin et al, 1983; Garcia et al, 1984), and are also unhelpful with regards to the analysis of what has been called 'mild' or early dementia, which is for most writers little more than a form of mini-dementia (Henderson & Huppert, 1984).

Access to the corrective power of longitudinal information has made these difficulties only occasionally apparent or inconvenient to the clinician (Rabbitt, 1988). They might be, however, a serious disadvantage to the non-clinical scientist who depends upon borrowed cross-sectional evaluations. Most potential sources of misdiagnosis, such as faulty applications of the operational definitions or bad performance of evaluating instruments,

---

* Dedicated to the memory of Edwin Ackerknecht, foremost historian of medicine, deceased in 1988.

have been already explored (Miller, 1977; Wattis & Hindmarch, 1988). Attempts at ameliorating this problem have resulted in an ever-growing keenness to polish operational definitions and to create comprehensive instruments (Berrios, 1989*b*). In spite of these efforts, the problem has not gone away (Homer *et al*, 1988).

It is time, therefore, that the 'cognitive paradigm' itself be considered as a potential source of diagnostic embarrassment, particularly in relation to the concept of 'early dementia'. This lecture is about its history. To discharge this brief, one conceptual clarification will need to be made, and the history of the following examined: (a) memory and memory testing, (b) biostatistics, (c) mental faculties, (d) senility, and (e) dementia.

A conceptual clarification

The term 'paradigm', as originally used by Kuhn (1962), included up to 21 different meanings (Masterman, 1970) and was one in a suite of concepts created to explain scientific change (Hacking, 1981). Hence its usage in this lecture requires some justification. The original semantic confusion is still apparent today. For example, some use 'paradigm' in the strong sense of being analogous to a perceptual filter (i.e. controlling the way in which scientists may 'see' the world) (as in the 'Necker cube' simile; Rogers, 1988); others use it in a weaker sense, as another name for 'scientific view' (Klerman, 1988). The confusion remains in spite of Kuhn's later suggestion (1970) that paradigms include both a 'cognitive' and a 'communal' component. The issue still is about the nature of the 'control' that the cognitive component might exercise upon the mind or behaviour of the scientist.

In this lecture the word 'paradigm' will be used in a pre-Kuhnian fashion to mean "archetype, idea, exemplar, according to which all things are made" (Oxford English Dictionary). 'Cognitive paradigm' of dementia will therefore mean 'the idea or view that dementia is essentially a disorder of cognition'. At no time will it be implied that users of this view were or, indeed, are perceptually or socially controlled.

Two contrasting definitions of dementia

A useful way to pose the problem is to contrast the current definition of dementia with that entertained, say, in 1889, when it was considered as an exogenous psychosis, a reversible syndrome, a final common pathway to a number of psychiatric and neurological disorders (Dagonet, 1876; Ball & Chambard, 1882; Kowalewski, 1886). Then it included, in addition to cognitive symptoms, hallucinations, delusions, volitional defect, motility disorders, behavioural failure and psychosocial incompetence (Clouston,

1888). A hundred years later dementia is defined as: "an acquired global impairment of intellect, memory and personality, but without impairment of consciousness . . . as such it is almost always of long duration, usually progressive, and often irreversible" (Lishman, 1987, p. 6).

Three main differences are apparent. The first relates to a change from the psychotic to the cognitive; that is, in 1889 dementia could still be legitimately diagnosed on the basis of a combination of insanity and psychosocial incompetence. Nowadays, "Global impairment of intellect is the central and essential feature . . . dementia should not be used unless intellectual deterioration can be identified" (Lishman, 1987, pp. 6–7). The second difference relates to the lesser diagnostic role currently played by delusions, hallucinations and other non-cognitive symptoms. The third refers to reversibility. This lecture deals only with the first difference, namely the development of the cognitive paradigm (the issue of non-cognitive symptoms is dealt with by Berrios (1989*a*)).

The historical hypothesis

Stage 1

By the 1860s a process had started whereby the clinical boundaries of the concept of dementia began to be reduced. Clinical states such as melancholic pseudodementia (Berrios, 1985*a*; Bulbena & Berrios, 1986), vesanic dementia, stupor (Berrios, 1981*b*), confusion (Berrios, 1981*a*), and chronic cognitive defects relating to brain injury, underwent translocation. The result was the creation of a narrow clinical class which essentially encompassed the senile and arteriosclerotic dementias (Cullere, 1890). The historical forces guiding this process included the development of morbid anatomy (Maulitz, 1987), the reaffirmation of intellectualistic psychology (Berrios, 1988*b*), a new awareness of neuropsychiatric principles (Ferrier, 1886; Hécaen & Dubois 1969; Young, 1970; Hécaen & Lanteri-Laura, 1977; Jeannerod, 1985), and the changing views on the nature of senility (Zeman, 1950; Birren, 1961; Halpert, 1983).

Stage 2

Concepts and techniques in morbid anatomy had developed by the 1890s to the point that replicable microscopic descriptions were possible (Ramón & Cajal, 1952, 1981; Long, 1965; Albarracin, 1983). For example, in the Berlin meeting of 1883 it was agreed to discard many early data on brain pathology on the basis that the changes described had occurred post-mortem (Anonymous, 1883). Reliable histological techniques soon led, for example, to the separation of melancholic from senile dementia (Berrios, 1985*a*).

This correlational work, inspired as it was, in the anatomoclinical model

(Ackerknecht, 1967), encouraged clinicians to improve their definition of dementia both in relation to its clinical scope and to ways of measuring its severity. In the event, the new definition was made to revolve around the state of the intellectual functions. But since the study of memory was, of all cognitive functions, the only one supported by an adequate technology of measurement, mnesic deficits were to become, *de facto*, if not *de jure*, the central feature of dementia.

Stage 3

A number of factors contributed to the view that intellectual deficit was the hallmark of dementia. First of all, there were the clinical facts: observation of institutionalised patients did indeed reveal frequent cognitive incompetence (Crichton Brown, 1874). Secondly, the 19th century had inherited a strong intellectual tradition, particularly with regards to the definition of madness (Berrios, 1985*b*). Thirdly, during the second half of the century the view had grown popular that intellectual weakness, resulting from degeneration of the original seed, was the common denominator to the states of dementia shown by the mentally ill, the elderly, the idiot, the mongolic, and the cretin (Talbot, 1898; Bateman, 1897; Barr, 1904; Ribot, 1906; Huertas, 1987).

This latter view had itself been an offshoot of evolutionism (Thomson, 1908; Mayr, 1982), degeneration theory (Génil-Perrin, 1913; Friedlander, 1973) and of the Lamarckian creed (Lamarck, 1984; Jordanova, 1984). According to the latter view, exogenous factors such as alcoholism (Magnan & Legrain, 1895) caused, in certain sections of society, behavioural and physical stigmata which were then passed on to succeeding generations in the form of melancholia, mania, and finally dementia. In this regard, it is no coincidence that the central drive of the British eugenics movement, as started by Galton (1883, 1979) and Pearson (see Semmuel, 1958), was the intellectual betterment of future generations (Blacker, 1952).

So, it can be tentatively concluded that the choice of intellectual impairment as the core of dementia was based on clinical, conceptual, and social factors. Explanation for the historical fact that, as said above, memory was to receive preferential attention, must be sought in the history of memory itself. It will be seen that by the 1890s the psychometry of memory (Burnham 1888–89; Young, 1923) together with that of reaction time and perception (Boring, 1961) and fatigue (Berrios, 1989*c*), had developed to the point that it began to be used in the assessment of patient groups. Psychiatrists with psychological training such as Kraepelin, Ziehen, Oehren and Meumann (Young, 1923) were active in this regard.

Consequences of the creation of the cognitive paradigm

This historical process led to two clinical consequences. One was the need to explain away the presence of non-cognitive symptoms in subjects diagnosed as demented according to the narrow definition. Thus, delusions, hallucinations, motility and affective disorders began to be accounted for as having resulted from 'grafted' psychoses, superimposed delirium, pathoplastic effect of personality, and arteriosclerotic changes (Berrios, 1989*a*).

The second consequence was that, for the first time, dementia was to be considered as irreversible (Kowalewski, 1886). This view was supported by histopathological evidence (Marcé, 1862; Mills & Schively, 1897), by the growing acceptance of an association between senility and dementia (Ball & Chambard, 1882), and by degeneration theory.

History of memory

Research into the history of memory is important for at least four reasons. Firstly, most current models of memory have been discussed under different names in earlier periods (Burnham, 1888–89; Levin *et al*, 1983). Secondly, most memory models have developed as explanations for clinical findings and their history is related to the mnesic vicissitudes of a few famous patients. Thirdly, the study of memory includes the analysis of a conceptual dimension whose consideration is relevant to the solution of boundary disputes (Edgell, 1924). For example, should the psychological impairment exhibited by subjects with depressive pseudodementia (Bulbena & Berrios, 1986), schizophrenic dementia (Rund, 1988; Kirkpatrick *et al*, 1986), fugues (Benon & Froissart, 1909), confabulation (Berrios, 1986) or *déjà vu* (Bernard-Leroy, 1898) be considered as a 'memory' impairment? This question cannot be solved by additional testing of the cases concerned; indeed it belongs to what should be called the meta-analysis of memory. Fourthly, the history of memory can help, in our case, to understand how the cognitive paradigm of dementia was created (Berrios, 1989*d*).

Tulving (1983), using as criterion amount of experimental work, has called the period before Ebbinghaus the 'dark ages' in the history of memory. This is historically unhelpful. The 19th century, in fact, was a period rich in conceptual analyses of memory (Murray, 1976). This is particularly so after the 1820s, when the impact of phrenology began to be felt (Berrios, 1988*b*). The problem was that during the 1860s memory reverted to being considered, as it had been up to the 17th century (Janet & Séailles, 1902), as a 'faculty of the mind'. Examples of this view are to be found in Great Britain in the work of Mill (1869), Hamilton (1859) and Bain (1864). This 'psychological view' shifted the onus of explanation from brian mechanisms to phenomenology of content and to speculation on laws of retention and association.

But after 1870 this view was once again to change as a result of Ewald Hering's lecture on "memory as a universal function of organized matter" delivered before the Imperial Academy of Science at Vienna. Hering (1870) made two crucial points. One was that: "memory is a function of brain substance whose results, it is true, fall as regards one part of them into the domain of consciousness, while another part escapes unperceived as purely material processes. . . ." The other that: "we have ample evidence of the fact that characteristics of an organism may descend to offspring which the organism did not inherit, but which it acquired owing to the special circumstances under which it lived . . . an organized being, therefore, stands before us a product of the unconscious memory of organized matter. . . ." Hering's views influenced Ribot (see Gasser, 1988) and culminated in the work of Semon (see Schachter *et al*, 1978), and others interested in the notion of engram (Gomulicki, 1953).

Hering was in fact claiming that knowledge on brain sites was important to the understanding of memory, and that a Lamarckian mechanism was in operation. The timing of his claims also proved right: both evolutionary (Mayr, 1982) and degeneration theory (Saury, 1886) were in need of an internal machinery that explained how new genetic information might be incorporated into the system.

Herings's views were not lost to neuroscientists working in the field of memory. If memory depended upon organic mechanisms it could not just be considered as a given, as a part of the make-up of the mind: sites and mechanisms had to be searched for. As dictated by a methodology of medical research popular during the late 19th century, this was best done in subjects exhibiting memory deficits.

But the analysis of cases required instruments and, at the time, it was not yet quite clear whether tests developed for the study of memory in the normal could be applied to the demented. A 'discontinuity' view (between the normal and the pathological) had been popular in psychiatry during the first half of the 19th century to the point that a parallel psychometric tradition for patients had been created (Bondy, 1974). Hering's counter-suggestion of a 'continuity view', at least in the area of memory, and other conceptual changes occurring at the time (Canguilhem, 1966) were, in the event, sufficient to provide a justification for the free use of tests, regardless of their origins.

But in testing abnormal subjects, a number of clinical phenomena were found which did not fit into the old one-storage model of memory. Paramnesia, false recognition, *déjà vu*, confabulation, delusions of memory, and specific amnesic syndromes (Kraepelin, 1886–87; Pick, 1903; Bernard-Leroy, 1898; Lalande, 1893; Dugas, 1894; Korsakoff, 1889; Rouillard, 1885) required for their understanding far more than a 'retention mechanism'. Their irreducibility to conventional memory models caused at the time some theoretical consternation.

The dementia syndrome, however, provided a perfect instance of memory failure. Ribot (1882), for example, used dementia to illustrate his law of dissolution: "to discover this law it is essential that the progress of dementia should be studied from a psychological viewpoint" (p. 117). He concentrated on dementia as a medical syndrome regardless of aetiology: "physicians distinguish between different kinds of dementia according to causes, classing them as senile, paralytic, epileptic, etc. These distinctions have no interest to us. The progress of mental dissolution is at bottom the same" (p. 117). This view is typical for the period. In England, Shaw (1892) stated, "sometimes the existence of dementia is only shown by loss of memory or loss of energy and there are no positive signs of acute disturbance" (p. 348). The testing of memory, however, depended upon the making of certain assumptions, discussed presently.

History of memory testing

Successful memory testing in the way that Kraepelin, Ebbinghaus, Galton or Jung were to carry it out depended upon the assumptions that it was conceptually legitimate to quantify psychological phenomena, and that the resulting number arrays contained extra information.

Conceptual changes had, however, taken place before this period to justify both assumptions. With regards to numerical descriptions, the work of Weber and Fechner, in the area of perception, of Hering in audition, and of Donders in reaction time (Cattel, 1890; Boring, 1942, 1950), had convinced psychologists that psychological phenomena were ready for mathematical treatment. This led in fact to an important debate, at the very end of the century, between Dilthey (1976) whose notion of 'understanding' (*Verstehen*) was to influence Jaspers (see Berrios, 1989*e*; Walker, 1988), and Ebbinghaus (1964) himself (Caparrós, 1986).

Kimball Young (1923), in his superb history of mental testing, has identified four quantificatory strands in 19th-century psychology: psychophysics, the study of difference limens, and mental and physiological measurement. These trends were not lost to those keen on the measurement of memory. Ebbinghaus (1964) himself acknowledged this in so many words: "in the realm of mental phenomena, experiment and measurement have hitherto been chiefly limited in application to sense perception and to the time relations of mental processes . . . we have tried to go a step further into the workings of the mind and to submit to an experimental and quantitative treatment the manifestations of memory" (p. xiii).

The ensuing number arrays, however, required analysis. This could be done only if techniques were available to identify patterns and relationships hidden in the number matrices.

History of biostatistics

By the second half of the 19th century, psychiatrists has come round to agree with Louis and Quetelet on the value of statistical analysis (Underwood, 1951; Ackerknecht, 1967; Murphy, 1981; Hilts, 1981). This was clearly expressed in the International Congress of 1856, when statistical techniques were discussed in relation to clinical description, classification, and treatment outcome (Parchappe, 1856; Renaudin, 1856). Parallel developments also occurred in the application of evolutionary theory to biology (Sheynin, 1980).

The use of statistics on medical data, however, depended upon a shift in medical beliefs with regard to the status of information obtained by means of measurement. One concerned the so-called measures of central tendency (e.g. means and medians) and the value of probabilistic approaches to bodily functions; the other the epistemological value of patterns and relationships such as they might be discovered by statistical manipulation. Not everyone agreed that this shift was required. For example, Claude Bernard (1957) opposed, on methodological grounds (Sertillanges, 1943), the view that averages or indeed statistics could ever lead to exact science (Bernard, 1957, pp. 138–140). Others, like Kraepelin, were not sure about the true status of hidden patterns in data. It must not be forgotten that he did not appoint a statistician to the Munich Psychiatric Institute until 1916 (Kraepelin, 1983).

The discovery of hidden patterns in raw data required techniques other than percentages which had until then been the main form of statistical description (Perrot & Woolf, 1984). Inferential statistical techniques were required and of these, correlations were the first to develop (Hilts, 1981). Since the late 18th century, astronomers had been preoccupied with what they called 'entanglement of observations' (and what Bravais was to call 'correlation' in 1846), that is, the notion of concomitant variation (Porter, 1986). These techniques reached psychiatry and psychology only during the second half of the century (Galton, 1883; Zupan, 1976). Its most important application was to be found in the belief that functional deficit and severity of brain lesion might covary and that their covariance could be taken as evidence of association.

But the correct interpretation of statistical correlations necessitated a stable conceptual matrix with regards to the way mental functions or modules might hang together.

The question of unitary v. multiple mental functions

This important aspect of the history of 19th-century neuropsychiatry is in need of much research. Basically, the debate was about whether or not faculties or modules of the mind might become affected by illness in an independent manner (Falret, 1864, pp. 430–433). Those who believed that they could not, tended to subscribe to a unitary view of mental functions and opposed most of the claims of brain localisation. These views have since been intermittently revived in the work of Head, Lashley, Mourgue, Minkowski and in the group of the so-called Gestalt neuropsychiatrists such as Goldstein and Konrad (see Hécaen & Lanteri-Laura, 1977). Those who believed that mental functions could become independently impaired defended a modular view of the mind similar to what Marr (1982), Fodor (1983) or Shallice (1988) have proposed in our own day, and supported brain localisation.

The outcome of this debate much affected the development of the cognitive paradigm of dementia. The last 30 years of the 19th century were a period of rampant localisationism (Tizard, 1959) and the parallel influence of Faculty Psychology and Associationism generated a variety of analytic approaches to the mind (Berrios, 1988*b*). All these were based on the view that psychological functions were modular in organisation, susceptible to measurement, and covaried with brain structure (Luys, 1881, pp. 389–520).

The fact that, for better or worse, we still live in a world of linear correlations is, thus, owed to morbid anatomy researchers from this period. Belief in brain localisation instigated a form of blatant cross-sectional approach where findings from post-mortem material were correlated with telescoped and two-dimensional versions of mental states as recorded in the case notes. This was in marked contrast with the predominant historicist (long-term follow-up) approach introduced by Kraepelin (Berrios & Hauser, 1988). This drifting away from the 19-century historicist mentality also appeared in other areas of knowledge, such as linguistics, where the anti-historicist reaction was led by Saussure (1960) (see also Koerner, 1982).

In addition to whatever brain changes might have accrued from injury or disease it was, at the time, strongly suspected that memory changes might also be caused by endogenous factors. Of these old age was the most conspicuous.

The concept of senility

Current operational definitions of dementia contain an ambiguity caused by its double referent (Small & Jarvik, 1982). They point, on the one hand, to a syndrome, and hence do not need to include an age criterion; on the other, they refer to the senile dementias in which case they carry an oblique reference to old age. This tension was felt even more keenly during the 19th century, as shown by a number of studies into the development of the medical (Zeman, 1950) and psychological (Birren, 1961) views on old age, and on the meaning of senility (Halpert, 1983). On the other hand, terms such as old age, dotage, and senility were themselves contaminated by references to dementia, and hence were often used to *explain* the presence of memory deficits.

Thus, during the middle of the 19th century, the view almost came to be accepted that old age was a form of disease, and that it was not possible to distinguish the normal from the pathological (Charpentier, 1885; Biaute, 1889). Charcot (1881) in his excellent review of the books on old age published up to his time stated: "a common feature is visible in most of the writings which have just been mentioned: it is a manifest tendency to refer to the peculiarities which distinguish the diseases of old age as much as possible to the anatomical or physiological modifications which the organism undergoes by the mere fact of old age" (p. 27). But then he was forced to conclude: "we shall have to remark among other things that the changes of texture impressed on the organism by old age sometimes become so marked, that the physiological and pathological states seem to merge into one another by insensible transitions, and cannot be clearly distinguished" (p. 27).

This continuous view may also partially explain why the senile amentias and dementias, already described during the late 18th century, did not catch on as diagnostic entities. For example Cullen (1827) clearly distinguished between amentia congenita, acquisita and senilis. The latter he described as: "involving perception and memory and getting worse with age", and subclassified as *"Amentia senilis, S.sp 1. Amnesia senilis*, sp. 2" (p. 317). Likewise, Pinel (1818): "dementia may be congenital or caused by advanced age; when acquired it may be caused by intemperance, debauchery, strokes, brain injury, great fear, and excessive intellectual work" . . . and it was clinically characterised by "alternating and disconnected ideas and emotions, disordered motility, extravagant acts, total forgetting of previous experiences, marked diminution or abolition of the capacity to perceive, failure in judgement, aimless hyperactivity, and automatic existence; occasionally [there was] forgetting or confusion of words and of the signs that allow the organization of ideas" (p. 130).

The force of the continuous view also helps to understand why a disease such as Alzheimer's, which there is no reason to suspect was less common during the 19th century, took so long to be clinically recognised. Other factors also contributed. It is likely, for example, that the disease was lost in the large group of the senile insanities. Since non-cognitive symptoms played, as mentioned above, such an important diagnostic role, any dementia accompanied by psychotic symptoms was classified as a senile insanity; the presence of marked cognitive impairment not being a problem for it was explained away as resulting from old age. Likewise, the histological features around which the concept of Alzheimer's disease was eventually to crystallise, were not yet technically possible. Indeed, the earliest important work in this area, much neglected by historians, is that by Marcé (1863), who has surprisingly achieved fame for his contribution to puerperal insanities, an area in which he was not a creator, but a compiler. The anatomopathological contributions of Krafft-Ebing (1876) and Beljahow (1887) must also be mentioned in this regard.

By the 1880s, however, the narrowing down of the concept of dementia helped to throw the senile states into preeminence.

The history of dementia during the late 19th century

The 19th century inherited a concept of dementia which included all states of chronic behavioural incompetence, whatever the original disease (Berrios, 1987a). The term 'dementia' was used to refer both to the medical and legal aspects of these states; age and irreversibility were not part of the meaning of the term (Esquirol, 1814).

This concept soon proved too wide as it could not be easily fitted into the anatomoclinical concept of disease (López-Piñero, 1983) which necessitated not only a clear organic lesion but also an operational definition of the disease. Charcot (1881), when lecturing on early-19th-century medicine, described this in vivid tones: "whilst symptoms were formerly considered in an abstract manner, and to certain extent, as outside the organism, to-day they are closely bound up with it. We have to search for the seat of the mischief . . . while disease was formerly considered as a being independent of the organism today it is nothing but a disturbance of the inherent properties of our organs. We have to do not with the appearance of fresh laws, but with the perversion and de-arrangement of pre-existing laws" (pp. 3–4). Towards the end of the century the phenomenon of cerebral ageing was already being discussed in cellular terms (Marinesco, 1900).

The work of Bayle (1826) began to show the way. Here there was, at last, a form of dementia which could be related to a more or less recognisable lesion (Marie, 1906, pp. 163–164). Indeed, Bayle (1826) went as far as saying: "all that I have said of paralysis also applies to dementia" (p. 559). But he was also interested in the need to develop clear descriptions of disease (Berrios, 1985a). From then on, efforts were made to identify what nowadays might be called the positive symptoms of dementia. These in the 1880s still included cognitive and non-cognitive symptoms (Ball & Chambard, 1882; Parisot, 1897).

After this period the narrowing down of the *classes* of dementias started in earnest. The first group to go were the melancholic stupors (Berrios, 1981b), then the defect states caused by brain injury; the amnesic states *á la* Korsakoff, and finally the so-called vesanic dementias (Gombault, 1900; Ball & Chambard, 1882, pp. 597–600). In the event only the dementias of old age, classified as senile and arteriosclerotic, and the presbyophrenias (Berrios, 1986) were left behind.

All three groups became the subject of intense anatomopathological study. Soon after the turn of the century the early results began to appear in the work of Alzheimer, Fischer, Bonfiglio, and Perusini (Amaducci *et al*, 1986; Bick *et al*, 1987; Beach, 1987; Berrios, 1989*f*).

The aftermath

Perusal of the literature on dementia just before World War I has a familiar ring. Two famous papers (Jaspers, 1910; Puillet & Morel, 1913) had revised in detail all the difficulties related to the quantification of the dementias. Bolton (1903) had published his major article reporting the Claybury Hospital research work on the physical basis of mental disease including dementia. Toulouse & Mignard's (1914) classic paper criticising the broad definition of dementia had appeared on the eve of the Great War as had Ziehen's (1911) masterly piece on the classification of the dementias. A concept of Alzheimer's disease had already been accepted (Fuller, 1912).

Progress since has concentrated on refining the distinction between the functional and organic psychosis of old age, dispelling the mythology surrounding the concept of vascular dementia, finding a home for the higher cortical syndromes (Berrios, 1987*b*), and more fundamentally, pushing the cognitive paradigm to the very limits of its clinical resolution. This has been a great achievement and one must be grateful to those who created the cognitive paradigm. But each age has its own problems and ours is the creation of adequate models for the longitudinal analysis of disease (Berrios, 1989*b*).

Discussion and conclusions

So, to conclude, now more than ever clinicians require a definition of dementia that includes sufficient signs and symptoms to achieve adequate sensitivity and specificity. The cognitive paradigm has proved to be of use only in relation to the study of the intermediate stages of dementia. However refined the cognitive instruments might become, they are unlikely to help with the identification of 'early dementia' as its symptoms may not even be cognitive (Liston, 1977; Gustafson & Nilsson, 1982). Nor can they help to evaluate the chaotic behaviour of the very late stages of dementia when subjects have become untestable; during this terminal stage, however, patients may still show behavioural signs of the kind which might bear correlation with an ever-worsening brain pathology. A cautious broadening of the cognitive paradigm might, therefore, be warranted, to include non-cognitive symptoms such as hallucinations, delusions, behavioural and personality changes, and affect and motility disorders (Berrios, 1989*a*).

The creation and acceptance of the cognitive paradigm by 19th-century psychiatrists was the result of a complex interaction of scientific and social factors. Hence, it must not be considered as immutable. Like the rest of psychopathological descriptions (Berrios, 1984), that of dementia reflects now, as it did in the late 19th century, honest efforts by clinicians to represent in words and in numbers complex behavioural changes, occurring both in space and in time. This noble task can, therefore, be described as a veritable form of analogical to digital conversion (Berrios, 1989*b*).

If so, its success will depend upon the quality of the signal emitted by the patient, and also upon the parameters and rate of sampling as practised by clinicians. While nature controls the parameters of the signal, clinicians can control their own sampling activity, as they indeed seem to have done in the past according to the indicators of history and the cognitive paradigm. This lecture should be viewed as a plea to change some of those sampling parameters, and as a historical demonstration that the cognitive paradigm may be in need of revision.

References

ANONYMOUS (1883) Association of German Physicians Practising in Lunacy. *British Medical Journal, ii,* 1198–1199.

ACKERKNECHT, E. H. (1967) *Medicine at the Paris Hospital 1794–1848.* Baltimore: The Johns Hopkins Press.

ALBARRACIN, T. A. (1983) *La Teoria Celular.* Madrid: Alianza Editorial.

AMADUCCI, L. A, ROCCA, W. A. & SCHOENBERG, B. S. (1986) Origin of the distinction between Alzheimer's disease and senile dementia. *Neurology,* **36,** 1497–1499.

BAIN, A. (1864) *The Senses and the Intellect* (2nd edn). London: Longman, Roberts, and Green.

BALL, B. & CHAMBARD, E. (1882) Démence. In *Dictionnaire Encyclopédique de la Science Médicale,* vol. 26 (ed. A. Dechambre), pp. 559–605. Paris: Asselin.

BARR, M. W. (1904) *Mental Defectives. Their History, Treatment and Training.* Philadelphia: Blakiston's Son & Co.

BAYLE, A. L. J. (1826) *Traité des Maladies du Cerveau et de ses Membranes.* Paris: Chez Gabon et Compagnie Libraires.

BATEMAN, F. (1897) *The Idiot. His Place in Creation and his Claims on Society.* London: Jarrold & Sons.

BEACH, T. G. (1987) The history of Alzheimer's disease. *Journal of the History of Medicine and Allied Sciences,* **42,** 327–349.

BELJAHOW, S. (1887) Pathological changes in the brain in dementia senilis. *Journal of Mental Science,* **35,** 261–262.

BENON, R. & FROISSART, P. (1909) Les fugues en pathologie mentale. *Journal de Psychologie Normale et Pathologique,* **6,** 293–330.

BERNARD, C. (1957) *An Introduction to the Study of Experimental Medicine.* New York: Dover.

BERNARD-LEROY, E. (1898) *L'Illusion de Fausse Reconnaissance. Contribution á l'Etude des Conditons Psychologiques de la Reconnaissance des Souvenirs.* Paris: Alcan.

BERRIOS, G. E. (1981*a*) Delirium and confusion in the 19th century: a conceptual history. *British Journal of Psychiatry,* **139,** 439–449.

—— (1981*b*) Stupor: a conceptual history. *Psychological Medicine,* **11,** 677–688.

—— (1984) Descriptive psychopathology: conceptual and historical aspects. *Psychological Medicine,* **14,** 303–313.

—— (1985*a*) Depressive pseudodementia or melancholic dementia: a 19th century view. *Journal Neurology, Neurosurgery and Psychiatry,* **48,** 393–400.

—— (1985*b*) The psychopathology of affectivity. Conceptual and historical aspects. *Psychological Medicine,* **15,** 745–758.

—— (1986) Presbyophrenia: the rise and fall of a concept. *Psychological Medicine*, **16**, 267–275.

—— (1987*a*) Dementia during the seventeenth and eighteenth centuries. *Psychological Medicine*, **17**, 829–837.

—— (1987*b*) The nosology of the dementias. In *Dementia* (ed. B. Pitt), pp. 19–51. Edinburgh: Churchill Livingstone.

—— (1988*a*) History and philosophy of psychiatry: overview. *Current Opinion in Psychiatry*, **1**, 585–587.

—— (1988*b*) Historical background to abnormal psychology. In *Adult Abnormal Psychology* (ed. E. Miller & P. J. Cooper), pp. 26–51. Edinburgh: Churchill Livingstone.

—— (1989*a*) Non-cognitive symptoms and the diagnosis of dementia. Historical and clinical aspects. *British Journal of Psychiatry*, **155** (suppl. 4), 11–16.

—— (1989*b*) Measuring human problems in organic psychiatry. In *Measuring Human Problems* (ed. D. Peck & C. Shapiro). Chichester: Wiley (in press).

——(1989*c*) Feelings of fatigue and psychopathology: a conceptual history. *Comprehensive Psychiatry* (in press).

—— (1989*d*) Disorders of memory and psychiatry: a conceptual history. *Psychological Medicine* (in press).

—— (1989*e*) Phenomenology, psychopathology and Jaspers: a reassessment. *British Journal of Psychiatry* (in press).

—— (1989*f*) Alzheimer' disease: a conceptual history. *International Journal of Geriatric Psychiatry* (in press).

—— & HAUSER, R. (1988) The early development of Kraepelin's ideas on classification: a conceptual history. *Psychological Medicine*, **18**, 813–821.

BEAUTE, T. (1889) Maladies mentales des viellards. *Annales Médico-Psytchologiques*, **47**, 63–78.

BICK, K., AMADUCCI, L. & PEPEU, G. (eds) (1987) *The Early Story of Alzheimer Disease*. New York: Liviana Press.

BIRREN, J. E. (1961) A brief history of the psychology of aging. *Gerontologist*, **1**, 69–77.

BLACKER, C. P. (1952) *Eugenics, Galton and After*. London: Duckworth.

BOLTON, J. S. (1903) The histological basis of amentia and dementia. *Archives of Neurology*, **2**, 424–612.

BONDY, M. (1974) Psychiatric antecedents on psychological testing (before Binet). *Journal of the History of the Behavioral Sciences*, **10**, 180–194.

BORING, E. G. (1942) *Sensatin and Perception in the History of Experimental Psychology*. New York: Irvington Publishers.

—— (1950) *A History of Experimental Psychology*. New York: Appleton-Century-Crofts.

—— (1961) The beginning and growth of measurement in psychology. *Isis*, **52**, 238–257.

BRANCONNIER, R. J. & DeVITT, D. R. (1983) Early detection of incipient Alzheimer's disease: some methodological considerations on computerized diagnosis. In *Alzheimer's Disease* (B. Raisberg), pp. 214–227. London: Free Press.

BULBENA, A. & BERRIOS, G. E. (1986) Pseudodementia: facts and figures. *British Journal of Psychiatry*, **148**, 87–94.

BURNHAM, W. H. (188–89) Memory, historically and experimentally considered. *American Journal of Psychology*, **2**, 39–90; 225–270; 431–464; 568–622.

CANGUILHEM, G. (1966) *Le Normal et le Pathologique*. Paris: Presses Universitaires de France.

CAPARRÓS, A. (1986) *H. Ebbinghaus. Un funcionalista Investigador Tipo Dominio*. Barcelona: Publicacions Universitat de Barcelona.

CATTELL, J. McK. (1890) Mental tests and measurements. *Mind*, **15**, 373–381.

CHARCOT, J. M. (1881) *Clinical Lectures on Senile and Chronic Diseases* (trans. W. S. Tuke). London: New Sydenham Society.

CHARPENTIER, T. (1885) Des troubles mentaux dans la sénilité précoce et rapide. *Annales Médico-Psychologiques*, **43**, 276–296.

CLOUSTON, T. S. (1888) Presidential Address. *Journal of Mental Science*, **34**, 325–348.

CRICHTON BROWN, J. (1874) Senile dementia. *British Medical Journal*, **i**, 601–605; 640–643.

CULLEN, W. (1827) *The Works* (ed. J. Thomson), 2 vols. Edinburgh: William Blackwood.

CULLERRE, A. (1890) *Traité Pratique des Maladies Mentales*. Paris: Baillière et fils.

DAGONET, H. (1876) *Nouveau Traité Élémentaire et Pratique des Maladies Mentales*. Paris: Baillière.

DILTHEY, W. (1976) *Selected Writings*. Cambridge: Cambridge University Press.

DUGAS, L. (1894) Observations sur la fausse mémoire. *Revue Philosophique*, **37**, 34–45.

EBBINGHAUS, H. (1964) *Memory. A Contribution to Experimental Psychology* (trans. H. A. Ruger & C. E. Bussenius). New York: Dover.

EDGELL, B. (1924) *Theories of Memory*. Oxford: Clarendon Press.

ESQUIROL, J. E. (1814) Démence. In *Dictionnaire des Sciences Médicales par une Société de Médicins et de Chirurgiens*, pp. 280–294. Paris: Panckouke.

FALRET, J. P. (1864) *Des Maladies Mentales et des Asiles d'Aliénés. Leçons Cliniques & Considérations Générales*. Paris: Baillière.

FERRIER, D. (1886) *The Functions of the Brain*. London: Smith, Elder & Co.

FODOR, J. A. (1983) *The Modularity of the Mind*. Cambridge: MIT Press.

FRIEDLANDER, R. (1973) *Benedict-Augustin Morel and the Development of the Theory of Degenerescence (The Introduction of Anthropology into Psychiatry)*. PhD dissertation, University of California.

FULLER, S. C. (1912) Alzheimer's disease (senium praecox): the report of a case and review of the published cases. *Journal of Nervous and Mental Disease*, **39**, 440–455; 536–557.

GALTON, F. (1883) *Inquiries into Human Faculty and its Development*. London: MacMillan.

GALTON, F. (1979) *Hereditary Genius*. London: Friedmann.

GARCIA, C. A., TWEEDY, J. R. & BLASS, J. P. (1984) Underdiagnosis of cognitive impairment in a rehabilitation setting. *Journal of the American Geriatric Society*, **32**, 339–342.

GASSER, J. (1988) La notion de mémoire organique dans la oeuvre de T Ribot. *History and Philosophy of the Life Sciences*, **10**, 293–313.

GÉNIL-PERRIN, G. (1913) *Histoire des Origines et de l'évolution de l'Idée de Dégénérescence en Médicine Mentale*. Paris: Leclerc.

GOMULICKI, B. R. (1953) The development and present status of the trace theory of memory. *British Journal of Psychology Monograph Supplements*, vol. 14. Cambridge: Cambridge University Press.

GOMBAULT, T. (1900) De la démence terminale dans les psychoses. *Annales Médico-Psychologiques*, **58**, 231–249.

GUSTAFSON, L. & NILSSON, L. (1982) Differential diagnosis of presenile dementia on clinical grounds. *Acta Psychiatrica Scandinavica*, **65**, 194–209.

HACKING, I. (ed.) (1981) *Scientific Revolutions*. Oxford: Oxford University Press.

HALPERT, B. P. (1983) Development of the term 'senility' as a medical diagnosis. *Minnesota Medicine*, **66**, 421–424.

HAMILTON, W. (1859) *Lectures on Metaphysics and Logic*, vol. 2. Edinburgh: William Blackwood and Sons.

HÉCAEN, H. & DUBOIS, J. (1969) *La Naissance de la Neuropsychologie du Langage (1825–1865)*. Paris: Flammarion.

—— & LANTERI-LAURA, G. (1977) *Evolution des Connaissances et des Doctrines sur les Localisations Cérébrales*. Paris: Desclée de Brouwer.

HENDERSON, A. S. & HUPPERT, F. A. (1984) The problem of mild dementia. *Psychological Medicine*, **14**, 5–10.

HERING, E. (1870) *Über das Gedächtnis als eine allgemaine Funktion der organisierten Materie*. Vortrag gehalten in der feierlichen Sitzung der Kaiserlichen Akademie der Wissenschaften in Wien am XXX, Wien. (Trans. S. Butler (1880) *Unconscious Memory*. London: Trübner.)

HILTS, V. L. (1981) *Statist and Statistician: Three Studies in the History of Nineteenth Century English Statistical Thought*. New York: Arno Press.

HOMER, A. C., HONAVAR, M., LANTOS, P. L., *et al* (1988) Diagnosing dementia: do we get it right? *British Medical Journal*, **297**, 894–896.

HUERTAS, G. A. R. (1987) *Locura y Degeneración*. Madrid: CSIS.

JANET, P. & SÉAILLES, G. (1902) *A History of the Problems of Philosophy* (trans. A. Monahan & H. Jones), vol. 1, pp. 145–165. London: MacMillan.

JASPERS, K. (1910) Die Methoden der Intelligenzprüfung und der Begriff der Demenz. *Zeitschrift für des gesamte Neurologie und Psychiatrie (Referate & Ergebnisse)*, **1**, 402–452.

JEANNEROD, M. (1985) *The Brain Machine. The Development of Neurophysiological Thought*. Cambridge: Harvard University Press.

JORDANOVA, L. J. (1984) *Lamarck*. Oxford: Oxford University Press.

KIRKPATRICK, B., JOHNSON, M., MCGUIRE, K., *et al* (1986) Confounding and the dementia of schizophrenia. *Pschiatry Research*, **19**, 225–231.

KLERMAN, G. L. (1988) Competing scientific paradigms in American psychiatry. *American Journal of Psychiatry* (in press; pre-publication copy).

KOERNER, E. F. K. (1982) *Ferdinand de Saussure. Génesis y Evolución de su Pensamiento en el Marco de la Lingüística Occidental.* Madrid: Gredos.

KORSAKOFF, S. (1889) Etude médico-psychologique sur une forme des maladies de la mémoire. *Revue Philosophique,* **28**, 501–530.

KOWALEWSKI, P. J. (1886) Sur la curabilité de la démence. *Annales Médico-Psychologiques,* **44**, 40–53.

KRAEPELIN, E. (1886–87) Uber Erinnerungsfälschungen. *Archiv für Psychiatrie und Nervenkrankheiten* **17**, 830–843; **18**, 199–239; 395–436.

—— (1983) *Lebenserinnerungen.* Berlin: Springer.

KRAFFT-EBING, R. (1876) De la démence sénile. *Annales Médico-Psychologiques,* **16**, 306.

KUHN, T. S. (1962) *The Structure of Scientific Revolutions.* Chicago: University of Chicago Press.

—— (1970) *The Structure of Scientific Revolutions* (2nd edn). Chicago: University of Chicago Press.

LALANDE, A. (1893) Des paramnésies. *Revue Philosophique,* **36**, 485–497.

LAMARCK, J. B. (1984) *Zoological Philosophy.* Chicago: University of Chicago Press.

LEVIN, H. S., PETERS, B. H. & HULKONEN, D. A. (1983) Early concepts of anterograde and retrograde amnesia. *Cortex,* **19**, 427–440.

LISTON, E. H. (1977) Occult presenile dementia. *Journal of Nervous and mental Disease,* **164**, 263–267.

LISHMAN, W. A. (1987) *Organic Psychiatry* (2nd edn). Oxford: Blackwell.

LONG, E. R. (1965) *A History of Pathology.* New York: Dover.

LÓPEZ-PIÑERO, J. M. (1983) *Historical Origins of the Concept of Neurosis* (trans. D. Berriois). Cambridge: Cambridge University Press.

LUYS, J. (1881) *Traité Clinique et Pratique des Maladies Mentales.* Paris: Delahaye et Lacrosnier.

MAGNAN, V. & LEGRAIN, P. M. (1895) *Les Dégénérés.* Paris: Ruef et Cie.

MARCÉ, L. V. (1862) *Traité Pratique des Maladies Mentales.* Paris: Baillière.

—— (1863) Recherches cliniques et anatomo-pathologiques sur la démence sénile et sur les différences qui la séparent de la paralysie générale. *Gazette Médicale de Paris,* **34**, 433; 467; 497; 631; 761; 797; 831; 855.

MARIE, A. (1906) *La Démence.* Paris: Doin.

MARINESCO, G. (1900) Mécanisme de la sénilité et de la mort des cellules nerveuses. *Comptes Rendus Hebdomadaires des Séances de L'Academie de Sciences,* **130**, 1136–1139.

MARR, D. (1982) *Vision.* San Francisco: Freeman.

MARSDEN, C. D. & HARRISON, M. J. G. (1972) Outcome of investigation of patients with presenile dementia. *British Medical Journal,* **ii**, 249–252.

MARTIN, B. A., THOMPSON, E. G. & EASTWOOD, M. R. (1983) The clinical investigation of dementia. *Canadian Journal of Psychiatry,* **28**, 282–286.

MASTERMAN, M. (1970) The nature of a paradigm. In *Criticism and the Growth of knowledge* (ed. I. Lakatos & A. Musgrave), pp. 59–89. Cambridge: Cambridge University Press.

MAULITZ, R. C. (1987) *Morbid Appearances. The Anatomy of Pathology in the Early Nineteenth Century.* Cambridge: Cambridge University Press.

MAYR, E. (1982) *The Growth of Biological Thought.* Cambridge: Belknap Press of Harvard University Press.

MILL, J. (1869) *Analysis of the Phenomena of the Human Mind.* London: Longman, Green Reader and Dyer.

MILLER, E. (1977) *Abnormal Ageing.* New York: Wiley.

MILLS, C. K. & SCHIVELY, M. A. (1897) Preliminary report, clinical and pathological, of a case of progressive dementia. *American Journal of Insanity,* **33**, 201–211.

MURPHY, T. D. (1981) Medical knowledge and statistical methods in early nineteenth century France. *Medical History,* **25**, 301–319.

MURRAY, D. J. (1981) Research on human memory in the nineteenth century. *Canadian Journal of Psychology,* **30**, 201–220.

NOTT, P. N. & FLEMINGER, J. J. (1975) Pre-senile dementia: the difficulties of early diagnosis. *Acta Psychiatrica Scandinavica,* **51**, 210–217.

PARCHAPPE, J. (1856) Rapport sur la statistique de l'aliénation mentale. *Annales Médico-Psychologiques,* **2**, 1–6.

PARISOT, P. (1897) Quelques caractères des hallucinations de l'ouie dans la démence sénile délirante. *Revue médicale de l'Est (Nancy)*, **39**, 585–594.

PERROT, J. C. & WOOLF, S. J. (1984) *State and Statistics in France 1789–1815*. London: Hardwood Academic Publishers.

PICK, A. (1903) Clinical studies. III. On reduplicative paramnesia. *Brain*, **26**, 260–267.

PINEL, P. (1818) *Nosographie Philosophique*, vol. 1, Paris: Brosson.

PORTER, T. M. (1986) *The Rise of Statistical Thinking 1820–1900*. Princeton: Princeton University Press.

PUILLET, P. & MOREL, L. (1913) De la méthode des connaissances usuelles dans l'étude des démences. *Journal de Psychologie Normale et Pathologique*, **10**, 25–36; 111–133.

RABBITT, P. (1988) Social psychology, neurosciences and cognitive psychology need each other; (and gerontology needs all three of them). *Psychologist*, **12**, 500–506.

RAMÓN Y, CAJAL, S. (1952) *Neuronismo o Reticularismo. Las Pruebas Objetivas de la unidad Anatómica de las Células Nerviosas*. Madrid: CSIC.

—— (1981) *Recuerdos de mi Vida: Historia de mi Labor Científica*. Madrid: Alianza Editorial.

RENAUDIN, E. (1856) Observations sur les recherches statistiques relatives a l'aliénation mentale. *Annales Médico-Psychologiques*, **2**, 339–360.

RIBOT, TH. (1882) *Diseases of Memory*. London: Kegan Paul, Trench & Co.

—— (1906) *L'Hérédité Psychologique*. Paris: Alcan.

RIESE, W. (1959) *A History of Neurology*. New York: MD Publications.

ROGERS, D. (1988) Psychiatry and the Necker cube. Neurological and psychological conceptions of psychiatric disorder. *Behavioural Neurology*, **1**, 3–10.

RON, M. A., TOONE, B. K., GARRALDA, M. E., *et al.* (1979) Diagnostic accuracy in presenile dementia. *British Journal of Psychiatry*, **134**, 161–168.

ROUILLARD, T. (1885) *Essai sur les Amnésies. Etiologie des Troubles de la Mémoire*. Paris: Jules Leclerc.

RUND, B. R. (1988) Cognitive disturbances in schizophrenics: what are they, and what is their origin? *Acta Psychiatrica Scandinavica*, **77**, 113–123.

SAURY, H. (1886) *Etude Clinique sur la Folie Héréditaire*. Paris: Delahaye and Lecrosnier.

SAUSSURE, F., DE (1960) *Course in General Linguistics* (trans. W. Baskin). London: Peter Owen.

SCHACHTER, D. L., EICH, J. E. & TULVING, E. (1978) Richard Semon's theory of memory. *Journal of Verbal Learning and Verbal Behavior*, **17**, 721–743.

SEMMUEL, B. (1958) Karl Pearson: socialist and Darwinist. *British Journal of Sociology*, **9**, 111–125.

SERTILLANGES, A. D. (1943) *La Philosophie de Claude Bernard*. Aubier: Montaigne.

SHALLICE, T. (1988) *From Neuropsychology to Mental Structure*. Cambridge: Cambridge University Press.

SHAW, T. C. (1892) Dementia. In *A Dictionary of Psychological Medicine*, vol. 1 (ed. D. H. Tuke), pp. 348–351. London: Churchill.

SHEYNIN, O. B. (1980) On the history of the statistical method in biology. *Archives for the History of the Exact Sciences*, **22**, 323–371.

SMALL, G. W. & JARVIK, L. F. (1982) The dementia syndrome. *Lancet*, ii, 1443–1446.

SMITH, J. S. & KILOH, L. G. (1981) The investigation of dementia: results in 200 consecutive admissions. *Lancet*, i, 824–827.

TALBOT, E. S. (1898) *Degeneracy. Its Causes, Signs and Results*. London: Walter Scott.

THOMSON, J. A. (1908) *Heredity*. London: Murray.

TIZARD, B. (1959) Theories of brain localization from Flourens to Lashley. *Medical History*, **3**, 132–145.

TOULOUSE, E. & MIGNARD, M. (1914) Comment caractériser et definir la démence. *Annales Médico-Psychologiques*, **72**, 443–461.

TULVING, E. (1983) *Elements of Episodic Memory*. Oxford: Clarendon Press.

UNDERWOOD, E. A. (1951) The history of the quantitative approach in medicine. *British Medical Bulletin*, **7**, 265–274.

YOUNG, K. (1923) The history of mental testing. *Pedagogical Seminar*, **31**, 1–48.

YOUNG, R. M. (1970) *Mind, Brain and Adaptation in the Nineteenth Century*. Oxford: Clarendon Press.

WALKER, C. (1988) Philosophical concepts and practice: the legacy of Karly Jaspers' psychopathology. *Current Opinion in Psychiatry*, **1**, 624–629.

WATTIS, J. P. & HINDMARCH, I. (1988) *Psychological Assessment of the Elderly*. Edinburgh: Churchill Livingstone.

ZEMAN, F. D. (1950) Life's later years. Studies in the medical history of old age. Part XII. The nineteenth century. *Journal of Mount Sinai Hospital*, **17**, 53–68; 241–246.

ZIEHEN, T. (1911) Les démences. In *Traité International de Psychologie Pathologique*, vol. 2 (ed. A. Marie), pp. 281–381. Paris: Alcan.

ZUPAN, M. L. (1976) The conceptual development of quantification in experimental psychology. *Journal of the History of the Behavioral Sciences*, **12**, 145–158.

Index

Compiled by STANLEY THORLEY

212